The Amateur Astronomer's Handbook

THE
Amateur Astronomer's
HANDBOOK

James Muirden

THOMAS Y. CROWELL COMPANY

NEW YORK

Established 1834

By the Author
Stars and Planets
Astronomy with Binoculars
The Amateur Astronomer's Handbook

Also published in Great Britain under
the title *Astronomy for Amateurs*.

Designed by Susan Gibson

Printed in the United States of America

L. C. Card 67–12406

For J. L.,
watcher of the skies

Note

This book is written primarily for readers in the northern hemisphere. In the southern hemisphere some of the compass directions given here may have to be reversed, as indicated in the text.

Acknowledgements

A great number of people have assisted me, in various ways, in the writing of this book, but I am particularly indebted to Dr. W. H. Steavenson and R. M. Baum, two British amateur observers of distinction, who made valuable comments on the first draft of the manuscript. In more general terms I must thank Patrick Moore, the well-known writer and broadcaster, for his help and encouragement over the years.

British, American, and Continental observers have been of material assistance in supplying notes and photographs, and acknowledgement, where due, is made in the text.

I must finally thank my many Greek friends, particularly Giorgos Markoulakis, for their overflowing hospitality during the time I spent amongst them, observing the sky and writing this book.

Foreword

Astronomy introduces us simultaneously to the most theoretical of abstractions and the most practical of realities. From whichever angle one approaches it, the field for activity is enormous. Some researches have been conducted sitting at a desk with a calculating machine or computer at hand; others have been based entirely on practical observation with a telescope. The results of both kinds of investigation have shown that much work remains to be done.

In *Stars and Planets* (1964), to which this book may be considered a companion volume, I attempted to survey our present knowledge of the principal branches of astronomy. This field is so vast that a whole book could scarcely do it justice, let alone expand on the practical side of the subject. This book is intended to complete the picture: to show just what observations can be made by an enthusiastic amateur; how they can be made most effectively; and to what use they can be put.

Even so, sacrifices have had to be made. If all the data likely to be needed by an active amateur had been included, the book would have had to be twice as long; instead, I have given references to texts covering the relevant subjects. Star charts, for instance, have been omitted, because excellent large-scale atlases are available. Telescope-making also falls within the scope of the title, but it could not possibly receive adequate treatment in a single chapter, and has been covered instead in the Bibliography.

In writing this book, I have drawn very largely on the work of other observers. Acknowledgement is made elsewhere to those amateur astronomers who have kindly offered much practical assistance; but it would be a mistake—and is, indeed, an error often made by modern writers on the subject—to overlook the wealth of experience accumulated by those observers who lived before this modern age of research. Times have changed, of course, but not everything has changed with the times. The technique of telescopic observation always has been and always will be based on unending practice and training of the eye. In this connection, the great observers of the past were certainly no less competent than the leading ones of today; especially when we consider the difficulties with which they coped. One cannot become a successful amateur astronomer without the inspiration that is kindled from a love of the night sky and an unshakable determination to succeed.

This book should not be considered as more than a guide for the would-be observer. I have, however, tried to bridge the gap between works that deal with the spectacular "wonders of the sky" and the formal handbooks full of facts. The latter are of great value once a start has been made, but in themselves they are almost meaningless. In short, this is intended to be a survey of the *technique* of amateur astronomy, from the selection of an instrument to the conduct of actual observation. A certain amount of basic astronomical knowledge has been assumed, since no one book can cover everything, and many have failed from trying to be too ambitious!

We must always remember, however, that astronomy has much more to offer us than the delight of scientific investigation. The element of wonder and frank incomprehension is, in many ways, of far more personal account than an explanatory theory. The unknown being more fascinating than the known, I hope my readers will feel inclined to pay as much attention to those branches of observation in which they have no hope of pronouncing a "verdict" as they do to the more orthodox lines of research. By all means let us continue the amateur's tradition of observing Venus, Jupiter, and variable stars, and making valuable reports, but let us also never forget that astronomy loses half its meaning for the observer who never lets his telescope range across the remote glories of the sky "with an uncovered head and humble heart."

JAMES MUIRDEN

Contents

List of Figures and Plates

PART

I

EQUIPMENT

1

The Telescope and Its Development

We live in the Age of Leisure; and, in this age, recreation has become part of man's estate. There are a thousand pastimes open to us, most of which are not technically "useful," but simply hobbies with which we occupy our spare hours. Yet it is curious that in a world revolutionized by science and technology, so few people consider turning to science in their leisure time.

Perhaps this is not so curious when we remember that the golden age of the amateur scientist has long since passed into history. Universities are now turning out technologists by the thousand, and it is clear that no amateur scientist would have the basic knowledge, let alone the facilities, to perform original work in most of the modern sciences. But there are still a few openings for research, in which the amateur can play a useful, even vital, part. Astronomy, geology, and archeology come to mind at once—and of these, astronomy is perhaps the most demanding and rewarding. Who has never wished, even subconsciously, that he might probe the secrets of a starry night? For there is art as well as science here, and the amateur—humble though his telescope may be—is, in a sense, as well equipped as the professional.

It is mainly the art of astronomy that appeals to the spare-time observer with a small telescope, an art that usually reveals itself in terms of perseverance. Indeed, this is the demarcation between the two classes of astronomer, and it explains why the amateur still has a part to play. For the night sky, which appears so placid and unchanging to the casual glance, is really a turmoil of activity: planets spin on their axes, meteors fly, stars slowly brighten or fade, and sometimes a comet creeps into view from the blackness of outer space. A professional astronomer, working on some particular problem, may not even glance at the sky for weeks on end. But amateurs are tied by no such schedules; they can let their attention wander according to the state of things. Scavenging in this way, they sometimes emerge with quite remarkable prizes, prizes that might otherwise have passed through our hands without notice and without profit.

The fact is that observations requiring endless persistence, and not necessarily needing complex equipment, are highly suitable for the amateur. It must be remembered that a professional astronomer is employed by his university or observatory to get through a certain amount of work in a given time, and this time is obviously severely rationed by the need of other workers to use the same telescope. This means that he is mainly confined to those lines of research likely to show a fairly swift return. No such necessity dogs the amateur. His time is his own, his telescope is his own, and he can observe the same object for years on end if he so wishes, waiting for something unusual to happen. If it does, the chances are that he will be the first to notice it.

A good example of this is Earth's neighbor planet, Jupiter. A small astronomical telescope will show a great amount of detail on its surface, but consistent watching over many months or years is required before valuable results are likely to emerge. This means that the observation of Jupiter's markings is almost entirely in the hands of amateurs scattered all over the world. Even Galileo was technically an amateur when, on that memorable night in January 1610, he pointed his primitive "optick tube" at Jupiter and discovered four bright satellites. Nowadays we can see these bodies through a pair of binoculars, but the wonder of that original observation remains.

Progress in astronomy has gone hand in hand with instrumental developments. It may therefore be enlightening to look back across the 350 years that have passed since Galileo's first peek at the stars. One wonders with what expectations he awaited that first nightfall, his tiny leaden-tubed telescope lying at hand. Did he realize that he was about to plunge into an uncharted universe a hundred times larger than the one that had absorbed men's minds for the past five thousand years? What were his feelings when he began to sweep the sky and found that for every star visible with the naked eye, his telescope showed a dozen? Surely, even at that early stage, he must have started thinking in terms of bigger and bigger telescopes, a yearning shared by every astronomer since. The greater the aperture of the telescope, the fainter and more distant are the stars it will reveal—and the larger the observable universe!

It is not hard to see why this should be. Under perfectly dark conditions, the iris of the human eye has an opening about $\frac{1}{3}$-inch across, with which it can detect stars down to a certain degree of faintness. The luster of the stars is calibrated in terms of *magnitude*, a term that refers to *brightness*, not to size; broadly speaking, the brightest stars in the sky are said to be of zero magnitude, while the faintest visible with the naked eye are of the 6th magnitude, the magnitude number rising with increasing faintness. If we now apply the eye to a telescope whose main lens, or *object glass*, has an aperture of one inch, we shall see a star as nine times brighter, because the light forming the image has been collected from an area nine times greater than that of the human iris. Correspondingly, the faintest star visible through the telescope will be nine times fainter than a 6th-magnitude star. Since a magnitude division represents a step in brightness of about $2\frac{1}{2}$ times, a 1-inch aperture telescope should reveal stars as faint as the 9th magnitude.

Early refractors

Galileo's telescope, which used a lens to gather and focus the light from a star, is known as a *refracting* telescope, or *refractor*. The word refraction refers to the bending of a ray of light when it passes from one transparent medium (in this case, air) through another of different density (in this case, glass). The principle on which the refractor works is shown in figure 1. The light from the star passes through the object glass, is refracted into a cone, and comes to a focus at the bottom of the tube. A star is rather faint for the purpose, but it is easy enough to catch the focal image of the sun or moon on a sheet of paper. However, when the telescope is being used for visual observation, an *eyepiece*, or *ocular*, is employed to magnify the image. This is a small lens placed close to the focal point and adjusted in position until a sharp view is obtained.

This eyepiece acts like a microscope. Just as a magnifying glass amplifies whatever is placed beneath it, so the eyepiece magnifies the image formed by the object glass, and gives a close-up view of the object concerned. Galileo's largest telescope had an aperture of about 2 inches and magnified some 30 times (written × 30). With this instrument, which is still on view in the Museum of Physics in Florence, he not only discovered the satellites of Jupiter but also saw the lunar plains and craters, spots on the sun, and the phases of Mars and Venus. He even made out some peculiar appendages to the planet Saturn. These were later found to be the rings, but he himself died in 1643 without realizing just what they were.

Figure 1. *Principle of the refractor.*

It is often claimed that Galileo was the first telescopic observer, but this is certainly incorrect. Simon Marius in Germany, as well as Thomas Harriot and Sir William Lower in England, was experimenting successfully during the same period. Harriot, indeed, unquestionably preceded Galileo in lunar observation, since he made a sketch as early as July 1609. Yet the Italian's work was of greater consequence, for all his observations were brought into the public eye by the publication of his *Sidereal Messenger* (1610) and *Dialogue* (1632), which discussed his then radical conclusions about the nature of the solar system, which led to his tragic struggle against the disapproval of the Holy Office in Rome.

Chromatic aberration

It soon became apparent, however, that the simple refracting telescope suffered from a grave defect. The image of a star or the edge of a planet was suffused with a colored halo that destroyed sharpness and made it quite impossible to use high magnifying powers. A tiny 1- or 2-inch-aperture telescope gave reasonable results, but astronomers were already impatient for more light and more power.

The explanation of this unhappy state of affairs, not known at that time, is given in figure 2. White light is actually an amalgam of all the colors of the rainbow, which is produced when sunlight is refracted by drops of water in the atmosphere. In addition to focusing light rays, a lens also splits them up into spectral colors. The light of shortest wavelength (blue) is refracted to a greater degree than the long-wave red light; consequently, the image of a star is actually a number of images, each in a different color, at different distances from the object glass. Since it is impossible to focus all these colors sharply at the same time, the image is inevitably faulty. This defect is known as *chromatic aberration*.

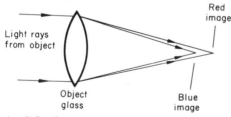

Figure 2. *Chromatic aberration. The effect is considerably exaggerated.*

Aerial telescopes

The early telescope-makers, not knowing the reason for the fault, could provide no real cure, but they did arrive at a workable compromise. This involved increasing the *focal length* of the lens. The focal length is simply the distance between the lens and the image it forms, and the simplest way of finding it is to form a sharp image of the sun on a sheet of paper and measure the distance between the lens and the paper. Galileo's 2-inch object glass had a focal length of about 3 feet; opticians now started grinding lenses of the same aperture, but with focal lengths of 30 feet, or even more. This had the beneficial result of separating out the images of different color, and so reducing the chromatic blur. The first systematic lunar observer, Johannes Hevelius (originally Hewelcke), of Danzig, used one of these *aerial telescopes* to produce the first reasonably accurate map of the moon, published in 1647. The Dutch observer Christian Huygens, well known as the constructor of the first practical pendulum clock, made an instrument giving such good definition that, in 1656, he discovered the true form of Saturn's rings.

Aerial telescopes, like all devices exploiting some form of distortion, enjoyed spectacular, if absurd, progress. Hevelius' main instrument was 150 feet long; Huygens constructed one more than 200 feet long, and a French optician is said to have constructed a 600-foot monster! But, however great their optical advantages, mechanical problems made them almost useless. They had to be used in the open air, since no observatory large enough to accommodate them could be built; only the calmest weather was suitable for their employment, and when they were not in use they had to be dismantled and stored. It is significant that the most memorable discoveries were achieved with relatively modest instruments. Huygens discovered Saturn's rings with a 90-foot telescope, but the Italian observer J. D. Cassini discovered the famous division in the rings, as well as two satellites, with a 17-foot instrument. It is a measure of the modern observer's good fortune that he can see all these features, and others more delicate, with great clarity in a telescope only three or four feet long!

The astronomers of the mid-seventeenth century must have looked at their unwieldy arrangements of masts and rigging and sighed for something more manageable, capable of better performance. But was there any alternative? How could a telescope be made that did not use an object glass? Failing that, how could an object glass be made that did not produce false color?

Early reflectors

It was a Scottish optician, James Gregory, who first suggested a plan for a *reflecting* telescope. As he pointed out in a small book published in 1663, a concave mirror will form an image in the same way as a lens, though by reflection rather than refraction; better still, it cannot produce any chromatic effect. Gregory created a design for what is known as a *Gregorian* reflector but, since his talents were confined to theory, did not

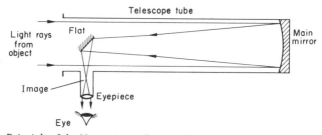

Figure 3. *Principle of the Newtonian reflector. The mirror's curve is greatly exaggerated.*

make such an instrument himself. In any case, the Gregorian reflector has rarely proved satisfactory for astronomical work. The world's first reflecting telescope, constructed in 1668 by none other than Isaac Newton, is still preserved in the apartments of the Royal Society in London.

The principle of the *Newtonian* reflector is shown in figure 3. The light from the star falls on the curved front surface* of the main mirror, or *speculum*, which reflects it back up the tube. Before it forms an image, however, it is again reflected, through a right angle, by a second mirror (this time plane), known as the *flat*. The light then passes through a hole cut in the side of the tube and comes to a focus where the eyepiece is positioned. Thus, instead of looking "up" the tube, as with a refractor, the observer peers more comfortably into the side, thus avoiding backbreaking contortions while observing an object high in the sky. There can be no doubt that of the two types, the reflector is the more comfortable instrument to use.

Newton's telescope was tiny, with a mirror only 1 inch across; astronomically it was useless, but he had shown the way. Opticians gradually turned their attention from the cumbersome refractor to the splendidly compact reflector, whose mirror could be ground to have a relatively short focal length. But the problems they faced were formidable. In the first place, the two mirrors had to be ground much more accurately than the surfaces of the object glass; secondly, there was the difficulty of finding a suitable material. Chemists had not yet discovered a way of precipitating silver out of a solution onto a glass surface, so the early mirrors had to be made of a substance known as *speculum metal* (an alloy of copper, tin, and other elements), which took a good polish but tarnished rapidly; it was also very fragile.

The first really workable speculum-metal reflector was made by an Englishman, John Hadley, in 1720. With the unheard-of aperture of 6 inches, and a focal length of only 6 feet, it caused a sensation; for, despite its handy convenience, it was equal in performance to any of Huygens' or

---

*All mirrors used in optical instruments reflect from the front surface, not from the second surface—as in the case of an ordinary looking glass, which is silvered on the back.

Cassini's unwieldy instruments. Soon after this, James Short, of Edinburgh, developed a technique for the production of fine optical surfaces and set himself up as a manufacturer of reflecting telescopes. By 1740, Short's telescopes were much in demand; but the finished instruments were in no sense permanent, despite their good performance. When their mirrors became tarnished they had to be repolished, and this process was quite enough to affect the delicate "figuring" of the surface, so that the optician had to be called in again to restore the original curve. There was no cure for this. The observer of those days had to choose between the unwieldy refractor or the efficient but impermanent reflector, finding no real satisfaction in either.

Achromatic refractors

However, the second half of the eighteenth century saw spectacular progress. The resurgence of the refractor began when Chester Moor Hall, an English "gentleman scientist," began looking into the root causes of chromatic aberration. After some experimenting, he actually managed to construct an object glass, 2½ inches across and only 20 inches focal length, that produced a relatively colorless image. This he achieved by making the lens from two different kinds of glass: one of low density (crown), the other of high density (flint). The chromatic light produced by the crown lens in focusing the light rays was then recombined into white light by the flint lens, as is shown in figure 4.

This compensating effect occurs because the two lenses are curved in the opposite sense. When a beam of white light passes through a prism (figure 4A), it is dispersed into a spectrum; correspondingly, a spectrum can be recondensed into white light if passed through a suitable prism. It is not hard to see that a beam of white light will emerge as white light it it passes through two correctly arranged prisms; this, in effect, is what happens when it is refracted by the two components of an achromatic object glass.

This was a sensational discovery. The object glass of a refractor could now be worked to almost as convenient a focal length as the mirror of a reflecting telescope. Yet, for some unknown reason, Hall chose to keep this

Figure 4. *Achromatic object glass. The distance between the crown and flint components is increased for the sake of clarity.*

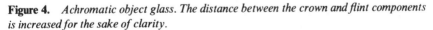
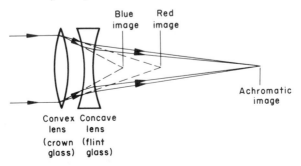

discovery to himself, and it was not until 1758 that the English optician John Dollond grasped the principle and began manufacturing *achromatic* refractors on a commercial scale. We can imagine with what relief astronomers consigned their ungainly aerial telescopes to the rubbish pile, and seized on Dollond's compact and efficient refractors! The new telescopes presented no tarnishing problem, and the definition was even better than that of Short's reflectors. Yet there was one big drawback: glassmakers could not yet cast large disks of glass of sufficient perfection to make big lenses, and a refractor with an object glass of more than 3-inch aperture was a rarity indeed. Therefore, reflectors, having no such drawback, remained on an equal footing. Shortly they were to receive an unprecedented boost when a Hanoverian musician, settled in England, decided to try his hand at telescope making and concentrated, for reasons of light-grasp, on the reflector. His name was William Herschel.

William Herschel

There are few fields of human endeavor in which one cannot point to one figure, whether past or present, as a prototype. The giant of observational astronomy is Herschel; in him, the separate but dependent arts of instrument making, observation, and analysis were combined in the highest degree. Absorbed by the unfathomed challenge of the sky, and faced, for want of money, with the necessity of making his own instruments, he brought the reflecting telescope to so high a pitch of perfection that its performance, in the 1780's, was comparable to that of the best modern instruments. In 1789, Herschel erected in his garden at Slough, England, a monster telescope with a mirror *48 inches across*. This remained the most powerful telescope in the world until, in 1845, Lord Rosse built his 72-inch reflector in Ireland. It is a sobering thought that Herschel's telescope was bigger than any in use in the British Isles today, although a 98-inch reflector has just been installed in the Royal Observatory at Herstmonceux.

Herschel, who built other instruments of smaller aperture, was for some time unaware of the excellence of his telescopes. Not until 1782, when visiting Greenwich Observatory in London, did he have a chance to compare one of his 6-inch reflectors with a 9½-inch reflector made by Short. Its mirror was markedly inferior to Herschel's, despite its extra aperture, so Herschel decided to make telescopes for sale, in order to subsidize his more ambitious projects. Since dozens of these first-rate instruments were distributed throughout the world, one might imagine that this would have been of wide benefit to observational astronomy. But nothing could be further from the truth. Only two observers—Pound in England and Johann Schröter in Germany—put them to worthwhile use; the others fell into the hands of dilettantes who had neither talent nor enthusiasm, both of which are part of the equipment of the observational astronomer. Indeed, Herschel might have exhausted himself by working on the means to the end had not King George III financed his further astronomical labors with a royal grant.

The lesson to be drawn from this instance is still applicable. During the last ten or fifteen years, hundreds of firms have been marketing astronomical equipment, some of it worthless, but much of very high quality. Yet this easy availability is not in itself of the slightest benefit to amateur astronomy. If a person has enough enthusiasm, he will find a way of obtaining a telescope; if he is deterred by immediate difficulties, then he will never make a first-class observer!

Resurgence of the refractor

Yet at the same time that Herschel was extending the limits of both his telescopes and his observations, Pierre Guinand, a Swiss optician, was laying the foundation for the resurgence of the refractor, whose limiting factor had proved to be the glass. If a lens is to refract light truly, its material must be perfectly homogeneous, without any flaws or strains that will deflect the tiny star-beams from their correct path; and in Guinand's day, pieces of optical glass more than 2 or 3 inches across were a great rarity. There were several reasons for this: the poor quality of the raw materials, the technique of heating and stirring the molten glass, and the final and immensely important *annealing* process. This is the gradual cooling of the red-hot mass, a process that must take place very slowly and regularly. Uneven cooling will produce disastrous flaws, and possibly cracks; and the larger the pot, the longer the annealing takes. Guinand was the first to study these various aspects of glassmaking; after many years of patient work he saw produced optical disks 4, 6, and even 8 inches across. Now the stage was set for someone with the skill and patience to grind such disks into fine lenses that would justify the caster's efforts.

It was a once poor orphan of Munich, Joseph von Fraunhöfer, who ushered in the age of the modern refracting telescope. Supported in his research by money compensating him for an almost fatal accident in his youth, he soon designed lenses on a slightly different pattern from Dollond's, although the basic crown-flint principle was the same. Joining forces with Guinand, he turned out a series of the finest object glasses the world had yet seen. This labor culminated in the completion of one $9\frac{1}{2}$ inches across, which was mounted in the Dorpat Observatory in eastern Estonia in 1824 and remained for several years the largest refractor in the world.

So far, the story of the telescope's development has been an exclusively European one. But it was not destined to remain so. Soon after the completion of Fraunhöfer's Dorpat refractor, Alvan Clark, a portrait painter living in Cambridge, Massachusetts, became intrigued by his son's efforts to grind an astronomical mirror. The two of them finally succeeded in completing it, only to find that tarnish immediately set in. Discouraged by the caprices of speculum metal, but absorbed by the principles involved, Alvan Clark began making object glasses. By 1853, news of their excellence had reached astronomers throughout the world.

Now it so happened that the founding of Alvan Clark & Son coincided with a sudden awakening of American interest in astronomy. Observatories were springing up in various universities—one of the first was at Harvard College, in Clark's home town—and, since the reflector was at its nadir of disfavor, Clark soon found himself overwhelmed with national demands for instruments. His first really big telescope, an 18½-inch refractor, was completed in 1862, and it is wonderful to record that by the end of the century the Clarks' firm had made what are still the two biggest refracting telescopes in the world: the 36-inch at Lick Observatory in California, and the 40-inch at Yerkes Observatory, Williams Bay, Wisconsin. With more than half a century of use behind them, these magnificent instruments are still in constant employment, eloquent testimony to their makers' genius.

The giant reflectors

It was now time for the refractor's rival to summon itself for the final and conclusive effort. Even in 1845, the great success of Lord Rosse's 6-foot-aperture colossus in detecting extremely faint nebulae proved that the mirror would one day achieve what the lens could not. It was already obvious that object glasses could not grow in size indefinitely. Quite apart from the extreme difficulty of casting huge disks of optically perfect glass, there was the serious drawback of flexure; a lens could be supported only around the rim, whereas a mirror could be held rigidly across the back. So there was no doubt, if only the tarnish problem could be overcome, that reflecting telescopes could be made of a size to shame the greatest refractor.

It was chemistry's turn to aid astronomy; the breakthrough came in 1856, when the German astronomer Carl von Steinheil suggested that a mirror made of glass—an absolutely permanent foundation—could be made highly reflective by the precipitation of silver on the curved surface. If and when the silver tarnished, it could be dissolved off and a fresh coat laid. Moreover, since the glass merely acted as a base for the reflecting layer, it did not need to be as perfect as that required for a lens. The idea was an immediate success, and with the construction in 1879 of a 36-inch reflector by the English amateur A. A. Common, the modern era of giant instruments was truly born. Common himself went further: In 1891, he completed a 60-inch reflector, which must stand as a final tribute to the great age of amateur opticians. For the writing was on the wall. Only the wealthiest of the wealthy could afford to subsidize the building of such tremendous instruments, and such individuals were less and less inclined toward astronomical interests.

Astronomers were now realizing in full measure the importance of more telescopic power. Astounding new facts were coming to light; theories about the stars demanded more research, which itself prompted fresh speculations; and with every increase of aperture, new discoveries were made. On the night of the unveiling of the 40-inch refractor at the Yerkes Observatory by Wisconsin's Lake Geneva, one of the little group of astronomers noticed a faint new star shining beside Vega, the brilliant, blue-white star that passes overhead in late summer in north temperate latitudes. This discovery greatly impressed another in the group, George Ellery Hale, an American solar astronomer.

Indeed, it was Hale who had brought the Yerkes Observatory into being. Having heard that two 40-inch disks, suitable for a colossal new lens, were on the market, he had pestered the Chicago millionaire Charles Yerkes into, first of all, buying them; then into paying the Clarks to grind them; and, finally, into building the entire observatory. Now, realizing that the future hopes of astronomy lay in larger and larger telescopes—and also recognizing that the 40-inch refractor would probably remain king of its kind—he determined to search out funds for new and bigger reflectors. His success is proved by the construction, through his own efforts, of the 60- and 100-inch reflectors at Mount Wilson Observatory in California and the gigantic 200-inch at Mount Palomar. Completed in 1948, the latter is still the largest telescope in the world and will remain so until the Russian 236-inch is installed at the Crimea Observatory.

Yet the magnitude of the modern instrument makers' achievements must not blind us to the fact that useful observations can be made without a huge telescope. Astronomers at the world's greatest observatories are concerned with highly specialized problems that often hover at the very edge of telescopic detection; here the amateur cannot hope to compete, and there is no reason why he should want to, for his domain lies closer to Earth. The details of the surfaces of the moon and planets have been largely neglected by professional astronomers, who mostly devote their time to studying distant stars and galaxies. No matter how humble his equipment—be it no more than a pair of binoculars—anyone can gain a lifetime of pleasure and profit by gazing at the sky, provided he possesses the main essential—perseverence.

2

Simple Telescopes

The construction of a simple refracting telescope should form part of the initiation of every amateur astronomer. For those beginners who cannot yet afford a proper instrument, it will in any case be a matter of necessity; and, no matter how poor the definition, the constructor will certainly learn more about how a telescope works than he can by merely reading a book. It is all very well to have a fine instrument, but if it is to be used with profit it must also be used with insight and wisdom.

This simple telescope will naturally have a single lens for the object glass, and, to combat the chromatic aberration with which the early observers were grimly familiar, it is necessary to choose one with as long a focal length as possible. A very weak, positive spectacle lens is one answer (the sort used to correct farsightedness), but if the local optician does not possess one of the right sort, a camera supplementary lens will do very well. These are designed to fit in front of a camera lens so as to take extremely close-up photographs; they are rated in strengths of 1, 2, or 3 diopters. A diopter is a measure of the focal length of a lens, expressed in terms of the reciprocal of a meter, so that the higher the rating in diopters, the shorter the focal length. A 1-diopter lens has a focal length of one meter, and will serve the purpose admirably; if, in addition, a 2-diopter lens (half the focal length) can be purchased, some interesting experiments can be performed. Both lenses should have the same aperture, and of course be as large as possible—probably about $1\frac{1}{2}$ inches across.

Focal length and image scale

The first task is to measure the focal lengths of the two lenses. This is done by casting an image of the sun on a sheet of paper and measuring the distance from the screen to the lens. If the lenses have been accurately made, their focal lengths should be about 39 inches and 20 inches.

While in this case the focal length is the distance between the lens and its image, this is true only *when the object is at infinity*. If we cast an image of, say, a distant street lamp, the screen will have to be moved a little farther away; the closer the object, the farther away the image is formed. This is why a camera has a focusing screw that varies the distance between the lens and the film. This, however, is of no importance to an astronomer, for all the objects he observes are effectively at infinity.

In the process of measuring the focal lengths, it will become apparent that the sun's image differs in size with each lens; accurate measurement of its diameter will show that the image cast by the 39-inch lens is twice as big as the other. This is because the image size is directly related to the focal length: the longer the focal length, the bigger the image. The relationship can be expressed by a very simple formula:

$$I = \frac{F}{57}$$

Here, I is the scale of 1° and F is the focal length. For example, if the lens has a focal length of 57 inches, an object in the sky 1° across will be exactly 1 inch across on the screen. Since the sun appears as roughly $\frac{1}{2}$° in diameter, it will make an image only $\frac{1}{2}$-inch across. If we want a 1-inch focal image of the sun, the object glass must have twice the focal length: about 9 feet.

Many people begin with the impression that what affects the size of the image is the diameter of the lens. This is quite wrong; the focal length is the only quantity that matters. This can be proved easily enough by placing small diaphragms over the lenses. The smaller the aperture, the fainter the image—but its size remains the same.

Tube and eyepiece

The next task is to mount the two lenses in telescopic form so that their performances can be compared. A cardboard tube will be ideal if it is of the right diameter, with the lens held in at one end by two retaining rings glued to the inside of the tube (figure 5). It is most important to get the lens accurately square-on to the tube; otherwise the image will be distorted. Both refractors and reflectors are equipped with adjusting screws to insure the correct inclination of object glass or mirror. The inside of the tube must be

Figure 5. *A simple refractor.*

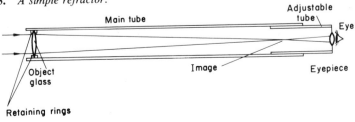

painted mat black to avoid stray reflections when the telescope is pointed to a bright object, and it should be cut off about three inches shorter than the focal length, so that a second, smaller tube can slide stiffly inside for focusing purposes. This smaller tube carries the eyepiece.

The job of the eyepiece is to magnify the image, which it does by allowing the observer's eye to get very close to the image formed by the object glass. It follows from this that the shorter the focal length of the eyepiece, the greater the magnification. For example, most people cannot focus their eyes on anything less than about 6 inches away; if, however, a 1-inch-focus lens is placed before the eye, an object can be seen sharp at a distance of only 1 inch, which gives a magnification of × 6 over the ordinary view. There is no essential difference between examining an insect on a microscope slide and the image of a planet formed by a telescope's object glass. In each case, if we want a high magnification the lens used must have a short focal length. In this particular case, an eyepiece with a focal length of 1 inch will be ideal; only one is needed, for it can easily be interchanged.

(It should be pointed out here that whereas mirrors and object glasses are rated by their aperture—e.g., 3-inch refractor, 6-inch reflector—eyepieces are rated by their focal length: 1 inch, $\frac{1}{2}$ inch, $\frac{1}{4}$ inch, etc.)

It may well be that a simple, short-focus lens is lying around in a drawer somewhere. It will not be in spruce telescopic condition, but it may serve. Or, you can take the eyepiece out of a pair of binoculars; this will be properly corrected by consisting of several lenses and will give a better image than a single-lens eyepiece. If an astronomical eyepiece is available, so much the better. On the whole, it will be beneficial to use a proper achromatic eyepiece, since the performance of the object glass must be tested and eyepiece flaws will only confuse matters. (See Chapter 4 for types of eyepieces.)

The telescope's performance

Once the eyepiece is fitted into the tube and is found to focus the image properly, it is time to point it at something. A distant building will be a useful beginning. The first drawback of the telescope will appear at once: It is quite impossible to hold it steady by hand, and the tube must be rested on a firm support. With a telescope of this size and weight, the mounting problem is relatively minor; later on, when a full-scale astronomical telescope is being used, its importance will become paramount.

The second drawback is often an unpleasant surprise, for the object viewed appears upside down. A terrestrial telescope, or a pair of binoculars, contains an extra lens or prism that reverses the light rays and gives an erect image; but this extra component does its work at the cost of a slight loss of light. Every time a light ray strikes a glass surface, about 4 per cent of its strength is reflected back, and a further small amount is absorbed by the glass. While this loss is imperceptible by ordinary standards, astronomical telescopes must focus every scrap of available light into the observer's eye; the erecting component is therefore always left out. Thus, *every astronomical telescope gives an inverted and reversed view*. Though confusing to the beginner, this soon becomes an accepted feature of observation.

Once the telescope has been found to focus satisfactorily, it is time to try it out at night. The moon is the best object with which to begin, for it is bright enough to be found easily, and its surface is a mass of detail. *A telescope must never be pointed at the sun without efficient protection.* Even a 1-inch-aperture telescope can focus enough heat to result in permanent blindness, and it is senseless to take such a risk.

The first view of the moon will certainly come as a surprise to anyone who has never before viewed it telescopically. No matter how imperfect the image, a great deal of detail can be made out. The immense dark areas can be seen, and along the line separating lunar day and night the craters cast black shadows and are seemingly thrown up into relief. This is probably a better view than old Galileo ever enjoyed with his tiny spyglass. To realize that these features are brought out by a telescope made with one's own hands doubles the pleasure; it is a great pity that so many amateurs miss this simple delight by immediately buying a far more sophisticated instrument that somehow lacks the romance!

If the telescope is now turned to a star (preferably a white one, for an orange tint will bias the experiment), the effects of chromatic aberration can be examined. When the eyepiece is pushed inside the position of best focus, the star image turns blue, since the eye is now focused on the point where the blue rays come to a focus. If the eyepiece is pulled out slightly beyond the best focus, the image turns red, since the red rays have a longer focus than the blue. At the position of best focus, the star's image is yellowish, surrounded by a purple haze. This is because yellow lies in the middle of the visible color spectrum; also, it is the tint to which the eye is most sensitive. The surrounding haze is composed of the out-of-focus red and blue elements.

Magnification and resolving power

Comparison of the views afforded by the two telescopes will bring home three main differences:

1. The long telescope gives better definition.
2. It shows the moon larger.
3. It shows a smaller area of sky.

Point 1 is accounted for by the fact that the relatively long focal length reduces the chromatic aberration. Points 2 and 3 are explained by the higher magnification.

The *magnification* of a telescope, which is measured in diameters, is found very simply: divide the focal length of the object glass or mirror by the focal length of the eyepiece. Thus, the 1-diopter lens used in conjunction with the 1-inch eyepiece gives a magnification of about × 40; the other lens, whose focal length is only 20 inches, gives × 20. The same eyepiece will therefore give different magnifications, depending on the focal length of the telescope with which it is used. Similarly, if we wish to achieve different magnifications with the same telescope, eyepieces of various focal lengths are required.

This explains why the moon appears twice as large in the long telescope, and it is not hard to see why the actual field of view should be reduced when a higher magnification is used. If the eyepiece is removed and the bright sky viewed through it, a circular disk of light is seen whose angular diameter may be anything from 30° to 60°. This is called the *apparent field of view*. Dividing this value by the magnification afforded by the eyepiece gives the *real field of view*. If the eyepiece in question has an apparent field of 40°, it will show just 1° of sky when used with the long-focus lens (× 40), but 2° when used with the other lens at a magnification of only × 20.

Another way of ascertaining the field of view is by direct measurement of the field lens of the eyepiece. The larger this is, the greater the area of the image formed by the mirror or object glass that can be seen at one time. If the objective has a focal length of 57 inches, which means that 1° of sky is represented by 1 inch at the focal plane, then an eyepiece with a field lens $\frac{3}{4}$ inch in diameter will show $\frac{3}{4}$° of sky at one view.

It is natural to suppose that the amount of detail that can be seen through a telescope depends solely on the magnification used. For example, if we have a glossy black-and-white photograph and wish to see some fine detail in it, we use a magnifying glass. But a glossy photograph is not at all a correct analogy of a telescopic image, which may be compared to a newspaper photograph (a coarse-screen halftone). When viewed from a distance (analogous to a low magnification) its outlines seem perfectly sharp, but from close range (high magnification) the detail is lost in a grid of dots. In the case of a 1-inch telescope of the best quality, the image begins to break down with a magnification of about × 100, and nothing is gained by using more powerful eyepieces; the area of the image will expand, but no additional details will be brought out.

For ordinary terrestrial use, where the magnification is relatively small, this sophistication is of little account. But astronomical telescopes have much greater demands made upon them, and when we start using high magnifying powers it soon becomes apparent that the amount of detail visible—for example, on the moon—varies greatly from telescope to telescope, even though the magnification used in all cases is exactly the same! The best way to prove this is to cut a half-inch hole in a piece of cardboard and fit it in front of the object glass. Take note of the smallest visible lunar feature; then repeat the observation with the diaphragm removed. It will be immediately obvious that much finer detail is now visible. The image is also much brighter, but this is a matter of illumination and has nothing to do with the question of *resolution*, or the ability of the mirror or object glass to distinguish objects that are close together.

Continuing our halftone analogy, we might say that the smaller the aperture, the coarser the screen. Putting it more elegantly, *the resolving power of a telescope is proportional to its aperture*. For instance, a 6-inch telescope will reveal a crater on the moon that is only $1\frac{1}{2}$ miles across, but it requires a 12-inch instrument to make out one only $\frac{3}{4}$ of a mile across. No matter what magnification is used on the 6-inch, it cannot exceed this $1\frac{1}{2}$-mile limit. So, if an observer wants to see fine detail on the moon or a planet, or if he wants to make out individually two stars that are very close together in the sky, he must use a large telescope. The astronomer's hunger for bigger and bigger apertures is as much a desire for improved resolution as for increased illumination.

The stars themselves form the best illustration of this effect, for without exception they are so far away that they appear as only points of light, despite the fact that many are far larger than our sun. No telescope can show even the closest one as a real disk, and it is unlikely that such an instrument can ever be built, for it would need to be several times larger than the 200-inch reflector—itself a masterpiece of both optical and mechanical technique. Instead, a telescope shows a star as an artificial disk, named after Sir George Airy, the nineteenth-century mathematician and British Astronomer Royal. This *Airy disk* is produced as a result of diffraction, the converging light beams interfering with each other and spreading out into a tiny disk rather than forming a true point. Its size depends on the aperture of the telescope: The bigger the telescope, the smaller the disk; hence, the better the resolution. A star viewed with a 3-inch telescope appears to have a diameter of about $1\frac{1}{2}$ seconds of arc (written $1''\cdot5$); the same star, if observed with the 40-inch Yerkes refractor, would appear to be only $0''\cdot11$ across. However, when we remember that $1''$ is equal to the diameter of a silver dollar seen from a distance of 6 miles, it is clear that a star disk appears very small even with a 3-inch telescope!

It so happens that many stars are twins. The two components may be separated by several seconds of arc, or they may be very close indeed. At all events, it is clear that a given telescope cannot resolve such a pair if they are closer than this critical resolving limit. Two stars 4″·5 apart can just be resolved with a 1-inch telescope; if they are closer than this, the instrument will show them as either a single star or an elongated disk, and a larger aperture must be resorted to. These values necessarily assume fine optics; it must not be expected that the primitive refractor we have described will attain its theoretical limit. At any rate, it can be tested on some of the double stars listed in Chapter 21.

However, it is well within the handyman's power to make an astronomical instrument far superior to the simple refractor described. A 6-inch mirror for a reflecting telescope can be ground in a few weeks, and it is such an absorbing business that every amateur, whether or not he wants a complete telescope, is strongly recommended to try it. The glass, carborundum powder, and other necessary materials need not cost more than about $6 (£4); and a knowledge of optical work will lead directly to better understanding of a telescope's performance. *Standard Handbook for Telescope Making*, by N. E. Howard, is very complete on the subject.

Opera glasses and binoculars

Despite the passing of the old chromatic telescope, there is one form—in fact, the original form used by Galileo—that is still in use today: the opera glass. Many amateurs have found a pair to be an invaluable addition to their kit. The opera glass is merely a pair of simple telescopes fitted side by side, having object glasses of very short relative focus and eyepieces giving a magnification of × 2 or × 3. The principle on which it works is shown in figure 6. Note that each eyepiece consists of a concave lens placed inside the focus of the object glass. These eyepieces are never used with astronomical telescopes, since the apparent field of view is very small, but in this case they tend to correct some of the color faults of the objective; and since the magnification of an opera glass is extremely low, the field of view is still sufficiently large to make it an invaluable instrument for quickly scanning large areas of the sky. It will presently be seen that magnification is not always desirable; sometimes it is positively objectionable, and it is on these occasions that the opera glass comes into its own.

The big brother of the opera glass, the field glass, has a somewhat larger aperture—about 2 inches—and a magnification of between × 3 and × 6,

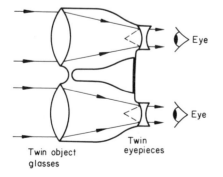

Eye

Eye

Twin object glasses

Twin eyepieces

Figure 6. *Opera glass. Note that each eyepiece, which is negative, is placed inside the focal point.*

which somewhat restricts the field of view. If a higher-powered instrument is required, and it will certainly prove to have many uses, the best answer is to buy a proper pair of binoculars.

Binoculars—which are, or should be, truly achromatic—work on the folded-beam principle. Generally speaking, an achromatic object glass gives the best performance when its focal length is between 10 and 15 times its aperture. If the *focal ratio*, as it is called, is less than 10 (written f/10), it becomes extremely difficult to correct the lens adequately for chromatic effects. If it is longer than f/15, on the other hand, the image scale becomes large and it is impossible to get a wide field of view using normal eyepieces. Since object glasses smaller than about 1¼ inches (30mm) admit too little light to give a really bright view, the only way of making an achromatic instrument really portable is somehow to fold up the long focus into a more compact unit. By using two prisms between each object glass and eyepiece, this is exactly what binoculars do (figure 7). For instance, if the instrument has a 2-inch aperture, the distance to the eyepiece is reduced from the nominal 10 or 15 inches to about 6.

Obviously, a pair of binoculars is anything but simple. Both the object glass and eyepiece in each optical system consist of at least two lenses (often three), and the three functioning surfaces of each prism have to be worked to optical accuracy. They therefore contain at least fourteen separate surfaces, all scrupulously polished and gauged—so that the wonder is not that binoculars are expensive, but that they are so cheap.

Every amateur astronomer should own a pair of binoculars. They are invaluable for learning one's way around the fainter stars in a constellation, for glancing at the moon to see what formations are well placed for observation with the main instrument, for picking up Venus in daylight or other planets in twilight, for observing bright variable stars, and for examining any really bright comet that may come along. For holding them steady, all that is needed is a broom-handle; sharpen one end to a point and fit a cradle to the other in which they can be rested. The observer can then sit comfortably in a chair, sweeping his glass across the sky and altering his attentions with a freedom and speed that is just not possible at the eye end of a large and ponderous telescope.

Figure 7. *Binoculars.*

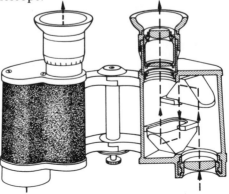

When choosing binoculars for astronomical work, the aperture is the principal bargaining point. Magnification is relatively unimportant—except to the extent that the widest field of view goes with the lowest power, so that it is really of negative account.

Binoculars are always catalogued in the form A × B, A referring to the magnifying power and B to the aperture in millimeters. Thus, 8 × 30 means that the magnification is × 8 and the object glasses are 30mm across. This is the most popular formula for terrestrial work, where there is usually plenty of light available; but for stellar observation a 50mm aperture will be far more effective. The two standard magnifications for this aperture are × 7 and × 10; 10 × 50 glasses will show difficult objects, such as the inner satellite of Jupiter, more easily, but the field of view is restricted. For general use, the 7 × 50 pattern is probably the best. These have a field of view of about 9°, whereas the more powerful types include only about $6\frac{1}{2}°$ and hence show only half the area of sky.

Binoculars can, of course, be had with apertures much larger than 2 inches; 12 × 60 glasses, widely available, will reveal correspondingly fainter stars, and just occasionally one comes across real freaks, often designed for night work during the war. The binoculars used by George Alcock, the English amateur astronomer who has so far discovered four comets and one nova, are rated 25 × 105; naturally, they require a massive stand of their own. However, such an instrument could hardly be used for casual sky-sweeping, and, all in all, the 7 × 50 model will best suit the requirements of the ordinary amateur.

Finding a usable second-hand opera glass is largely a matter of luck. New 8 × 30 binoculars cost from about $40 (£14); 7 × 50 from about $50 (£18); but real bargains can often be found in government and industrial surplus stores specializing in scientific instruments, which often prove to be an inexpensive source of much optical gear. When buying binoculars, it is most important to insure that each eyepiece can be focused independently to allow for individual anomalies; if possible, a star test should be made before final purchase, since the stellar points of light often reveal errors of definition that might go unnoticed on terrestrial objects. Minor scratches on the lenses do not matter, for they make no noticeable difference to the view, but a network of tiny scores, which can be produced by careless cleaning with a dirty cloth, will diffuse faint light into the field and obscure the dimmest stars.

3

Telescopes and Mountings

We have already seen that the astronomer has two completely different types of telescope available for his needs: the achromatic refractor, and the reflector, each having its own advantages and drawbacks. The time has come to decide just which type to choose. The observations to be made and the amount of money that can be spent are the deciding factors—to which might be added the temperament and the mechanical ingenuity of the observer himself. Obviously, a hopelessly heavy-handed individual will not want to worry over delicate adjustments, and he certainly would not even consider making the whole thing himself. Yet many telescopes—and very powerful ones, at that—have been made by amateurs who could not afford the price of a factory-made instrument. For $50 (£20) and the expenditure of a great deal of patience, it is possible to make an instrument worth ten times that sum; and the persevering qualities of the telescope-maker are exactly those required by the good observer. In fact, many people forced by financial circumstances to make their own telescope have found the experience so fascinating that they have ended up as both amateur optician and astronomer!

Reflector or refractor?

Anyone wanting to make his own instrument must choose the reflecting type. This is not because a lens is more difficult to grind than a mirror (in some respects it is easier), but because the manufacture of an object glass requires the use of some rather specialized equipment that is unlikely to be available to the casual amateur. A telescope mirror, on the other hand, can be ground and polished with the simplest of materials; and if this is considered too ambitious, the mirror can be bought separately and fitted into a homemade mounting.

For the moment, however, it will be assumed that the amateur wishes to buy his telescope complete and ready for use. In this case, the choice lies roughly between a refractor of 3 or $3\frac{1}{2}$ inches aperture and a reflector of 6 inches aperture. Anything smaller than this will be ineffective for serious observation, and anything larger will be more expensive, less convenient, and will require more experience on the part of the observer if it is to be used profitably. It is a frequent and natural wish of the beginner to lay his hands on as large a telescope as possible, in the belief that he will see more; but this is a grave mistake. All the greatest observers started out with modest equipment, and it was in the process of overcoming its drawbacks that they trained themselves to excel in the art of observation. This is a vital point, one which we shall discuss in more detail in Chapter 5.

The great advantage of a refracting telescope over a reflector is its ruggedness. The object glass, screwed securely into its cell, requires no attention; once accurately squared-on, so that it forms a symmetrical image, it should not need readjustment for years. The tube itself is strong enough to take many knocks without coming to harm, and the focusing device merely requires an occasional touch of grease.

But a reflecting telescope is altogether a more delicate matter, although it must be admitted that performance varies enormously from maker to maker. In many types, the main mirror, which is held in an adjustable cell at the bottom of the tube, tends to come out of alignment rather easily. More susceptible still is the small plane mirror, or *flat*, which is held opposite the eyepiece at the correct angle by a system of three or four vanes. From time to time this has to be realigned. In addition to this, the reflective coating applied to the front surface of both mirrors has to be protected from harmful particles in the air when the instrument is not in use. In short, the reflector is hardly the sort of telescope that can be stored in the garden shed and brought out ready for use whenever wanted. The best models are fairly trouble-free, and may be used for months without requiring any attention at all, but the owner of a reflector must be prepared to spend more time on upkeep than he would with a refractor.

The question of relative performance, like the controversy over the origin of the lunar craters, has been raging for a hundred years. In apertures up to about 12 inches, a refractor is undoubtedly more effective than a reflector of equal size; and it is a fact that more reflectors than refractors turn out to be optically defective. The recent surge of interest in astronomy, welcome though it is, has in a sense made things more difficult for the prospective telescope purchaser. There is a bewildering choice of instruments available, and the novice cannot be expected to know the good from the bad.

One reason for the refractor's superiority is that its single lens transmits more light to the image than do the reflector's two mirrors.* Secondly, the obstruction of light by the flat slightly affects the resolving power. A third, and perhaps the most important reason, is that mirrors are commonly made f/8 or even f/6, whereas refractors are usually f/15, and the long relative focal length gives a better image. (The necessity of having the eyepiece at the top of the tube makes it impractical to make mirrors of such long relative focal length.) A fourth mitigating factor is that the tube of the refractor is closed at both ends, whereas the reflector's tube is open at the top, which can produce swirling amalgamations of hot and cold air that interfere with the steadiness of the image. These so-called *tube currents* are usually more objectionable with a reflector than with a refractor.

The refracting telescope does not have all the bonus points, however. Though it is true that an object glass of given size is superior to a mirror, the mirror happens to be much cheaper. A first-quality 3-inch object glass costs at least $100 (£40), while the same money will purchase an 8- or 9-inch mirror; and the rough equivalent of the 3-inch lens—i.e., a 6-inch mirror—costs about $40 (£15), complete with the flat.

No would-be astronomer should buy a reflector of less than 6 inches aperture. This is the smallest standard size; most of the 3-, 4-, and 5-inch reflectors that are often seen advertised are incapable of serious work. Money spent on them would be far more wisely invested in a mirror of reasonable aperture, even if the mounting has to be made at home.

For the construction of the homemade mounting, too, the reflecting telescope is a better proposition. An object glass must be mounted in a solid tube, and a lathe is required to do the job properly. The tube is then mounted on a tall tripod, which must itself be rigid. But a reflector has a relatively short tube, and since the eyepiece is located near the top, the stand on which it is mounted is low and therefore easier to make solid. The handy position of the eyepiece also means that, of the two telescopes, the reflector is the more comfortable to use.

A third advantage possessed by the reflector is its perfect achromatism. The reflecting mirror makes no differentiation between light of different wave lengths, but no object glass of the two-element type can be made to give an absolutely colorless image. If the lens is a good one, this slight remaining color (a faint bluish tint) is quite unobtrusive; it will be notice-

---

*Large lenses, on the other hand, transmit relatively *less* light than mirrors, because of the great thickness of glass. The object glass of the 40-inch Yerkes refractor absorbs roughly one-third of the light passing through it. In terms of light transmission, the two types of telescope are comparable at apertures of about 15 inches.

able only when a very brilliant object, such as the moon or Venus, is under observation. But if photography is to be attempted, the perfect achromatism of the reflector will prove to be an immense advantage.

To sum up so far: If a foolproof, ready-to-use telescope is required, $250 (£100), or so will buy a new 3-inch refractor. Alternatively, by very careful perusal and selection (an astronomer friend is of great service here), a second-hand refractor can be picked up for less than $100 (£40). It may need slight attention here and there, but so long as the object glass is good, the focusing movement works smoothly, and the mounting is steady, the telescope should give excellent results.

Buying a new reflecting telescope, on the other hand, is a different matter altogether; here, the pitfalls for the unwary are much greater. For, while the refracting telescope has changed little in either construction or appearance during the past century, the relative delicacy of the reflector has led to a number of different theories about mirror supports, tube design, and so on.

At the turn of the century, two of the greatest names in the amateur reflecting-telescope market were John Browning and George Calver. The success of these makers was logical enough, for both had been amateur astronomers, and they were well aware of the little necessities that are so essential to the observer but would be overlooked by the engineer who was simply asked to "design a telescope."

With the death of their firms came the virtual end of reflecting-telescope manufacture, until the postwar period, when the situation changed. The rapid rise of interest in astronomy and space travel produced a phenomenal demand for small telescopes. But, unhappily, the new firms that sprang up were not headed by men like Browning and Calver, and their telescopes were, and still are, designed by draftsmen having little or no knowledge of observational astronomy, and who are content to produce an efficient engineering job that takes little or no account of the conditions under which the instrument will actually be used. The long and short of the matter is that a person buying a new reflector may well pay out a great deal of money (at least $250 to $300 [£80 to £100], for a 6-inch) for an instrument that is markedly inferior to many homemade types. Though there are one or two exceptions to this rule, it should be clear that buying a reflecting telescope is, to say the least, a chancy business, and it would be foolish to invest a lot of money without taking the advice of an experienced observer.

For this reason, it should be repeated that anyone wanting a reliable, ready-made telescope would be best advised to buy a refractor, whereas the person with less money and a modest workshop can make himself a tube and mounting for a reflector and also, if he feels inclined to experiment, the mirror itself.

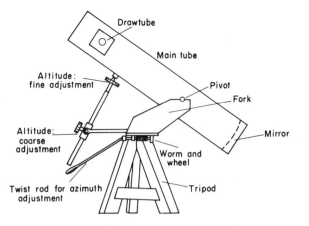

Figure 8. *Altazimuth mounting. This type of stand is suitable for a reflector of from 6 to 12 inches aperture.*

Simple mountings

It is ironical how often the emphasis is put on the excellence of the mirror or object glass, while the mounting itself is given only secondary consideration. The performance of the mounting is quite as important as that of the optics—perhaps even more so. A good lens mounted on a shaky stand is useless, whereas a second-quality lens solidly mounted will at least show something!

Figure 8 shows a simple homemade mounting for a reflecting telescope. The accent is clearly on solidity. The legs of the stand are thick and braced, and the tube itself swings in a fork made of ⅜-inch steel plate. The horizontal pivot is the hub axle of a car, a smooth and rigid axis that has been utilized in many an amateur's telescope.

This stand also includes apparatus for giving a fine adjustment to the position of the tube. Such "slow-motions" become very useful indeed when a star or planet is being viewed under high magnification, for the earth's rotation is also magnified and the object is soon carried out of view. The slow motion in altitude consists of a long rod that can be clamped at the approximate position required, after which a threaded bar screws in and out to provide the fine adjustment. The horizontal (azimuth) motion is provided by a worm-and-wheel arrangement, the wheel (about 6 inches across) being fixed to the top of the tripod stand and the worm to the underside of the fork that carries the telescope itself. This worm can be unclamped when it is necessary to move the instrument through a large arc. This mounting was made with nothing more complicated than a drill gun, hacksaw, and other simple tools that are to be found in any workshop; altogether it cost about $10 (£4) to construct.

One often hears would-be purchasers asking whether such-and-such a stand is "portable." In this, they are begging for trouble, for it is virtually impossible to combine real solidity with true portability. To perform well, a stand must not only be rigid; it must also be heavy. Nor should it contain any folding joints; they can never be locked as rigidly as unjointed members. In short, a light, collapsible telescope stand that can be packed away in the car will never perform satisfactorily when high magnifications are used; any commercial mounting advertised as being "portable" should therefore be viewed with the deepest suspicion.

Naturally, this is not meant to imply that the instrument should be totally immovable. One of the great advantages of a small telescope is that it can be moved over short distances to avoid trees and other obstructions that might block the view of some celestial object. Large apertures really require a well-laid concrete base if they are to be truly steady; if such a telescope is subsequently acquired, the smaller instrument will be found very useful when some infuriating blockage occurs. But this is an entirely different matter. Any compromise between steadiness and portability will inevitably be to the telescope's disadvantage.

Tubes and fittings

Before we discuss the various types of mounting, the telescope tube and immediate fittings deserve attention. The layout of a typical refractor is shown in figure 9; this varies little from model to model. The object glass itself is safely enclosed in a cell, which is screwed into a mount at the top of the tube. This mount is secured to the main tube by three sets of adjustable screws, as shown, so that it can be set and locked absolutely square-on. This is a most important adjustment, since if the object glass is even slightly tilted the telescopic image will be faulty. Projecting in front of the lens, for a distance of at least three diameters, is a tube with a blackened interior called a *dew cap;* this, as its name suggests, decreases the tendency for the lens surface to become dewed in damp weather (see p. 48). Inside the tube are one or two stops, which serve to suppress stray reflections; and, of course, the inside of the tube must be painted mat black. At the other end of the tube is a large knurled knob that allows the eyepiece (which itself screws or slides into a narrower tube) to be focused correctly. In the best telescopes, this is worked by a rack-and-pinion drive inside the tube; some cheaper ones use a simpler friction method. All that matters is that the resultant motion be slow and regular.

A reflecting telescope (figure 10) is rather more complicated. The mirror

Figure 9. *Refractor: tube and fittings.*

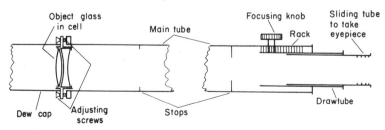

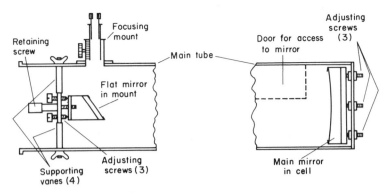

Figure 10. *Reflector: tube and fittings.*

should be held inside a metal cell, which of course has a solid back; this cell is secured to the base of the tube by three adjustable screws which allow it to be lined up correctly. Near the top of the tube, four thin vanes support a metal disk, to which the small flat mirror, in its own cell, is secured. Because of diffraction effects, a three-vane support produces six rays of light around the image of a bright object. A four-vane support gives only four, and is therefore preferable. The flat is elliptical, so that when inclined at the correct angle of 45° and viewed through the eyepiece tube, it appears circular. The flat itself must be adjustable; so must the length of the vanes so that it is located exactly in the center of the tube. It can be seen at once that the business of lining up, or *collimating*, a reflector is rather more complicated than with a refractor; there are also more components to adjust.

The last essential is the focusing mount, opposite the flat, which adjusts the position* of the drawtube into which the eyepiece fits; also, both the mirrors need covers to protect them from dirt and damp when the telescope is not in use.

All refractors have solid (i.e., totally enclosed) tubes; so have many reflectors, but many observers have found that reflecting telescopes work better with framework tubes, which reduce the disturbing tube currents. Briefly, the argument is this: During the day, the telescope and all its components warm up; at nightfall, when the temperature drops, they begin to cool. The metal tube cools very rapidly, giving up its warmth to its surroundings; which means that the air in contact with the tube's surface is cooled, gains density as a result, and sinks down the tube. Soon a system of convection currents is set up, and the swirling air inside the tube so disturbs the image that it is impossible to do any observing until the whole system has cooled down.

The "open tube" enthusiasts point out that if a mere framework is used,

---

*The drawtube must always be fitted in a horizontal position to the east side of the tube (which means that the mouth of the tube is to the observer's left and the mirror to his right). Any other position will upset the orientation of the image.

the air currents can flow freely away from the light-path. This is un-doubtedly true; but it also means that other heat currents, such as those from the observer's body or from the rest of the stand, can get in the way. With an open tube there is also less protection from stray light, although if the observer lives in the country this is of little account. Other experi-menters have found that heating effects are less marked if the tube or framework is made of material that is a poor conductor, such as wood or plastic, but these substances are not, unfortunately, as rigid as metal, and the mirrors will probably need to be collimated more often. If a solid metal tube is desired, one excellent idea is to make it considerably larger than the aperture of the mirror. The swirling air currents, which tend to spiral up around the wall, are then kept clear of the incoming light rays.

A survey of the mass of material available on the subject suggests that the telescope's site has at least as great an influence on image steadiness as has the form and material of the tube. Some solid metal tubes perform quite adequately, especially when inside an observatory, while identical instru-ments elsewhere prove troublesome; there is no hard-and-fast rule, and every amateur will soon develop his own ideas on the subject.

Equatorial mountings

The mountings that have been considered so far have had motion in both altitude and azimuth, and are for that reason known as *altazimuth* mount-ings. Provided they are well made, they perform satisfactorily enough; illustrious proof of this is afforded by Herschel, who mounted all his telescopes in an altazimuth style of his own. As a more recent example, the famous English planetary observer William Frederick Denning was awarded the Royal Astronomical Society's Gold Medal for his work on Jupiter, done with a 10¼-inch Browning reflector on an altazimuth stand. Many contemporary observers own similar equipment. But this type of mounting does have the drawback that adjustments must continually be made in both altitude and azimuth in order to compensate for the earth's rotation. This effect, though normally imperceptible to the naked eye over a period of five or ten minutes, can carry an object right across the field of a high-power eyepiece in ten or fifteen seconds, so that the observer's hands are kept fully occupied manipulating the slow-motions. When he must make a drawing at the telescope, his problems are multiplied!

It is encouraging, therefore, to find that there is a way in which this objection can be partly or entirely overcome. The stars and planets seem to move across the sky because the earth is rotating on its north-south polar axis. If one of the telescope's axes is tilted so that it is exactly parallel to the earth's axis, it is clear that rotation about this axis—in a sense, opposite to

Figure 11. *Principle of the equatorial mount.*

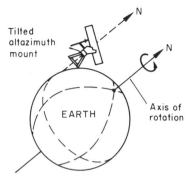

that of the earth—will keep the telescope firmly pointed to any particular celestial object (figure 11). This so-called *equatorial* mounting therefore requires continuous adjustment to one axis only (the *polar* axis), and, since it rotates at a constant speed—once in 23 hours 56 minutes—it can be controlled by a geared-down motor. An old-fashioned phonograph motor performs excellently, for its speed can be varied until exactly the right rate is found.

At right angles to the polar axis is the *declination* axis. This needs adjusting only when finding and locking on to the star; after this, it is clamped and should not require readjustment.

The equatorial stand is clearly a great advance on the simple altazimuth, for even without an automatic drive, the observer need do only half the work to keep the object in view. In addition, such a stand is essential if any sort of celestial photography is to be undertaken. For these reasons, it is worth examining the various available forms of equatorial.

The simplest way of making an equatorial mounting is merely to tilt an ordinary altazimuth stand until its azimuth axis points at the celestial pole (the North Pole is marked approximately by Polaris, the pole star). The telescope shown in figure 8 could be converted in this way, but the result would not be very satisfactory, for the tube could not point to the low southern sky. The mounting would also be out of balance, throwing an unnecessary strain on the slow-motions. Clearly, some reorganization is necessary.

The commonest equatorial mounting is the *German* type, invented by the Jesuit astronomer Christoph Scheiner in Galileo's time, but which first became popular at the hands of Fraunhöfer. Virtually all refractors are mounted in this way, and so are many small reflectors; the principle is shown in figure 12. The mounting is in the form of a T; the stem forms the polar axis, which rotates once a day, having the crosspiece as the declination axis. This carries the telescope tube at one end; at the other end a counterweight maintains the balance. The German-mounted telescope is extremely compact—an especially valuable feature should any sort of observatory be involved.

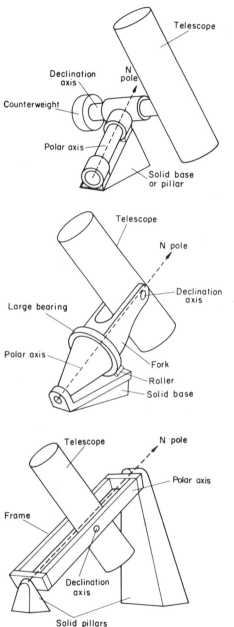

Telescope

Declination axis
N pole
Counterweight

Polar axis

Solid base or pillar

Figure 12. *German mounting. In the case of a refracting telescope, the mounting would be raised above the ground on a tall pillar to make the eyepiece accessible.*

Telescope

N pole

Declination axis

Large bearing

Polar axis

Fork
Roller
Solid base

Figure 13. *Open fork mounting.*

Telescope   N pole

Polar axis

Frame

Declination axis

Solid pillars

Figure 14. *English mounting, or polar frame.*

Some astronomers, however, object to the counterweight's excess baggage; and, in certain positions, the tube can foul the supporting pillar. When this happens, the polar and declination axes must both be turned through 180° to bring the telescope to the other side of the pillar, a process known as "reversing." The *open fork* mounting (figure 13) does not suffer from this defect; it also avoids the use of a counterweight, since the telescope tube is slung between the arms of the fork at the end of the polar axis. Unfortunately, it has drawbacks of another sort. In the first place, it cannot be used with a refracting telescope, since the eyepiece is inaccessible when the tube is pointed near the celestial pole; secondly, the weight of the telescope at the end of the fork means that the polar axis must be extremely rigid, with an especially large bearing at the north end.* A well-built mounting of this type is illustrated.

The *English* mounting (figure 14), also known as the *polar frame*, avoids this second objection, though at the cost of taking up much more

*This book is intended for readers in the northern hemisphere. The polar axes of telescopes used in the southern hemisphere must point to the south rather than the north.

German mounting. *Below left: A 12-inch Calver reflector on a rugged stand made by Calver. It originally belonged to T. E. R. Phillips, a famous planetary observer, and is now in the observatory of A. W. Heath. The upper part of the tube rotates to bring the eyepiece into a convenient position.*

Open fork mounting. *Below right: A 10-inch reflector made and used by G. Turner. The large dimensions of the north bearing on the polar axis insure stability. (G. Turner).*

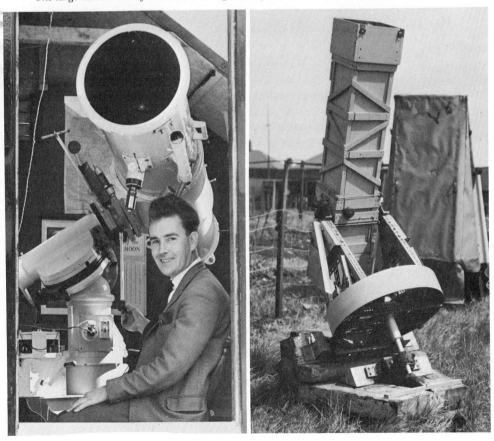

English mounting. *A. Sanderson's 10-inch reflector, mounted in the English style with the declination axis raised above the frame so that the telescope can point to the north celestial pole. The construction is entirely of wood. (The Staveley Iron & Chemical Co., Ltd.)*

room, by swinging the tube inside a closed frame that is pivoted at both ends. This design makes for extreme rigidity; structurally, it is the most stable of the three. Once again, it is unsuitable for refractors because of the length of tube involved, and the region around the celestial pole is blocked by the north bearing, but this latter difficulty can be overcome by raising the tube pivots above the level of the frame. The 60-, 100-, and 200-inch telescopes of the Mount Wilson and Palomar observatories are all mounted on this principle; the 120-inch reflector of the Lick Observatory is the open fork type, and the big refractors all have German stands.

There are, naturally enough, many modifications of these mountings. As figure 15 shows, the frame of the English mounting can be reduced to a single beam, with the telescope pivoted at one side and a counterweight at the other; this, the *modified English* mounting, is a halfway stage between the English and German types. There are plenty of other varieties too, but these three patterns provide the basic choice from which the amateur can design his own mounting. It is worth pointing out that virtually all commercially made stands, whether for reflectors or refractors, are of the German form, since this is economical of both materials and space and can take either type of telescope.

Proof that an equatorial mounting need be no more difficult to construct than an altazimuth is given by the photograph of a 6-inch reflector mounted in the English style. The construction is almost entirely of wood, and the bearings are made stiff enough to hold the telescope firmly in any position and yet allow free motion when required. If this is not considered sufficient,

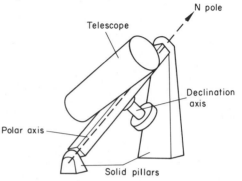

Figure 15. *Modified English mounting.*

English mounting. *A very simple equatorial mounting for a 6-inch reflector, made by L. Pointon. The construction is of wood. There are no slow motions, the pivots being sufficiently stiff to hold the telescope firmly in any desired position. (G. Turner).*

a driving wheel can be added to the polar axis, the main difficulty being in finding a sufficiently large wheel. In order to guide smoothly, especially if a mechanical drive is being used, a diameter of at least 6 or 8 inches is required, and the bigger it is the better. Motion is supplied through a worm wheel.

The English mounting is probably the easiest type for the amateur to construct, since it is well balanced and simple bearings will serve quite well. The principal problem is making the frame stiff enough to prevent flexure. It must be built massively; if of wood, 3 × 2-inch beams are the minimum size suitable for a 6-inch reflector, and 4 × 3 would be better still. It must be remembered that such a telescope will often be used with magnifications of × 200 or × 300, and under these conditions the tiniest tremor is magnified to disastrous proportions. One other very efficient basis for a mounting (the modified English) is a car's complete rear axle. The shaft forms the polar axis, revolving on the hubs at either end, and the telescope is pivoted on the central differential, with a suitable counterweight at the other side. This will hold a 6- or 8-inch reflector very firmly, and a rear axle is not difficult to obtain. Really, anything goes in the world of amateurs' telescopes; there is no need to be shy of using unorthodox materials or ideas! Water-softening units and old geysers, or hot water boilers, are just two of the many surprising items to be found in homemade mountings, and large-diameter water pipe has a multitude of applications.

An entire book could be devoted to this subject; but since we must be brief, here is a short summary. There can be no doubt at all that an equatorial offers more convenient observing conditions than an altazimuth, and for photography it is indispensable. On the other hand, for anyone who has "horizon problems" and needs to move his telescope around to avoid obstructions, an altazimuth stand will be handier, since an equatorial mount must be aligned accurately with the earth's axis, and this adjustment should preferably remain undisturbed. An equatorial can also be used to find very faint stars at night, or bright planets during the day, by a process employing celestial latitude and longitude; the same objects can usually be found with a telescope on an altazimuth stand, but the task is more difficult.

It has frequently been stated that for "serious" observation an equatorial mounting is "essential." This is utter nonsense. Apart from celestial photography, there are hardly any amateur observations that are impossible with an altazimuth stand as against an equatorial. The main difference is that with an altazimuth an amateur has to take more care, since life is that much harder for him; but, by learning to overcome these difficulties, he will gain experience as an observer and a much greater appreciation of the advantages offered by an equatorial telescope.

Two mountings to avoid

Just occasionally one comes across unwise mountings, and it is as well to be warned in advance. In the writer's experience there are two: ancient and modern. The traditional deathtrap of any telescope (usually a small refractor) is the *pillar and claw* mounting. Also known as the *table stand*, it consists of a vertical pillar about a foot high supported on three crablike legs. On the top of the pillar is a universal joint, to which the telescope is attached, and the whole device is supposed to be stood upon a table. It is hardly necessary to add that since tables are not normally made five feet high, it is quite impossible to look through the telescope at a star without grovelling on one's knees; in any case, so lightweight a mount lacks the necessary stability. Three-inch refractors on table stands often come at bargain prices and are well worth purchasing, provided the stand itself is disposed of and replaced by a proper tripod. In this connection, it is amazing how many manufacturers design their tripods for a race of dwarfs; the legs should be quite six feet long, so that the observer can stand comfortably erect when using the instrument.

The second device originated in the United States. It is known as the *Springfield* mounting, and is intended to satisfy the needs of the observer who wishes to remain stationary in a chair. The Springfield is certainly ingenious, for by the use of an extra mirror in the optical train, the eyepiece of a reflecting telescope is made absolutely stationary. However, this advantage is gained at the cost of a slight loss of light and, possibly, definition; in addition, the image is reversed, as compared with the ordinary telescopic view, which makes it almost impossible to refer to charts. The reasoning behind the Springfield may be sound, but the lack of published observations made with it suggests that it is the plaything of the amateur optician and mechanic rather than useful to the practical astronomer.

Collimation and testing

Any telescope, whether new or secondhand, must be tested before purchase to see how well it defines. Although the sight of a reputable maker's name on the side of the tube can inspire confidence, its excellence should not be assumed on this basis. This is because every mirror or object glass has to be given its finishing touches or "figuring" by a skilled craftsman; and as the skill varies from worker to worker, so will the resultant quality. There is no question of mass-producing fine optics; as a result, every telescope must be examined on its own merits. A star test is the safest guide to quality, but before this can be made, the optical components must be collimated.

Aligning a reflector's mirrors is an operation best done by daylight. First of all, remove the lenses from a high-power eyepiece so that only the diaphragm with the central hole is left, and screw this into the drawtube (alternatively, a diaphragm can be made from a piece of cardboard). On looking through this hole, the main mirror is seen reflected in the flat as a circle of bright light; the flat is then adjusted in inclination until the reflection of the main mirror appears central.* Provided the flat is in the center of the tube (an adjustment effected by altering the length of the vanes) and is directly opposite the drawtube, it can be locked and does not need further attention.

The outline of the flat itself is reflected in the main mirror, appearing as a central black spot, with arms (the vanes) radiating from it. The most tedious part of the operation is to adjust the main mirror, using its three screws, until the reflection of the flat is directly in line with the drawtube and symmetrical in the reflection of the mirror (figure 16). It is useful to remember that if the flat appears to one side of the mirror's reflection, the screw on the *opposite* side should be *advanced*. It is a great help if a friend can be enlisted to do the adjusting while progress is followed through the drawtube.

The collimation of a reflector is critical, since a mirror working at f/8 has a relatively narrow field of good definition, and if it is even slightly off axis the image will be imperfect. With a focal ratio as short as f/6, the adjustment is even more vital, and the reflector's bad record so far as performance goes may be partly due to the user's neglect in insuring that the mirrors are correctly aligned. It is an excellent idea to make a habit of checking the collimation before an observing session.

The adjustment of a refractor must be carried out at night. Select a fairly bright star (the polestar is a good choice for northern observers), and examine its image under a high power. If the alignment is perfect, the star will appear as a tiny spot that expands into a circular disk or system of rings both inside and outside the correct focus. If the expanded disk is

*Strictly speaking, the image of the mirror should appear slightly displaced towards the bottom of the tube, since a cone does not pass through an inclined ellipse symmetrically. However, this refinement is negligible with apertures smaller than f/5 or f/6.

Figure 16. *Adjustment of a reflector. This shows the correct alignment of the mirrors when viewed through the drawtube with the eyepiece removed.*

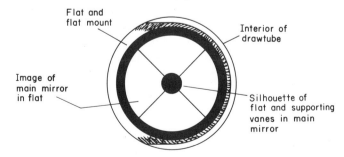

elliptical, however, it means that the object glass is not correctly squared-on, and it will be impossible to get a perfectly round, sharp image at the focus. In this case, the adjusting screws must be attended to until the necessary symmetry is obtained.

The optical quality of a telescope can most easily be ascertained by comparing the intrafocal and extrafocal images of a star. At the focus, it should appear as a tiny spot, almost a point, of light, and if the telescope is a refractor this spot should be surrounded by two or three faint and narrow rings called *diffraction rings*. Atmospheric conditions must, however, be steady to show this well. If the eyepiece is then moved slightly inside the point of best focus, the image expands into a disk; as it is moved farther inside, this disk should break up into a number of rings. The same sequence of events, giving precisely similar effects, should occur when the eyepiece is moved outside the focus.

A reflecting telescope, because of its shorter focal ratio, is very unlikely to show diffraction rings either around the focused image or in the expanded disk. Instead, these disks should appear evenly illuminated, with a black spot in the center representing the outline of the flat. If the mirror is perfect, the disks should appear identical at equal distances inside and outside the focus.

The advantage of the test just described—which should be performed with the most powerful available eyepiece—is that it can be carried out under almost any atmospheric conditions, even when the air is too unsteady to show the focused star as anything but a tiny, jiggling blur of light with no trace of the fair-weather diffraction rings. The disadvantage is that it is perhaps *too* sensitive. Many telescopes perform splendidly even when the expanded images are somewhat anomalous, and it can safely be said that if the disks are "more or less" alike, the telescope is a good one.

A reflector is perfectly achromatic, but a refractor needs to be examined for color correction as well as definition, and this can be assessed at the same time. A well-corrected lens will show a lilac-green fringe to the disk outside the focus, to be replaced by crimson when the eyepiece is advanced inside; at the point of focus there should be no extraneous color at all, unless the object is very brilliant, when a bluish halo will be apparent. If the lens is overcorrected (i.e., compensated too strongly) the outer fringe will be orange, the inner one bluish, and a very obvious bluish haze will surround the focused image. The characteristics of undercorrection, on the other hand, are turquoise and orange borders to the extrafocal and intrafocal images, respectively, and a red glare at the position of best focus.

The experienced observer can tell at once when a telescope's optics are first-rate. The planet Jupiter is a fine test object, and so is Venus when seen in a twilight sky. If the lens or mirror is a good one, the edge of the planet should come up critically sharp, and the slightest movement of the eyepiece should make an obvious difference to the definition. Atmospheric turbulence may make the image ripple and boil, but there is a clear difference between this effect and the misty outlines associated with poor optics. It is hardly necessary to point out that the eyepiece used in these tests should be of established excellence, for any inherent faults will certainly prejudice the telescope's performance.

If a star expands into an elliptical rather than circular disk, and the axis is crossed at a right angle inside and outside focus, *astigmatism* is present. This may have been caused by faulty alignment, but if this is not the case, it must be caused by one of the components. Astigmatism is almost always the sign of poor optical work or strained glass. Such an astigmatic telescope is worthless.

The villain can be weeded out by a simple process of elimination. An astigmatic component always distorts at a constant angle relative to itself, since it is effectively a good lens or mirror that has subsequently been slightly "bent" across the diagonal. Hence, rotation of the culprit will produce a corresponding rotation of the expanded ellipses. A reflector's flat is a likely source of trouble, or the fault may even lie in the observer's eye, although with an eyepiece of high power this effect is unlikely to manifest itself (see p. 64). Provided the mirror or object glass is good, however, it may be worth going ahead with the purchase and paying a little extra money to replace the faulty component.

4

Maintenance, Accessories, and Observatories

While the fundamentals of the telescope—objective, tube, and mounting—must rightly receive first attention, there are other important items to attend to. Indeed, unless the accessories are of the same quality as the instrument itself, its efficiency will certainly be reduced. In this category are eyepieces, finders, and other immediate accessories; the larger question of whether or not to build a proper observatory; and the all-important matter of keeping the optics of the telescope in good condition.

Types of eyepiece

Eyepieces, or oculars, are probably the chief culprits behind poor telescopic performance. It is amazing how many people spend a considerable amount of money on a first-class telescope, then buy a battery of cheap eyepieces that give inferior results. It is also a fact that many makers have the same bad habit; so it is clearly worth knowing something about the different kinds of eyepiece and their various characteristics.

Almost all eyepieces consist of two or more lenses. In some types, these provide better color-correction, while in others they give a wider field of sharp definition; a single lens gives good results only in the very center of the field, which is why it is rarely used. With a two-lens eyepiece, the component nearest the eye is called the *eye lens;* the other one, facing the objective, is called the *field lens.*

The most common type of eyepiece is the *Huygenian,* named after the seventeenth-century astronomer; it consists of two plano-convex lenses (i.e., one side flat, the other convex), with both flat sides facing the eye. Between the two components, at the focus of the eye lens, is a pierced diaphragm known as the *field stop*, which cuts off the badly defined margins of the field of view. A variation on the Huygenian eyepiece is the *Ramsden* type, in which the convex surfaces face each other. (Both types are shown in figure 17.) The advantage of the Ramsden is that the edge of the field is not so blurred; but neither of these eyepieces is truly achromatic, and for the finest definition a more sophisticated type must be used. This is especially important in the case of a reflecting telescope, since a Huygenian or Ramsden eyepiece will badly upset the perfect achromatism of the mirror.

An *Achromatic Ramsden*, similar though not identical to the *Kellner* (with which it is often confused), is often chosen for low magnifications. This consists of a plano-convex field lens and an achromatic eye lens, consisting of two separate components. An Achromatic Ramsden gives a fairly wide field of view, but it has one most annoying feature: The surface of the field lens is in the focus of the eye lens, so that any dust specks that happen to be present are painfully obvious. Another drawback is its tendency to internal reflections, so that bright stars often appear to have fugitive companions. These "ghosts" can be most misleading, and it is as well to remember which eyepieces in the battery are "haunted."

The *Orthoscopic* is another haunted eyepiece, but it gives a very wide field of view and a colorless image, although the definition falls off at the margins. It makes a very suitable eyepiece for low and medium powers. For high-power work, involving critical definition, the Tolles and Monocentric are very effective. The *Tolles* type, which is especially effective with reflectors, consists of a single glass cylinder, with both ends convex; the *Monocentric* contains three lenses cemented together. Since there can be no internal reflections in either of these types, they are quite ghost-free, and so

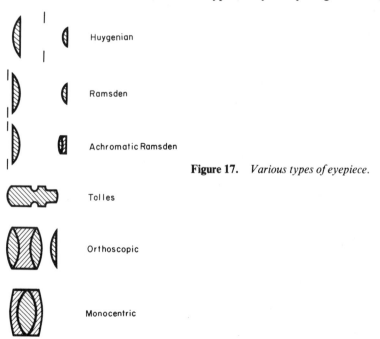

Huygenian

Ramsden

Achromatic Ramsden

Figure 17.   *Various types of eyepiece.*

Tolles

Orthoscopic

Monocentric

are exceptionally useful for hunting faint stars in the vicinity of bright ones. They are also ideal for planetary work, in which study their small fields of view matter little. The *Erfle*, another eyepiece that has become popular in recent years, is somewhat similar to the Orthoscopic and is useful for low powers since it has an extremely wide field of view, although it is badly haunted.

The choice is wide, and this makes it even more regrettable that few opticians have progressive ideas on ocular matters; they persist in dealing out Huygenians regardless of telescope and magnification. Most of these atrocities consist of a solid brass mount with a raised and threaded rim for a suncap, while the tiny eye lens is buried so deep in the mount that little or nothing can be seen. These should be arbitrarily rejected. Modern eyepieces are much improved, with the eye lens readily accessible, and these add immensely to the comfort of observing. Of course, the longer the focal length of the eyepiece (the lower the power), the larger the lenses can be. An eyepiece with a focal length of, say, $\frac{1}{6}$ of an inch, must clearly be a minute affair.

One way of achieving very high powers without the discomfort of using tiny eyepieces is to invest in an *Achromatic Barlow lens*. This is a biconcave "negative" lens, so called because it diverges the light rays passing through it instead of converging them to form an image, as does the usual convex "positive" lens. It is supplied in a short tube that fits inside the telescope's drawtube, some inches in front of the eyepiece. The Barlow effectively increases the focal length of the objective without necessitating a corresponding increase in the length of the tube, so that the magnification is stepped up by an amount depending on the actual position of the Barlow. Some enterprising opticians have designed variable-power eyepieces on this principle, incorporating a negative lens that can be slid to and fro to produce a wide range of magnifications.

Because of the longer focal ratio of the objective, Barlow lenses work better with refractors than with reflectors; however, if well made and truly achromatic, there is no reason why they should not give excellent definition with either type of telescope. The one slight disadvantage is that the introduction of an extra lens into the system makes the image slightly dimmer, since each glass surface reflects away about 4 per cent of the light falling on it; in the case of bright objects, such as the moon and Jupiter, however, this is of minor importance. If the image does appear too faint, though, it may be worth experimenting with a single lens, such as the eye lens taken from a high-power Huygenian. A single lens transmits more light than a compound eyepiece, and the extra brilliance of the image may well compensate for the lack of achromatism and sharpness away from the very center of the field. As a rough guide, the magnifying power of a Huygenian eyepiece is increased by about one third when the eye lens only is used.

Magnifying powers

To use a telescope to its fullest capacity, a number of different magnifications are necessary. A very low power, with a consequently wide field of view, gives the best results on extended objects, such as star clusters and comets; a medium power will show a large area of the moon in considerable detail; and a high power is necessary for the glimpsing of fine planetary markings and the resolution of close double stars. Depending on circumstances, each is essential, and it is no use trying to compromise. On the other hand, there is no point in buying great numbers of eyepieces. Four different magnifications are all that a small or moderate telescope really requires. Thus:

	Low	Medium	High	Very high
3-inch refractor	× 20	× 70	× 150	× 200
6-inch reflector	× 30	× 100	× 180	× 250
10-inch reflector	× 40	× 100	× 200	× 300

On excellent nights, it is possible to use powers as high as × 350 with a 6-inch or × 400 with a 10-inch, but it is doubtful whether such eyepieces will show detail more clearly than a lower power, for with very high magnifications the image of the moon or a planet is spread out over a large area and so appears much dimmer than when viewed with a lower power. The stars, being virtual points of light, are an exception to this rule and take magnification better. As a rough indication, it has been found that planetary observers using telescopes of between 6 and 12 inches aperture rarely employ powers greater than between 30D and 40D, where D is the aperture expressed in inches. A 3-inch refractor can give good results with powers as high as 70D; on the other hand, the great refractors at Lick and Yerkes give splendid performances with much lower relative powers. E. E. Barnard, one of the greatest observers of modern times, found that a power of × 1000 was on the whole too high for planetary work with the 36-inch telescope; and that powers of between × 350 and × 600 (roughly, between 10D and 20D) gave the best results.

The reason for this general deprecation of high powers lies not in the quality of the telescope but in the instability of the atmosphere. It is usually a gyrating mass of air currents at various temperatures, which refract the light irregularly and cause the image to swirl and flicker; thus, stars "twinkle" on very unsteady nights. Only when the air is calm and the image placid are very high magnifications feasible; even then, depending on the object under review, they may not be necessary. It will soon be learned from experience that, far from always using high powers, the lowest magnification that shows sufficient detail is much to be preferred. With a powerful eyepiece, not only is the image made dimmer and the field of view much reduced, but also every slight tremor of the telescope is augmented.

Opticians formerly had a very bad tendency to exaggerate the power of their eyepieces—in other words, to understate the focal length. Even today, it is unwise wholly to trust the figure inscribed on the side of an ocular. One of the easiest ways to find the true magnification given by an eyepiece is to use a measuring instrument called a *dynamometer* (shown in figure 18).

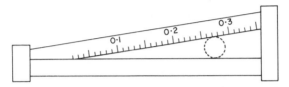

Figure 18. *Dynamometer. The value of the scale divisions depends on the angle between the two edges.*

Its working is self-explanatory, and it can be made from an old steel rule. The telescope, with the eyepiece in position, is pointed to the daylight sky; a small circular disk of light is seen in the eyepiece if it is examined at a distance of a few inches, and its diameter can be measured with the dynamometer. Dividing this into the diameter of the objective gives the magnification.

Good eyepieces cost from at least $8 to $10 (£3 to £4) each, and a Monocentric, the most expensive type, will undoubtedly cost much more. They therefore deserve careful treatment; cramming them into the observer's coat pocket does them no good at all! The best container is a small wooden box with a hinged lid and false bottom, in which are cut a number of 1¼-inch holes to take the eyepiece barrels. In this way, they cannot shift around and scratch each other, and if they are always stored in the same order it becomes a simple matter to pick out the right one in the dark. Should the lenses become dirty, as may be the case after several nights' use, the offending matter should be gently whisked off with a soft, damp brush. Rubbing the surfaces with a cloth will certainly produce scratches.

The care of objectives

Second-hand object glasses are often not only dirty on the outside; they may also be stained on the inside surfaces. This often happens when the cold lens is taken indoors; dew forms on the glass, and it cannot evaporate quickly in the confined space. The same "sweating" sometimes occurs outdoors when the air temperature happens to rise rapidly, and ordinary dewing is a common feature of autumnal nights. Since prolonged moisture is bad for the lenses, and may even stain them permanently, it is a good idea to give such an object glass a proper cleaning. After that, if reasonable care is taken, there is no reason why it should ever have to be taken apart again.

Many writers insist that a lens should be dismantled only by a qualified optician; but there is no real reason for this, provided elementary care is taken. First of all, unscrew the cell from the end of the tube and place it face down on a pad of soft cloth. Next, unscrew the retaining ring in the back of the cell. The two components can now be lifted out by placing a handkerchief over the rear (flint) lens, turning the whole assembly face up, and lifting the cell away from the lenses.

Before they are separated, examine the edges for two adjacent pencil marks. These indicate the correct orientation of the components with respect to each other and the lenses must be reassembled in the same way. Few object glasses are quite insensitive to orientation, usually through fractional errors in lens thickness at different points on the circumference; if this precaution is not observed, therefore, the performance will suffer.

Now lift off the convex lens and lay it aside. It may be that three tiny pieces of foil, known as *spacers*, have been placed around the circumference, to keep the two lenses slightly apart. If so, these too must be kept in a safe place. The lenses themselves can now be cleaned, preferably in warm soapy water, washed down afterwards with clean water and stood on edge to dry. Special care must be taken with the flint component, for flint glass scratches more easily than crown. Once they are thoroughly dry they can be reassembled, with great care to match up the edge marks. The retaining ring, incidentally, should be left with a tiny amount of slack, so that the object glass gives a slight rattle when gently shaken; a tight grip may strain the lenses and spoil the performance.

While all large lenses are of this "air-spaced" type, the components of some small ones may be cemented together with Canada balsam, a colorless adhesive. It need hardly be added that such cementing should not be disturbed—in any case, no dewing could possibly occur between the surfaces of such an object glass.

The mirrors of a reflecting telescope are altogether more accessible. If they are aluminized, a six-monthly wash in detergent will clean off the dirt and keep them highly reflective for years on end, provided they are kept covered when not in use. The old process of silvering has almost entirely vanished, for aluminium reflects light just as efficiently and lasts much longer—for five years, or even more.

The greatest enemy of an aluminized mirror is, oddly enough, salt. This forms a dull white chloride; for this reason the mirror's surface should never be touched with the fingers. It is interesting to find that some amateurs who live very near the sea find this effect so serious that silvered mirrors give better results. This is just one example of how local conditions can have an unexpected effect.

Mirrors must always be kept covered and dry when not in use. A circular disk of cardboard, covered with soft cloth and padded with cotton wool, is the best protection for the main mirror; this can be held down by the cap that fits over the cell. If the tube is of the solid variety, a small door somewhere near the bottom is required for the insertion and removal of the cover. A much lighter cap will serve for the flat. Similarly, in the case of a refractor, it is a good idea to put a pad of dry cloth inside the cap that covers the object glass.

Finders

The finder, a small, wide-field telescope fitted to the main instrument to allow it to be pointed quickly at the required object, is a most important accessory. This is another item that many manufacturers, being only remotely acquainted with the observer's many requirements, tend to dismiss summarily. They are often inconveniently placed, and may not even be adjustable. But the main trouble is that most finders are far too small. The usual type supplied with a 3-inch refractor has an object glass about $\frac{3}{4}$ inch across; and, while this is large enough to find the moon or Jupiter, it is far from satisfactory where fainter objects are concerned. The finder should be considered as an astronomical telescope in its own right. Nothing less than a $1\frac{1}{2}$-inch aperture will give a good view of the sky, and a 2-inch telescope is better still. Such an instrument will not only make it easy to pick up difficult objects, but it will also show very extended features, such as star clouds and bright comets, even better than the main instrument.

Some really excellent low-power telescopes are available in government and industrial surplus stores specializing in scientific instruments. These make ideal finders for any telescope of from 3- to 12-inch aperture. I once bought a 7 × 50 monocular with a prism system similar to that used in binoculars, and found that it makes an excellent finder for a $3\frac{1}{2}$-inch refractor. It had originally been designed as a gun sight, and the cost was less than \$12 (£5); so that two, if mounted side by side, would work out considerably cheaper than binoculars of the same specification and quality. The only drawback in using a relatively large finder is that the telescope tube needs some sort of counterweight to restore the balance. Such a telescope also has another advantage: It gives an erect image and so provides a direct comparison with the naked-eye view.

The finder should contain cross wires to mark the exact center of the view, so that this point can be matched with the field of a high-power eyepiece on the main telescope. If these are not already included, they can be supplied by stretching two pieces of spider web, or even human hair, across the field stop of the eyepiece, so that they appear in focus against the sky. Unfortunately, if the observer is favored with the truly black skies of rural sites, he will find that the cross wires disappear from view! In this case, provision must be made for illuminating the wires so that they stand out against the sky. The way of doing this is to cut a small hole in the side of the eyepiece so that the light from a low-voltage bulb, wrapped in red cellophane, can shine on the wires. The illumination must be sufficient to make the wires clearly visible, but no more, or the faintest stars in the field will be lost.

Dewing troubles

On a night when the air temperature falls rapidly and the air is calm, the active astronomer is apt to have a frustrating time. Such conditions often offer splendid atmospheric conditions, and the steady telescopic images are conducive to observation; but they also provide a heavy fall of dew, and this precipitation must at all costs be kept off the optical surfaces. It is infuriating to have to disrupt the observing session to let a component dry out; it is also harmful to aluminized surfaces, for repeated dewing can undermine the reflective film. Prevention being more satisfactory than cure, it is wise to see what can be done to combat this menace.

Dew falls on cold, exposed surfaces, and, in the case of a refractor, the best way of preventing precipitation on the surface of the object glass is to provide a dew cap. This is a long cylinder extending out over the lens. To be serviceable under all conditions its length should be about three times the aperture of the object glass; those supplied by the manufacturer are invariably too short, and it is best to make another one—preferably of some light material, such as tin—and line it with black blotting paper. If it is too long, however, the effective aperture of the telescope may be cut down slightly, and it is best to make it in the form of a funnel rather than a perfect cylinder. The object glass of the finder needs similar protection. If, during a night's work, the image begins to turn hazy—a sure sign of dewing—a piece of warm, dry cloth, such as a handkerchief, should be placed loosely inside the dew cap and a cover put over the end. The dew will vanish in a very few minutes.

In the case of a reflecting telescope, dewing troubles are dependent on the nature of the tube. It is almost impossible for the main mirror to dew up if protected by a solid tube, but the flat is more troublesome. In this case, it depends on how far the walls of the tube project beyond the position of the flat. The material of the tube can also have an influence, metal offering less protection than some nonconductor of heat such as wood.

There is no way of directly shielding a flat, as there is for an object glass; but some observers have successfully overcome dewing tendencies by heating the glass. This is not as drastic as it sounds; a tiny amount of heat will raise the temperature of the surface fractionally above that of the air, and under these conditions no dewing can possibly occur. The best way of applying the heat is to insert a small flashlight bulb, wrapped in tin foil so that no light can escape, inside the mounting of the flat. The wires can be led away along one of the vanes and thence to the power supply. A transformer working from the domestic supply is convenient, provided that all contacts are insulated against damp.

When wiring up the telescope in this way, it is extremely useful to include a dim red or green lamp for general illumination. This can be fixed to the tube or stand so that it shines down on the notebook; if a variable resistance is included in the circuit, the brightness can be adjusted so that it is just enough for reading or making notes without eyestrain. Too bright a light will dazzle the eye and make it unfit for viewing faint objects, so it is essential to achieve just the right level.

If the reflector has an open tube, the main mirror is far more susceptible to dewing troubles. A certain amount of protection is offered by wrapping some material, such as black cloth, around the lower half of the tube; but if damp persists in forming, it may be removed by placing the cover, previously heated in some warm place, over the cell. A mirror must never be closed up for the night when damp, as the reflective film will suffer.

The most dew-prone item of all is the ocular's eye lens, which quickly mists up in the presence of the observer's body warmth. As soon as the lens itself warms up, the trouble vanishes. The best way of accelerating the process is to wrap the eyepiece in a clean handkerchief and carry it in an inside pocket for some minutes before the observing session begins.

Notebooks and atlases

The organized observer, before going to his telescope, adopts a plan of campaign. He decides just what he is going to observe and what materials he will need. This decision will be dictated, in part at least, by weather conditions. If the sky is very dark and the stars twinkle a great deal, it is the sign of a transparent but unsteady atmosphere. Planetary observation on such a night will probably be a waste of time; on the other hand, it will offer splendid opportunities for hunting faint objects, such as nebulae or any comet that happens to be about. These must be marked on a star chart, and the purchase of a good star atlas is just as important as the acquisition of a telescope.

The best-known and most universal publication, used by astronomers and observatories all over the world, is *Norton's Star Atlas and Reference*

Handbook. The atlas covers the whole sky in sixteen separate charts showing all the stars visible with the naked eye and some fainter ones. It also includes a great many telescopic objects of interest. The associated handbook is no less useful, containing a multitude of facts and tables, and the work can rightly be termed essential for every practical observer.

Another widely available chart is the *Atlas Coeli*, compiled by A. Becvár of the Skalnaté Pleso Observatory in Czechoslavakia. This shows stars down to about magnitude 7·75, which is roughly the limit of a pair of 8 × 30 binoculars, and includes a catalogue that gives details of the color and type of all the naked-eye stars. While the atlas is more comprehensive, it is much more bulky than *Norton's* and not so convenient to use at the eyepiece. Becvár has followed this up with three large-scale atlases: *Borealis* (north), *Eclipticalis* (central), and *Australis* (south). Together, these atlases show more than 100,000 stars brighter than the 9th magnitude. These are obviously very useful if a very faint star or minor planet has to be identified, but the newcomer to astronomy is unlikely to require such sophisticated maps. Even more comprehensive is the *Photographic Star Atlas* compiled by a German amateur, Hans Vehrenberg. This shows stars as faint as the 13th magnitude, which is roughly the limit of an 8-inch telescope. Another useful publication is H. B. Webb's *Atlas of the Stars*, which shows stars down to magnitude 9·5 but does not cover the far southern regions. For observers in north temperate latitudes, however, this is no great handicap. N. E. Howard's *The Telescope Handbook and Star Atlas* includes fourteen maps showing stars down to the 6th magnitude, with the telescopic stars printed on transparent overlays. It also includes a listing of the Messier objects by season rather than by number.

Two famous atlases, which the amateur is unlikely to possess but which may be consulted in astronomical libraries, are Argelander's *Bonner Durchmusterung* and the Beyer-Graff *Stern Atlas*. The *B.D.* covers the northern half of the sky down to about 10th magnitude; the Beyer-Graff atlas descends farther south but shows stars only to the 9th magnitude.

Besides having a chart of the permanent features of the sky, the amateur needs to keep in touch with its changing aspects. The standard work on celestial movements throughout the year is *The American Ephemeris and Nautical Almanac*, published annually, its contents identical with the British *Nautical Almanac and Astronomical Ephemeris*. This contains daily positions of the sun, moon, and planets; details of the planets' rotation and the positions of their satellites; eclipse information; and a wealth of detail of far more complexity than the amateur is ever likely to require. The essential matter is included in another valuable publication, *Handbook of the British Astronomical Association*, which also gives details of expected comet appearances for the year in question. Unexpected events, such as new comet discoveries, are relayed through the *Announcement Cards* of the Harvard University Observatory and the *Circulars* of the British Astronomical Association. In addition to these, notes on coming phenomena are included in *Sky and Telescope*, an excellent monthly journal of astronomical affairs.

A scientist's worth is revealed by the state of his notebooks; from the beginning, the amateur astronomer must take the business of documentation seriously. If an observation is worth making, it is worth making well; one never knows whether a few innocent notes may not have an important bearing on some subsequent discovery. To begin with, when one is engaged in "learning the constellations," notes can be written up in a general observing book, preferably with alternate ruled and blank pages to allow drawings to be included. Later, when definite fields of observation are adopted, a separate observation book should be kept for each object; but it is also a good idea, as a sort of index, to make a brief note of such observations in the general book, using this for notes at the telescope, copying them later—a process, incidentally, that should not be delayed until memory has faded. Every observation must be prefaced by the date and time (preferably using Universal Time, which is 5 hours fast on E.S.T.), details of telescope and magnification, and the state of the air. The amount of care taken in documentation can make all the difference between an interesting observation and a definite record of permanent value.

Some luxury items

The observer's physical comfort is of paramount importance. At the instant of making a critical observation, every muscle in the body must be relaxed to allow the retina full play in picking up the faintest sensations. An observer's eye, as we shall see, must be educated to accomplish feats of vision considerably beyond what one might otherwise consider possible, and it is unreasonable to expect superhuman feats in the half-stooped, cramp-riddled posture one has to adopt with so many carelessly designed mountings. It is agonizingly uncomfortable to crouch halfway between standing and sitting in order to see through the eyepiece.

A set of *observing steps* provides the answer to this dilemma. Household steps (kitchen ladders) are serviceable, but are unlikely to be very comfortable to sit on, and a better answer is to make a special set, with ledges about 10 inches wide and rising to a height of about 3 feet. An attached rail or post allows one to keep perfectly still without clinging to the telescope itself, an act that will set the image dancing so violently that nothing can be seen.

All astronomers prefer to observe an object when it is high in the sky, since atmospheric conditions always improve with increased altitude, but a refractor is not altogether comfortable to use when the object under observation is almost overhead. One answer is to restrict one's observations to the period before or after the object crosses the *zenith*, or overhead point, since atmospheric conditions do not improve noticeably above about 60°. If this should prove inconvenient, one way of preventing vertebral contortions is to use a *zenith prism*, which effectively turns the eyepiece through a right angle and allows one to view at a much more comfortable angle. However, a zenith prism inverts the image from north to south, which is a nuisance when comparing the telescopic view with a chart, and it also involves a slight loss of light. Considering these severe drawbacks, it is amazing how many manufacturers apparently include them as more or less standard equipment with refractors—even for observation at low altitudes! Actually, zenith prisms do more harm than good, and they should be avoided wherever possible.

As already mentioned, a reflecting telescope is a most agreeable instrument to use, for when mounted on an altazimuth stand the eyepiece is always horizontal. An equatorial mounting, however, can give the observer some bending and crouching problems, and a rotating tube is a useful refinement. The usual way is to have the tube freely held in a cradle on the declination axis so that it can be twisted to bring the eyepiece into a convenient position, while some models have just the upper portion of the tube rotatable. Unless both mirror and flat are in the very center of the tube, this differential rotation may bring the optics out of alignment; so the former method is, on t' e whole, preferable.

Painting and upkeep

Only a small refractor can be carried indoors at the end of each observing session. Larger telescopes must endure the elements, but there is no reason at all why they should come to harm. The optical parts must be covered with scrupulous care, and all moving parts must be well greased; as for the rest, aluminium paint is an excellent protector of metal, and has the additional advantage of making the instrument conspicuous in the dark. The inside of the tube should be given an occasional sweep to remove any particles of rust or paint that might fall on the mirror and harm the surface when the cap is replaced, but except for these elementary precautions a well-made instrument should need no special attention.

The main war to be waged on behalf of an outdoor instrument is against insects. Beetles and cockroaches may take up residence in the stand, and spiders can spin their webs in the tube—even in the nether regions of a refractor. An open-tube reflector is particularly susceptible to this menace, and little preventive action can be taken. However, a lid can be fitted into the mouth of a solid tube, and an old eyepiece screwed into the drawtube will keep both insects and dust out of the interior. It is strange but fortunate that, even though the observer takes care to collect only good eyepieces, he always acquires a store of old Huygenians that are quite useless optically, but do serve this important function. Inevitably, too, the amateur will become intimately acquainted with an insect marauder when it crawls across the field lens of his eyepiece and appears projected with astonishing relief against the moon!

Observatories

Every amateur who has spent the quiet watches of the night communing with the stars and coping with the various problems of nature—dew, wind, and chill—has sighed for a proper observatory in the remote countryside, with a clear view of the whole sky and no artificial lights to dim out the fainter stars. Alas, few of us have much choice in the matter, and there is certainly little chance of being able to build an impressive domed structure in the back garden. But, even so, there is really no reason why a person who is capable of building a telescope mounting should not be able to construct some sort of observing shelter. The simplest contrivance is better than none at all, and will certainly add much to the comfort of observing. Astronomers are, by tradition, hardy folk, but this is no reason for courting unnecessary agony!

The simplest protective cover for an observatory is a run-off shed, which is simply a box on wheels that rolls away to reveal the telescope. This is very suitable for a reflector, since this type of telescope is compact, especially if on an altazimuth or German stand. A rigid timber or angle-iron framework provides the basis for the covering, which can be asbestos sheeting, wooden slats, or even heavy-gauge plastic. The box rolls on rails that are sunk into the ground. When it is in position with the door closed, the telescope is perfectly protected; moreover, if made sufficiently large it also forms a shelter in which the observer can write up notes during a night's work. Some form of illumination and a shelf for books and eyepieces makes this kind of shelter a very cheap and handy device.

The gravest drawback of this type of observatory is its instability. It is almost certain to be higher than it is broad, and if a strong wind chances to blow on either beam it may be upset, with possible disaster to the telescope. One way to prevent this possibility is to mount a second rail *over* the wheels, so they cannot lift off the ground. A less satisfactory solution is to fit low projections, either to the shed itself or in the ground, that will hold the observatory steady if it starts to tilt; these, however, may bring possible disaster to the observer!

The next step in sophistication is to have the walls of the shed permanent and merely slide the roof back. This, the sliding-roof observatory, is the best type of all, since it is cheap, protects the telescope and observer from wind, and permits coverage of the complete sky at one time. This is something that cannot be had from inside a dome, where only a segment of the sky is clear; in fact, a dome is a grave disadvantage for anyone who does not know the night sky intimately, since only a few constellations can be seen at any one time.

The main secret of building any sort of observatory that involves having permanent walls around the telescope is to allow plenty of room for the observer. An observatory should never be less than ten feet square, and preferably twelve; cramped conditions will merely hamper the observer's efficiency, and he would do better with a moveable shed. A second point is that the walls must be sufficiently low to allow the telescope to point down to the horizon. Since the tube of a reflector is usually mounted low down, this immediately cancels one of the advantages of this type of observatory, since the low walls will provide little or no protection. All things considered, the sliding-roof observatory works best with a refracting telescope.

Everyone will have his own ideas on the details of construction. The walls can be of slatted wood, or even brick, while the roof, which must slope, can be covered with fiberglass sheeting. Generally speaking, it is best to have the roof sliding off to the north, since this part of the sky is likely to receive the least attention and the obstruction will not be serious; but, whichever direction is adopted, a free-running motion is essential. Nothing is more infuriating than a roof or dome that persistently sticks. Depending on the observer's agility, he can either admit himself by a door or else vault over the wall when the roof is slid back.

The best observatory for a reflector is a totally revolving affair, like that illustrated here. In this type, the entire hut rotates, with a wide slit running across the roof and down one (or both) of the walls, so that the telescope commands an uninterrupted view from horizon to zenith. A revolving observatory requires a properly leveled concrete foundation, with a circular track to take the wheels, but otherwise it is a much less complicated affair than might be imagined; in the case of the observatory in the photograph, the only part that had to be made professionally was the 8-foot-diameter angle-iron ring, $\frac{1}{4}$-inch thick and with 2-inch sides, that is built into the base of the hut. This rotates on eight pulley wheels, which are held in the concrete. The rest of the building, made of wood and asbestos sheeting, involved only simple carpentry.

The disadvantage of a revolving observatory is that, since the slit is relatively narrow, it requires constant rotating if a large area of sky is being covered during the observing session. This particular structure

Simple observatory. *A. W. Heath's rotating hut.*

houses a 12-inch reflector that is used almost exclusively for planetary work, and it functions very well since the only shifting required is that needed to follow a planet's drifting across the sky. For anyone with free-range ideas, however, this type may prove rather limiting. It is difficult enough to make a critical observation, without having to attend to the observatory itself every five minutes.

Nevertheless, owning an observatory gives one a tremendous sense of purpose. Everything is at hand; books, atlases, eyepieces, and the miscellany of minor items that the observer is likely to need at a moment's notice, can all be reached immediately. Moreover, there is another point. When observing faint objects, it is vital to get the eye thoroughly dark-adapted. It takes about half an hour for the retina to become fully sensitive, and the interruption of having to return to a brilliantly lighted room ruins the adaptation, which must then start all over again. For this reason, the observatory should be lighted by the bare minimum of red or green light; it is even better if the actual intensity can be varied at will. It is also handy to have an ordinary white light for use before the session begins; but in this case, as in a photographic darkroom, the switch must be easily distinguishable in the dark.

When weighing the pros and cons of the matter, it is essential to keep a sense of proportion. An observatory is a desirable luxury, but no more, and money should certainly not be spent on building an elaborate structure that might better be invested in a larger telescope. Tarpaulins are cheap and will protect a small or medium-sized telescope from the worst ravages of weather; and no observer with the necessary zest will be put off by a frosty wind in his face. Some of the world's greatest amateurs have had nothing between them and the elements. Herschel put his telescope out on the lawn at the back of his house; so did Denning, one of the greatest planetary observers of recent times; and so do many leading observers today. The worth of a telescope is not to be measured in terms of its immediate environment; in the long run, its own quality and, above all, the quality of the man at the eyepiece, are what matter.

5

Atmosphere and Observer

Many beginners in astronomy are discouraged and their enthusiasm is sharply diminished when their first glance through a telescope proves disappointing. And with just one celestial exception—the moon—this will almost certainly be so. Great expectations of a canal-streaked Mars or a cloud-scribbled Jupiter come to nought when the novice's telescope shows a tiny, trembling blob of light on which little or no detail can be seen. His immediate reaction is that the telescope must be at fault, or the state of the atmosphere; everything is blamed except what is really responsible—the inexperience of the observer!

Learning to see

A little thought will show that this initial disappointment is only to be expected, for the discernment of faint detail through an astronomical telescope is perhaps the severest possible test of discipline for the human eye. In just the same way as a violinist's left hand is trained to a quite exceptional degree of suppleness and control, so an observer's eye must refine its reactions far beyond the level necessary for ordinary day-to-day vision. When the slightest glimpse of a wispy marking may herald a world-shaking change on the surface of a planet millions of miles away, it is hardly surprising that perceptual observations can be made only by the experienced eye. Tales are legion of how old hands, using a small telescope—perhaps a 3-inch refractor or 6-inch reflector—have perceived new details long before they became apparent to other amateurs possessing technically superior equipment, most of whose potential was nullified by the observer's inexperience. Sir William Herschel, whose visual acuity has been surpassed by few, summed the matter up as follows:

> *You must not expect to* see *at sight. Seeing is in some respects an art which must be learned. Many a night have I been practising to see, and it would be strange if one did not acquire a certain dexterity by such constant practice.*

The lesson is clear. No opportunity should be lost to train the eye to work with the telescope; to observe the same object with different powers so as to see the effect of magnification; to try to see faint stars; and to draw planetary markings. In the beginning, to be sure, this may all seem to be wasted effort; the observing book will fill up with valueless sketches and brief notes of failure. But this apparently empty labor is absolutely essential; for, as the weeks pass, a steady change will be taking place. Objects considered difficult or impossible to see will now be discerned at first glance, and fainter specters will have taken their place. Indeed, these former features will now be so glaringly obvious that the observer may suppose that some radical improvement has occurred in the observing conditions. But the credit belongs entirely to the eye, which, in Herschel's expression, is "learning to see"—and the more practice it has, the better it will see. Success in astronomical observation comes only with persistence; it cannot be emphasized too strongly that nominal telescopic power counts for relatively little against *the observer's perceptive powers*. Again and again, one hears a beginner sighing for a bigger telescope because the one he possesses "isn't powerful enough"! A 3-inch refractor—assuming, of course, that it is of good quality and well adjusted—will show far more detail than may at first be suspected; and its full potentiality must be mastered before the special advantages of a bigger telescope can be appreciated. The amateur who immediately arms himself with, say, a 12-inch reflector, will be severely handicapped over the observer who patiently educates himself with a small and manageable instrument.

Just occasionally one comes across feats of astonishing vision, far beyond that expected to be acquired from experience alone. The American observer S. W. Burnham discovered with a 6-inch refractor new double stars that had previously been seen as single with telescopes of two or three times the aperture. An Irish amateur, Isaac Ward, glimpsed two of the satellites of Uranus with a 4·3-inch refractor; they are usually fair tests of vision with even a 12-inch telescope! An English clergyman, W. R. Dawes, was also famous for his ability to detect very faint stars. Such achievements are too rare to be of application to the vast majority of amateur and professional observers, but they form interesting instances of exceptional development of one of the natural senses.

The atmosphere and "seeing"

Part of the reason the eye has to play an active rather than a passive part in making an observation lies in the dense atmospheric layer that extends for about ten miles above the earth's surface. Above this, the air is too thin to have any effect on the telescopic image, but the lower level, being hardly ever calm, can ruin it. The heating of the ground below this level and the movement of winds act together to mix the lower atmosphere into a soup of strata at different temperatures, and since the light rays from a star or planet are slightly refracted each time they change strata, the net result is frequently to produce a wobbling, blurred image, an effect that astronomers term "bad seeing."

Even on the best nights, there is still a slight tremor in the air, which is enough to mask the finest detail on a planet's surface; but just occasionally, for periods of a second or two at a time, the image suddenly shrinks and steadies itself into a neat, sharp disk. This is the moment when the eye must play its crucial part, rapidly picking out the faintest shades of texture so that the hand, when the moment of perfect vision has passed, can transfer them to the sketch. The same is true of attempts to see very faint stars, which may be glimpsed only when the image stops boiling and concentrates into a point. On such nights, by far the greatest proportion of the observing period is spent waiting for these moments.

Bad seeing affects different apertures in different ways, being more serious the larger the telescope; but it is certainly not true to say, as do some observers, that a small telescope is equal or even preferable to a large one! This misapprehension has probably arisen because there is greater general steadiness of the image in a small telescope. On most nights air waves of between 6 and 12 inches across, travel quite slowly at a height of several hundred feet above the ground. It is not hard to see that if these waves are larger than the aperture of the telescope, their effect will be to move the image bodily rather than to break it up into fragments, so that while the image of a planet will wobble no matter what telescope is used, it will maintain its general outline rather better with a small aperture. On the other hand, critical definition can be obtained only when a period of true steadiness occurs, and in such an interval a large aperture will show far more detail than a small one; a night on which a small telescope is constantly superior to a large one can be written off as quite impossible.

Low seeing, as this atmospheric condition is called, is produced by local agencies. For instance, anyone living on the lee side of a city will experience very bad conditions—at any rate, until the early hours of the morning, by which time the heat from chimneys and factories has died down. On the other hand, an observer actually in the city may enjoy quite favorable seeing, since he is in the center of the "warm spot" and the air above his head is relatively homogeneous; the haze associated with such conditions may also help to steady the lower atmosphere. Hilly surroundings also help produce turbulence, especially when a wind is blowing, and it is for this reason that so many big observatories have been built on plateaus at heights of between 4,000 and 7,000 feet, above the densest and dirtiest layer of the atmosphere.

Of more frustration to the observer, in the sense that nothing can be done about it, is *high seeing*. This effect occurs at heights of between five and ten miles, where winds spring up as a result of large-scale pressure changes associated with meteorological "fronts." Once again we have the disruptive effect of layers of air at different temperatures; but since the waves are much farther away from the telescope, the blurring effect is greater and the wobble less than that produced by low seeing. Being essentially a climatic phenomenon, high seeing varies with the observer's position on the earth's surface, being less serious at low latitudes because of the more uniform pressure.

The third atmospheric effect, *ground seeing*, is at least partly under the observer's control. This is the disturbance produced by heat waves rising from the warm ground in the immediate vicinity of the telescope; naturally, this occurs mostly during the day and in early evening. The trouble can be minimized by surrounding the telescope with grass or scrub, as has been done at such observatories as Mount Wilson and Palomar, since this radiates very little heat; but a town-based telescope will inevitably prove troublesome when used during daylight hours. Also, the observatory itself can radiate a great deal of heat from its walls and roof, and, since the air inside warms up during the day, it should be opened up at sunset to allow free circulation to take place.

Even more locally, ground seeing can affect the air lying within a few feet of the ground, producing a thick stratum of warm air that may extend only as high as the observer's shoulders. When this condition is severe, it may be found that a refractor on a tall tripod outperforms a reflector on a low stand, especially if the reflector has a framework tube that leaves the mirror immersed in the warm layer. In this connection, experiments with thermometers placed at various heights above the ground may prove of interest.

Transparency is also important to the observer. This has nothing to do with the stability of the air, but is instead a measure of how bright the stars appear. In this area of observation, the rural observer is at a permanent advantage; the clear skies of country districts show the stars in all their majesty, a sight denied the town-dweller, who can never hope to see diaphanous objects, such as nebulae and comet tails, in their true form.

Atmospheric steadiness, which frequently occurs in the haze and smoke of a large settlement, is of little help in observing such extended objects; transparency is the deciding factor. When trying to observe very faint stars, however, it is essential for the air to be still as well as clear, for turbulence will expand the tiny pinpoint of light, and may make it invisible.

Sky transparency varies from night to night. Under the best conditions, when the moon is absent and the sky a pure black, stars as faint as magnitude 6·5 can be seen by a keen-eyed person. (It is worth noting, in this connection, that naked-eye acuity gives little or no guide to a person's telescopic vision.) On other nights, the faintest stars are nowhere to be seen and the Milky Way is visible only as a vague stain. This may be due to haze, but it can also be caused by faint auroral activity in the upper atmosphere, making these nights, to the rural observer, noticeably brighter than others.

Scales of seeing

1. Image usually about twice the diameter of the third ring.
2. Image occasionally twice the diameter of the third ring.
3. Image of about the same diameter as the third ring, and brighter at the center.
4. Disk often visible; arcs (of rings) sometimes seen on brighter stars.
5. Disk always visible; arcs frequently seen on brighter stars.
6. Disk always visible; short arcs constantly seen.
7. Disk sometimes sharply defined. (a) Rings seen as long arcs. (b) Rings complete.
8. Disk always sharply defined. (a) Rings seen as long arcs. (b) Rings complete, all in motion.
9. (a) Inner ring stationary. (b) Outer rings momentarily stationary.
10. Rings all stationary. (a) Detail between the rings, sometimes moving. (b) No detail between the rings.

Users of refracting telescopes may care to class their images in accordance with this scale, devised by W. H. Pickering on the basis of observations carried out with a 5-inch refractor. Seeing 1–3 is considered very bad; 4–5 poor; 6-7 good; and 8-10 excellent. Since few reflecting telescopes will show diffraction rings, however, users of reflectors must base their estimates on the smallness and sharpness of the star disk itself. There is usually a difference of some three scale divisions between the seeing at altitudes of 20° and 70°.

Pickering's scale, being based on the appearance of star disks, is not very suitable for planetary work, where the observer is scrutinizing an extended image. The Greek astronomer E. M. Antoniadi, well known for his work on Mercury and Mars, produced the following seeing scale for planetary work:

1. Perfect seeing, without a quiver.
2. Slight undulations, with moments of calm lasting several seconds.
3. Moderate seeing, with large tremors.
4. Poor seeing, with constant troublesome undulations.
5. Very bad seeing, scarcely allowing the making of a rough sketch.

The scale used in recording observations must be specified; the best way is to write, for example, Pickering's seeing 3 as 3/10, and Antoniadi's as 3/5. Note that the two numerical sequences work in the reverse order.

Sky conditions and "changes"

By now, the reader should be aware that making a critical telescopic observation demands reconciliation of a number of independent factors. The three most obvious are the observer's acuity, the telescope's quality, and sky conditions. On top of these are the less definable influences such as dark adaptation, the telescope's collimation, the observer's mood, the particular eyepiece used, and so on. But of all these, atmospheric conditions probably have the most far-reaching effect. No two nights are exactly alike.

Burnham, the famous double-star observer, once said:

An object glass of 6 in. one night will show the companion to Sirius perfectly: on the next night, just as good in every respect, so far as one can tell with the unaided eye, the largest telescope in the world will show no more trace of the small star than if it had been blotted out of existence.*

Two facts emerge from this: Each night must be treated on its merits; and the most scrupulous care must be taken when comparing observations made under different conditions. It stands to reason that the telescope and magnification should remain unchanged if comparable views are to be had; but unless conditions are similar, "changes" will almost certainly be observed, for which responsibility must be placed not on the object under observation, but on the *atmosphere*.

Another overhasty conclusion indulged in by many people concerns the myth that some regions have "clearer" skies than others, in the sense that the air is more transparent. Thus, exotic regions, such as the Mediterranean, are endowed with star-crammed nights, whereas the much-maligned British climate is considered incapable of producing skies to the same specifications.

*Sirius, the brightest star in the sky, has a faint star close to it which is very difficult to see.

It is true, of course, that the Mediterranean and North African climate, like that of Arizona, favors cloudless nights; but on the question of transparency there is probably nothing to choose among different regions of the world. For vindication of British skies one need look no further than the work of Sir William Herschel; and the comet-hunter G. E. D. Alcock, who observes from a site near the large town of Peterborough, England, has made the following interesting comments:

> *Conditions have deteriorated in the Peterborough area during the past 35 years, but this has never been an ideal part of England for astronomical observation, and it is very easy to exaggerate any changes that may have taken place.*
>
> *Obviously, there are two. First, there is the glow from street lighting and advertisements; second, the polar air which comes with the passage of cold fronts is more filled with smoke from Birmingham, the Potteries, and above all the Sheffield and south Yorkshire industrial zone. Formerly, we could expect transparent dark skies with N.E. winds, but now the visibility falls to less than three miles, and the smoke is lit up by artificial lights.*
>
> *However, we can still have superb conditions; occasionally the skies of the East Midlands can surpass those of Italy and North Africa. On October 12, 1948, and again at dawn on December 4, 1964, the sky was so brilliant that the Galaxy [the Milky Way] appeared "granulated" with faint stars along the entire band of light. Between 1942 and 1945 I never suspected this effect in the Mediterranean area.*

Just occasionally, geophysical effects can interfere with sky conditions. The faint auroral glow is one, but there are sometimes more spectacular agents. The explosion of the Indonesian volcano Krakatau on August 27, 1883, released a tremendous amount of fine dust into the upper atmosphere and produced noticeable obscuration for many months; while the eruption of the Mt. Agung volcano on the Indonesian island of Bali, on March 17, 1963, reduced sky transparency all over the world, the effects lingering until the end of 1964.

Astigmatism

We have already seen that exceptionally sharp naked-eye sight does not necessarily mean that a person will excel in telescopic observation. This is because a telescope can be focused to anyone's individual requirements, so that even chronic shortsightedness or farsightedness is of no account. There is, however, one inherent eye defect that can be troublesome, and this is astigmatism, caused by the corneal lens being strained in one direction. Even

Figure 19. *Test for astigmatism.*

slight astigmatism in any of a telescope's optical components is ruinous to its performance, so it is scarcely surprising that astigmatic eyesight can also cause trouble. The best way to find out if one's eyes are astigmatic is to look at a system of radiating lines, as in figure 19. A normal eye will show all the lines equally sharp and dark, but, should astigmatism be present, one or more lines will be more sharply defined than the rest. Astigmatism can ordinarily be solved by wearing glasses, but it is difficult or impossible to use a telescope in this way; not everyone is able to tolerate contact lenses; and few have the resourcefulness of the observer who mounted a special compensating astigmatic lens in front of the eyepiece!

Luckily, astigmatism makes itself really objectionable only when low-magnifying powers are being used. The reason is not hard to understand. Every eyepiece has what is known as an *exit-pupil*, which effectively is the diameter of the beam of light leaving the eye lens and passing into the observer's eye. In measuring the circle of bright light seen in the eyepiece, to determine the magnification, we were measuring the diameter of the exit-pupil, the relationship being

$$E = \frac{D}{M}$$

where E is the diameter of the exit-pupil, D the diameter of the objective, and M the magnification. The lower the magnification, the larger the exit-pupil; and the larger the exit-pupil, the greater the area of the corneal lens that is used to form the image. If a high magnification is used, and the exit beam is narrow, only a small proportion of the corneal lens is called upon, and any inherent astigmatism will have less effect.

Low and high magnification

But even if the eye is perfectly formed, there is still a practical limit to low magnification; this is decreed by the aperture of the telescope. It is clear that, after struggling to obtain as large a telescope as possible, the observer will not want to waste any of his hard-won light; yet this is what will happen if he uses a magnification of, for example, × 6 with a 3-inch refractor. The exit-pupil will now be $\frac{1}{2}$ inch across—about twice as large as the maximum pupil opening—so that only a quarter of the light focused by the object glass is actually going into the eye.

In perfect darkness, the normal pupil expands to about $\frac{1}{3}$ inch; in dim twilight, it is about $\frac{1}{4}$ inch. This means that to use a magnification of less than 3D or 4D results in a waste of light; theoretically at least, the lowest feasible power with a 3-inch telescope is between × 9 and × 12; with a 6-inch, between × 18 and × 24; while a 12-inch telescope can never profitably use less than × 36 or × 48, depending on the conditions of darkness.

Thanks, however, to the conservatism of manufacturers, it is extremely doubtful whether anyone has ever managed to use a magnification of × 9 with a regular 3-inch refractor. If the telescope has a focal length of 36 inches, such a power would require a 4-inch eyepiece; and they are rarely to be found with focal lengths exceeding 2 inches. Furthermore, so low a power would require a field lens at least 2 inches across to provide a reasonable field of view, while the standard drawtube is only $1\frac{1}{4}$ inches across. Extensive modification would therefore be required to produce a really low-power, wide-angle instrument, although the results should be spectacularly worth-while.

In this connection, one frequently finds manufacturers skimping on the dimensions of the flat in a reflecting telescope. An undersized flat will serve for high powers, since the field of view is small; but if a low-power field is to be fully illuminated, the flat must be full size. To check on this, remove the eyepiece and rack out the drawtube until its rim is at the position of focus. Then view the reflection of the main mirror in the flat from all around the edge of the drawtube. If the marginal view shows the edge of the mirror cut off at the edge of the flat, then the flat is too small to give illumination over a wide field. In the case of a 6-inch f/8 reflector, the flat should have a shorter diameter (minor axis) of at least $1\frac{1}{4}$ inches, and $1\frac{1}{2}$ is safer; the slight extra loss of light caused by the larger silhouette is negligible compared with the improved light transmission to the borders of the field.

At the other end of the scale, as we have seen, the highest useful magnification is dictated mainly by atmospheric conditions; but even on nights of superb seeing (which occur mainly in observers' dreams), a power of more than about 60D for 3- to 6-inch telescopes, and about 40D for those of up to 12-inch aperture, will show no detail that is invisible with smaller magnifications. They effectively exceed the telescope's limit of resolution, so that for most purposes such magnification is "empty."

Temperature effects

The temperature drop at nightfall can, as we have seen, cause undesirable tube currents in a reflecting telescope, which can be overcome by using a square or framework tube. It can also, however, affect the actual quality of the image by temporarily distorting the mirror. This thermal effect can be very important indeed in the case of large telescopes, and is well worth investigating.

To give perfect definition, an astronomical mirror must be figured to within a very few millionths of an inch of the correct curve. This curve is not spherical, but *paraboloidal*, which means in effect that the mirror is slightly deeper than it would be were it a sphere. If the mirror were merely spherical, the image would be faulty and the defect would be termed "under-correction." If the mirror's curve were too deep, or *hyperboloidal*, it would be "over-corrected," and once again a star or planet would have a hazy appearance. These errors, however, are minute by all except optical standards. For instance, the curved surface of a 6-inch f/8 mirror is about 1/20-inch deep—hardly noticeable to a casual glance. To deepen such a spherical curve to a paraboloidal one involves the removal of a mere 1/80,000 of an inch of glass; yet the difference bridges the gap between an almost useless mirror and a splendid one!

The heating troubles arise because the glass has to be thick; were it thin, the mirror would sag under its own weight and ruin the definition. This explains why object glasses, where the lenses have to be supported around the edge, have a definite restriction on size. The disk for a 6-inch mirror is normally an inch thick, and the 6:1 ratio for diameter to thickness is a standard one; hence, large mirrors are very heavy indeed. As a result, when the glass is warm it expands and distorts the curve, and it may take an hour or more for a 12-inch mirror to cool down thoroughly by just a few degrees. During the time it is radiating heat, the correction is increased. A paraboloid becomes hyperboloidal, whereas an undercorrected mirror turns temporarily paraboloidal if the error is just right.

Most astronomical work is done during the night; this is why most good opticians intentionally make their mirrors slightly undercorrected, so that they perform well in the cooling air. The method is not, of course, foolproof, for unexpected temperature variations can have a prejudicial effect on the curve. The effect is usually slight, but for critical work it can be obvious enough, and it certainly pays to "know one's mirror" under various conditions of heating and cooling.

The observer

The final and most vital link in the whole chain is the observer himself, and on his competence, more than on any other factor, depends the success of the observation. Telescopic observation is an art, a fact too easily forgotten when large instruments are glamorized on their own merits, as if they themselves recorded the objects to which they were pointed! It is true that the introduction of photography has made many fields of observation a simple technical exercise; but in most amateur investigations the eye reigns supreme, the telescope being simply a tool that will do the job well or badly, depending on the skill and experience of its user. There are perhaps three broad headings under which an observer must discipline himself.

EDUCATION. We have already seen that the eye requires plenty of experience in telescopic work before it can hope to discern all that the telescope is capable of revealing. The interesting thing is that even after experience has been gained, many observers find their eyes particularly gifted in just one field of observation. E. E. Barnard, the famous American comet-hunter who also made stellar observations with the 40-inch Yerkes refractor, could glimpse very minute stars; yet he saw much less planetary detail than other observers using small telescopes. The same was true of the "eagle-eyed" Dawes, who had exceptionally acute stellar vision. Conversely, many successful planetary observers have proved defective when it came to glimpsing small satellites and faint stars. Seemingly, two different visual processes are involved, and it is clearly sensible to make observations in the field in which one's talents lie. One excellent idea is to train each eye separately, one for planetary work, the other for the observation of very dim objects.

PREPARATION. Spasmodic and ill-considered observation is not only useless, but also wastes energy and enthusiasm. The observer should know exactly what he intends to observe before he goes to the telescope; assuming that he has reached the stage of knowing the main constellations and the positions of the planets, it is possible to cover a wide field and yet work systematically. The best education of all, because it exercises the eye and also teaches one the layout of the night sky, is to survey each constellation in turn for its more prominent features: colored stars, double stars, star clusters, and nebulae. If a list is prepared in advance, they can be found, or "swept up," in conjunction with *Norton's*, and notes made on their appearance. After several hundred of these objects have been identified, the observer will have a vastly different attitude toward the apparent chaos of the sky, which will now have resolved itself into familiar and unforgettable patterns.

It is the same with lunar and planetary work. If it is decided to observe a certain region on the moon, or a particular planet, it must be viewed on every possible occasion when conditions are good enough. The aim should be to produce a series of observations that may be compared with one another, and this can only be done by being prepared whenever an opportunity presents itself.

RELAXATION. It is useless to try to make a critical observation under conditions of strain. The problem of muscular comfort can usually be solved by using some form of observing steps, but the effects of cold are less easy to combat; the only practical agent of warmth on the coldest nights is the observer's own enthusiasm! Once one becomes really uncomfortable, it is far better to close down, or at least go indoors for a while, since the reliability of observations made under such conditions is open to question, and no observation at all is better than a spurious one.

When observing, the idle eye should be kept open; the strain involved in shutting the lid has a prejudicial effect on one's vision. This takes a certain amount of practice; at first, the half-seen images seem to obliterate rather than improve the view, but after a time they can be ignored. Another physiological habit that must be mastered is the tendency of the eye, when fatigued or when trying to catch a detail at the limit of its powers, to focus on something near at hand rather than to relax at infinity. When this happens, the critical sharpness of the image may be destroyed without the observer realizing it. Therefore, it pays to pause every five minutes or so, throw the eyepiece out of focus, and then refocus carefully.

THE SOLAR SYSTEM

6

The Moon

The moon is without doubt the favorite object for observation by the beginner with a small telescope. The reasons for this are really too obvious to need mentioning: It is bright, it is visible regularly every month, and it is so close that a fantastic amount of detail can be made out. The fascination of seeing so literally unearthly a world in close-up never palls, and it takes no astronomical knowledge to be impressed by the way every rock casts its own sharp shadow, with the great craters looming up in indescribable magnificence.

The moon is the earth's natural satellite, and, whether or not it once formed part of the earth (few scientists support this theory nowadays), we can at least be sure that they were both formed at around the same time—some 4,500 million years ago. The moon is a small world, however, only 2,163 miles across, and it lost its internal heat and its atmosphere relatively quickly. These factors, together with the fierce scarring of its surface, have produced a world bearing absolutely no resemblance to the earth. Where there is no air there can be neither rain nor wind, and consequently no erosion; hence, the lunar topography, most of which is probably older than the most ancient mountain chains on our own planet, has been preserved in its original form, as if in some celestial museum. Only with the brief impact of Lunik II in September, 1959, has the moon begun to awaken to the present.

The fact that the moon is so unchanging—on the large scale, at least—means that modern observations can be compared directly with those of our predecessors. This is not so with the other planets of our solar system, whose surfaces show slow or rapid changes as the case may be. The dark lava plains, known generally as *maria* (seas), have made up the face of the "man in the moon" since the beginning, and a telescope not only brings these out in great detail, but also shows the vast walled plains, craters, craterlets, and mountain ranges that were first seen in 1609, following the invention of the telescope. Galileo compared them to the "eyes" in a peacock's tail, while an early British observer, Sir William Lower, described how he saw the "mountaintops shining like stars." Indeed, the first proper map of the moon was produced by Hevelius in 1647, and the formations that he charted can be clearly recognized.

Anyone possessing a 3- or 4-inch refractor or a 6-inch reflector can, with care, make useful and original lunar observations. This may sound surprising when it is remembered that the moon has been kept under observation for three and a half centuries, but the position is not quite as simple as that. In the first place, the tangle of detail is so intricate that to draw every feature visible with a 3-inch would take many lifetimes; secondly, the angle at which the sunlight strikes the lunar surface and hence casts shadows is changing all the time. This matter is so important that it is worth examining the motions of the moon at once.

Movements and phases

The moon revolves around the earth in an elliptical orbit; its mean distance is 238,866 miles, and this varies from around 228,000 at perigee to around 252,000 at apogee. Since most of the orbits in the solar system lie in roughly the same plane, we shall not be far wrong in drawing them all in plan view on a sheet of paper. Figure 20 shows a schematic view of the moon's orbit around the earth. It must be remembered, however, that the earth itself is revolving around the sun in the same direction (counterclockwise if viewed from the north).

The moon, like all the planets and satellites in the solar system, has no light of its own; in position *A*, therefore, where it lies roughly between the earth and the sun, it is invisible, since its night hemisphere is turned toward us. If the lunar orbit lay in exactly the same plane as that of the earth, it would always pass centrally across the sun and produce a solar eclipse; but there is a tilt of about 5°, which means that the *new moon*, as it is called in position *A*, generally lies either north or south of the sun in the sky, and

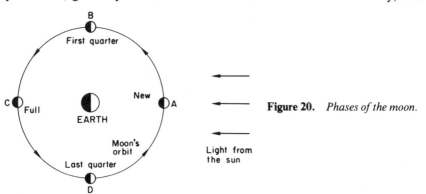

Figure 20. *Phases of the moon.*

only rarely does an eclipse occur. The usual new moon, masked by the solar glare, is utterly invisible.

The moon's counterclockwise motion carries it eastward around the earth at the rate of about 12° per day, so that in a couple of days' time a thin crescent can be seen in the evening sky after sunset. As the days pass, this crescent widens as more of the sunlit hemisphere is turned toward us and the moon moves farther away from the sun, until at position *B*, or *first quarter*, it forms a right angle with the sun and appears to us as a perfect half. The *terminator*, the line separating lunar day from night, is now straight, and the features across which it runs cast long shadows and are seen with great clarity. It is obvious that as the terminator sweeps across the lunar disk, different regions will be seen under low-lighting conditions.

The moon takes about 29½ days—the lunar month, or synodic period— to complete its cycle of phases, so that the period from new to first quarter is about 7¼ days. After this, the moon passes through the second quarter of its orbit. The phase becomes *gibbous*, or intermediate between half and full, with the terminator convex instead of concave; after a total of 14½ days it has reached position *C*. It is now on the far side of the earth from the sun, and appears fully illuminated. This is *full moon*, and, referring to the diagram, it follows that at this stage it appears as more or less opposite the sun in the sky, rises at sunset, and remains above the horizon all night. If the line-up is nearly perfect, it passes through the earth's shadow and suffers eclipse.

The full moon appears glaringly bright not only because the whole disk is illuminated, but because the sunlight is now shining down squarely on its surface. Just as a photographer places his camera so that the illumination on the model's face is slightly slanted, so for the most spectacular views we should see the moon when the sun is to one side. But at full moon, since the sun is behind our backs and no shadows are visible, the lunar disk appears as a blinding, patchy blur of light.

The moon now moves on toward *D*, or *last quarter*, and the evening terminator passes across the surface. The formations are now seen in their evening, as against morning, aspect; by the time the moon's last quarter is reached, half the disk has been lost in night. The moon has now moved to the west of the sun, so that it rises late in the night. Finally it shrinks to a crescent, visible just before dawn, and after the completion of the synodic period it is back at new again.

It is clear from this that the best time at which to observe any particular feature of the moon depends on its position. For example, if it is near the right-hand (western) edge, or *limb*, we shall have low illumination soon after new (sunrise), and again soon after full (sunset). On the other hand, a crater on the disk's meridian will be well seen at first and last quarters.

It should not be thought that observations can be carried out only when the object is near the terminator, but there is no doubt that the most spectacular views are to be had at this time.

The two hemispheres

The moon presents its features in the same relative positions from night to night; we enjoy this conveniently standard state of affairs because it keeps roughly the same face turned toward us. When it was young, it was much closer to the earth than it is today, and gradually the earth's gravitational pull slowed down its spin until one of its hemispheres remained in the "captured" state. At the same time the moon slowly receded; it is still spiralling outwards today, although unimaginably slowly, and it will be thousands of millions of years before it appears appreciably smaller to us. At all events, observers have only just over half the lunar surface at their disposal. (The map on page 78 shows the main features permanently visible on the disk.) We can, however, see part of the averted hemisphere because the moon's eastern and western limbs alternately advance and recede during the lunar month in a slightly swinging motion known as *libration*. The eccentricity of the moon's orbit is the reason for this. The moon itself, because of its captured rotation, spins on its axis at a uniform speed, but its orbital speed is not constant. When near perigee it is moving faster than when near apogee, so that the two motions move slightly out of synchronization, with a fortnightly presentation of each margin. Furthermore, the lunar axis is slightly tilted, which means that we can also peer a little way beyond the north and south poles. Altogether, in terms of area, 59 per cent of the moon's surface is at one time or another accessible to our gaze, and the splendid success of the Orbiter and Surveyor probes has given us a key to most of the hidden side.

Lunar observation

Though the moon is a bright and regular visitor, exhibiting the same formations month after month (except in the limb regions) and going through the same cycle of phases, lunar observation is far from being the simple matter that it may seem at first sight. There is little or no color on the moon; its surface tints are merely grays of various depths and textures, and we are highly dependent on shadows to mark out features and reveal tiny details. But all the time the terminator is creeping along, not only from night to night but also from hour to hour; in addition to this, the general angle of the sunlight is somewhat different with each revolution, or *lunation*.

Should a particular formation be under examination, and a vital night be missed because of clouds or poor seeing, it may be months before conditions are right again. Roughly comparable conditions occur at intervals of 2 and 15 lunations (59 days 1½ hours and 442 days 23 hours), but this does not take the effects of libration into account; these greatly affect one of the hunting grounds of the amateur—the marginal regions. The lunar observer must be systematic, must plan ahead, and must seize his chances as they are presented.

For obvious reasons, professional interest in the moon has stepped up in the last few years. Until the recent launching of the Apollo project, which suddenly made it necessary for a large-scale "official" map to be constructed, our satellite was considered as more of a nuisance than a benefit; astronomers, anxious to photograph faint stars and galaxies that are of far more cosmic importance than our diminutive solar system, have more or less to stop work during the fortnight around full moon, when the bright light fogs their sensitive plates. Formerly, only amateurs bothered to take the moon seriously; one of the pioneer lunar maps was produced in 1837 by two German astronomers, Johann von Mädler and Wilhelm Beer, using a 3¾-inch refractor. The next great advance occurred in 1878, when another German, Julius Schmidt, who observed from Athens, produced a chart more than six feet across. Shortly after this, in 1890, the British Astronomical Association (B.A.A.) was formed, and amateur astronomy became established on a more coordinated footing. Three different directors of the B.A.A. Lunar Section published charts, in 1895, 1910, and 1946. The spate of amateur observations became even more marked when, just after World War II, American observers banded together to found the Association of Lunar and Planetary Observers (A.L.P.O.), at University Park, New Mexico.

Recently, however, the position has changed. Photographic techniques have improved tremendously, and some professional observatories, such as the Pic du Midi in the Pyrenees, are taking photographs showing details considerably beyond the range of a small telescope. The publication in 1960 of the *Lunar Photographic Atlas*, compiled by Gerard Kuiper of the Lunar and Planetary Laboratory, University of Arizona, was a recent event of great importance. Obviously, photographic methods are more reliable than drawing, and it must be admitted that the earthward regions of the moon's surface are unlikely to reveal new details to telescopes of less than 8 or 10 inches aperture. Systematic work is also being carried out in Arizona, at the Lowell Observatory, the Goddard Optical Research Center, and the Lunar and Planetary Laboratory, as well as at various other centers. But it must never be forgotten that so far as visual observation is concerned the experienced amateur can be the equal of the professional. In addition, there are other fields of research, such as crater distribution and analysis, that do not depend merely on the recording of new detail.

It may be argued that the recent successful Luna and Surveyor probes have carried the moon far beyond the range of amateur observation. It is certainly true that they have transmitted detailed photographs of great clarity, and have told us more about the nature of the lunar surface than could ever be inferred from Earth-based work, but such efforts are necessarily limited to the examination of the moon's surface, under a single set of lighting conditions. Their greatest service so far is to show indisputably that much of the ground is firm, free from deep dust drifts, and evidently safe for spaceship landings.

The lunar features

The first step in becoming a lunar observer is to learn the moon's principal features. An outline map shows the main maria and the largest craters, and a few nights with a telescope (or even binoculars) will bring a good deal of order out of the initial confusion. Indeed, the surface presents a certain amount of harmony in the sense that, although it is covered with a tangle of objects, these can be organized into a number of different classes.

MARIA, OR SEAS. These form the lunar lowlands. The Latin name for "seas" (singular, mare) was bestowed on them by the early telescopic observers, who thought they really were liquid bodies; we now know there is no water anywhere on the moon. The maria, which differ in appearance from the highlands in being both darker and smoother, are evidently colossal lava plains, perhaps covered with a thin layer of dust. Winding ridges are common, and so are small hillocks and craterlets ("small" on the telescopic scale, of course), but there are few prominent craters in these regions. Here and there we find very low rings, often of considerable size; these "ghosts," so called because of their faintness, are evidently the walls of ancient craters that were overlaid by molten lava when the seas were formed.

Most of the maria run into each other, extending from the Mare Foecunditatis in the S.W., or Fourth, Quadrant, via the Maria Tranquillitatis and Serenitatis (N.W., or First, Quadrant), into the beautiful Mare Imbrium (N.E., or Second, Quadrant), and ending in the region of the Mare Nubium and Oceanus Procellarum, the latter being the largest sea, although somewhat ill-defined. All these maria have areas of a hundred thousand square miles or more. In addition, there are smaller dark areas which may be known as a lake (lacus), marsh (palus), or bay (sinus), all of which are offshoots of the maria.

Some maria are quite detached. The most prominent of these is Mare Crisium (First Quadrant), while four other examples lie along the western limb. One of these, Mare Australe, was first shown by the Lunik III photographs to extend into the averted hemisphere.

WALLED PLAINS. Although it is convenient to refer to all circular lunar formations as "craters," they actually fall into definite categories. The walled plains are the largest features, ranging from about 60 to 180 miles across, with a mountainous ring several thousand feet high overlooking an inner floor that may itself have some fair-sized craters embedded in its surface. Some are in good condition, with their walls entirely preserved, whereas others have been so broken down by later upheavals and remelting of the crust that the reduced ridges can be well seen only when near the terminator. Judging from the way in which so few are perfect, it seems probable that these immense formations are among the oldest of the moon's visible features, presumably originating when the crater-forming activity was at its most violent.

RING PLAINS. These are the most impressive of the lunar features. They are smaller than the walled plains, with diameters of between about 30 and 60 miles. The walls are relatively high, sometimes rising 10,000 feet or more, and the interior floor may be depressed below the level of the external terrain. These walls are often magnificent in themselves; they may be ridged or terraced with great complexity, especially on the inner slope. The floor itself often contains a central mountain mass that may rise to a height comparable to that of the wall, and this mass is often divided into separate peaks.

CRATERS. Similar in cross section to the ring plains, except that the walls are much less complex, are narrower, and the central mountain is either small or totally absent. They are smaller than the ring plains, with diameters as small as 5 miles, and many form the center of ray systems, deposits of bright matter that seem to radiate away from the crater across the outside surface. Craters, together with the smaller craterlets, occur all over the surface and are often plastered over much larger formations.

CRATER CONES AND CRATER PITS. These are very small features, requiring a moderate telescope for their detection. Crater cones are roughly conical, though not steep, formations, bearing tiny orifices at their summits. Crater pits are simply minute depressions in the lunar surface without recognizable walls; they are well shown in the Orbiter photographs.

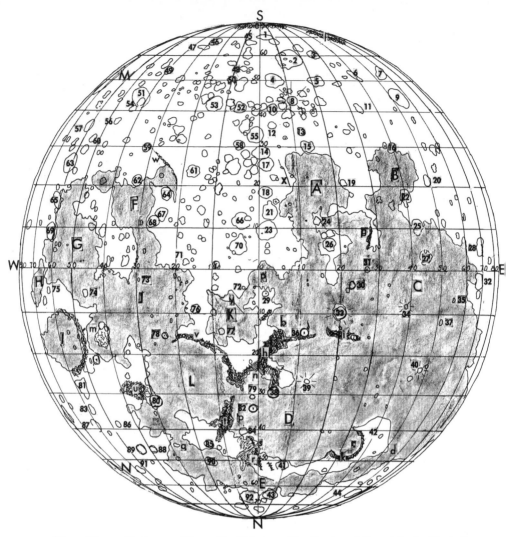

Map of Lunar Features. (From *The Telescope Handbook and Star Atlas* by Neale E. Howard, Thomas Y. Crowell Company)

A. Mare Nubium (Sea of Clouds)
B. Mare Humorum (Sea of Moisture)
C. Oceanus Procellarum (Ocean of Storms)
D. Mare Imbrium (Sea of Rains)
E. Mare Frigoris (Sea of Cold)
F. Mare Nectaris (Sea of Nectar)
G. Mare Foecunditatis (Sea of Fertility)

H. Mare Spumans (Foaming Sea)
I. Mare Crisium (Sea of Crises)
J. Mare Tranquillitatis (Sea of Tranquillity)
K. Mare Vaporum (Sea of Vapors)
L. Mare Serenitatis (Sea of Serenity)
M. Mare Australe (Southern Sea)
N. Mare Humboltianum (Humbolt Sea)

1. Moretus	32. Hevelius	63. Petavius
2. Clavius	33. Copernicus	64. Catharina
3. Scheiner	34. Kepler	65. Vendelinus
4. Maginus	35. Reiner	66. Albategnius
5. Longomontanus	36. Eratosthenes	67. Cyrillus
6. Schiller	37. Marius	68. Theophilus
7. Phocylides	38. Archimedes	69. Langrenus
8. Tycho	39. Timocharis	70. Hipparchus
9. Schickard	40. Aristarchus	71. Delambre
10. Orontius	41. Plato	72. Triesnecker
11. Hainzel	42. Mairon	73. Maskelyne
12. Lexell	43. Birmingham	74. Taruntius
13. Wurzelbauer	44. Pythagoras	75. Appolonius
14. Regiomontanus	45. Curtius	76. Julius Caesar
15. Pitatus	46. Maginus	77. Manilius
16. Doppelmayer	47. Mutus	78. Plinius
17. Purbach	48. Lilius	79. Autolycus
18. Arzachel	49. Vlacq	80. Posidonius
19. Bullialdus	50. Cuvier	81. Cleomedes
20. Mersenius	51. Janssen	82. Aristillus
21. Alphonsus	52. Stöfler	83. Geminus
22. Gassendi	53. Maurolycus	84. Cassini
23. Ptolemaeus	54. Fabricius	85. Eudoxus
24. Guericke	55. Walter	86. Franklin
25. Letronne	56. Rheita	87. Messala
26. Fra Mauro	57. Furnerius	88. Hercules
27. Flamsteed	58. Aliancensis	89. Atlas
28. Grimaldi	59. Piccolomini	90. Aristoteles
29. Pallas	60. Stevinus	91. Endymion
30. Reinhold	61. Sacrobosco	92. W. C. Bond
31. Landsberg	62. Frascastorius	

a. Sinus Medii (Central Bay)
b. Sinus Aestuum (Seething Bay)
c. Sinus Iridum (Rainbow Bay)
d. Sinus Roris (Bay of Dew)
e. Leibnitz Mountains
f. Doerfel Mountains
g. Riphaean Mountains
h. Apennine Mountains
i. Carpathian Mountains
k. Jura Mountains
m. Palus Somnii (Marsh of Sleep)
n. Palus Putredinis (Marsh of Decay)

o. Lacus Somniorum (Lake of Dreams)
p. Palus Nebularum (Marsh of Mists)
q. Lacus Mortis (Lake of the Dead)
r. Alps (mountains)
s. Alpine Valley
t. Caucasian Mountains
u. Taurus Mountains
v. Haemus Mountains
w. Altai Scarp
x. Straight Wall
y. Hyginus Cleft

CRATER CHAINS.   Many of these features are distributed in chains. The walled plains exhibit some impressive line-ups, such as the great series running roughly along the meridian in the southern hemisphere. The same is true of the craters and craterlets, which often occur in pairs and occasionally in long strings. It is obvious that the moon has been subjected to some immense "peppering" force, whether from without or within; and the crater chains prove that, in many cases at least, the process was not a random one. This tends to support the volcanic rather than the meteoric theory of crater formation.

DOMES.   These curious features, like low swellings or hillocks, are of heights up to 1,000 feet and diameters up to two miles; they can be seen well only when near the terminator. More than a hundred are known, but it is certain that many remain to be found, since they were first identified only thirty years ago. Many American and British amateurs are engaged in dome-charting. They may represent solidified lava pushed up by huge bubbles of gas.

VALLEYS AND CLEFTS.   Sometimes called *rills*, these range from colossal ravines more than a hundred miles long and several miles wide, to hairline cracks at the limit of telescopic visibility. The more delicate clefts are evidently true cracks in the surface, but some of the more prominent ones are seen to contain the remains of craterlets along their length. Great clefts often pass across the floors of walled plains, frequently breaking through the mountain wall and extending across the ground outside.

MOUNTAIN RANGES.   It is not surprising that a world showing such drastic primeval activity has thrown up superb mountain ranges. One of the finest, the Apennine Mountains, runs across the meridian in the northern hemisphere, while the highest peaks on the moon, some of which reach 30,000 feet, occur near the south pole. These, the Leibnitz Mountains, actually run along the limb, so that under suitable conditions of libration they can be seen in profile, their glittering summits poking out against the sky. Other mountain ranges also run along the eastern limb, as well as marking off the Mare Imbrium from the Mare Serenitatis.

NAMES.   The system of crater naming follows the plan suggested in 1651 by the Italian observer Giovanni Riccioli, who called them after famous scientists (reserving a fine formation for himself) and other prominent figures. The moon therefore houses such illustrious personages as Plato, Newton, Archimedes, and Copernicus. Riccioli himself supplied about two hundred names for the craters he had plotted, but subsequent work has naturally added many more; there are now more than a thousand listed formations. Unfortunately, the last "official" map was issued by the International Astronomical Union as long ago as 1935, and since that time two further charts have appeared, to which fresh names have been added. One was drawn up by the British amateur observer H. P. Wilkins, the other being compiled by the United States Air Force. In several cases the same craters have been given different names; it is therefore satisfying to find uniformity being restored in D. W. G. Arthur's new quadrant charts, issued from the Lunar and Planetary Laboratory of the University of Arizona.

Another serious reversal to conformity has appeared in the decision of the United States Air Force and the International Astronomical Union to reverse the east and west limbs. The present orientation has worked satisfactorily for three centuries; and, while this in itself is no strong reason for refusing to change, it is clear that utter confusion may well reign when comparing old and new observations. The well-established convention has, therefore, been retained throughout this book.

The best way of getting a general picture of the lunar surface is to follow the moon through its phases from crescent to full. In this way, all its major features will be seen as they are revealed by the slow progress of sunrise over its surface; and it will be noted how soon they lose their distinctiveness as the sun rises high over them and the shadows disappear. With this end in view, let us now assume two weeks of favored weather, and view the moon at two-day intervals throughout the first half of a lunation.

The thin crescent

It is interesting to see just how soon the young moon becomes visible with the naked eye in the evening sky. Conditions are most favorable in the spring, when it makes the greatest angle with the horizon. W. F. Denning, in his 1891 classic work, *Telescopic Work for Starlight Evenings*—unfortunately, a book difficult to obtain—mentions seeing the crescent when it was only 20 hours 38 minutes old. He also quotes a case in which the waning crescent was seen one morning before sunrise, and the young moon just after sunset on the following day. Another observer claims to have seen the crescent when it was only sixteen hours old. Challenges such as this, although of no particular scientific benefit, form an interesting test of vision and application.

Three days old

The most obvious feature of the young crescent is the Mare Crisium (Sea of Crises). This is one of the smaller lava plains, measuring 355 by 280 miles; but, although it is elongated in an east-west direction, foreshortening makes it appear to be extended along the north-south axis, and it compensates for its small size by the majesty of its mountainous surroundings. At this phase and, similarly, two or three days after full, the rugged border can be seen very well with a small telescope. There are also three small craters on its surface (Picard, Pierce, and Graham); these are just coming into view. Another interesting feature is a "quadrangle" of white streaks and tiny craterlets near the southwest corner. This can be seen easily with a 3-inch refractor when the sun is high, but it somehow escaped notice until thirty years ago. Several well-known amateurs have observed that some small features on the mare's surface appear unaccountably obscure at times; but these observations must be taken with a certain amount of reserve, for it is desperately easy to be misled by different conditions of seeing and illumination.

There are four other maria located in the crescent (Australe, Smythii, Marginis, and Humboldtianum), running from south to north, but these lie on the extreme edge of the disk and can be well seen only at conditions of western libration, when this part of the moon has swung its maximum extent toward the earth. Even so, they always appear extremely foreshortened, and our first good view of them was had from the Lunik III photographs.

The crescent phase reveals some fine walled plains. The southernmost, Furnerius, has been reduced by subsequent activity, but its walls still rise to 11,000 feet above the 80-mile floor. To the north is the magnificent crater Petavius. This is 100 miles across, and has a splendid central mountain, from which a great cleft runs to the southeast wall. This cleft is easily seen with a 3-inch, as is much other interior detail. North again is Vendelinus, as large as Petavius but badly destroyed. The fourth member of this chain, Langrenus, is 85 miles across and has a central mountain; its walls are only a little lower than those of Petavius. It is worth remembering that although these craters, and indeed almost all the craters on the moon, are roughly circular, they appear elliptical when they are near the limb because of the foreshortening effect.

Two 78-mile walled plains in the northern half of the crescent are worthy of attention. The first, Cleomedes, lies immediately north of the Mare Crisium, and has a fine central mountain; parts of its wall rise to 16,000 feet. Much nearer the north pole is Endymion, which has an unusually dark floor that seems to change in tone as the lunation progresses. Several craters show this effect, and we cannot yet be sure whether some change is really going on, or if it is simply due to contrast as the angle of illumination changes. Endymion and its companions are well worth systematic watching.

When viewing the crescent moon, it will be noticed that the entire disk is often visible, glowing faintly against the sky. This effect, known as *earthshine*, can be seen with the naked eye on some occasions, and a low magnification will reveal some of the darkest and brightest features on the night side. Earthshine is caused by the cloudy terrestrial atmosphere reflecting sunlight onto the moon, so that its distinctness is a measure of atmospheric conditions. It is strongest when the moon is near new, since at this point the earth would appear "full" to an observer on its surface.

Five days old

One of the major seas, Mare Foecunditatis (Sea of Fertility), is now revealed. It contains a few small craters dotted here and there, but none is more interesting than the "non-identical" twins Messier and Pickering. These lie close together in the center of the mare, and are easily found because a curious, double white streak projects from Pickering in a roughly easterly direction. Although they are small, about eight miles across, they are well worth observing. Beer and Mädler, in their 1847 map, described the two craters as exactly alike; Walter Goodacre, a well-known British observer, measured their diameters in 1932 and found Messier to be the larger of the two; and many amateurs often see Messier as smaller than Pickering! These "changes" are, of course, entirely optical effects, probably due to the different depths of the craters. R. M. Baum, a contemporary observer well known for his lunar work, has commented: "The apparent shallowness of Messier leads to internal reflection, and thus possibly, at the right phase, to some dilution of shadow intensity. By contrast, Pickering seems deeper and able to hold shadow longer." This example shows how easy it is to be misled by the subtle and varying play of light. Another instance was the fiasco of the supposed "bridge" discovered near the eastern shore of Mare Crisium in 1954, caused by unusual lighting conditions whose effects deceived an observer. The moon may be an almost dead world, but the progress of sunrise and sunset certainly breathes a ghostly life across its surface.

Mare Nectaris (Sea of Nectar), a smaller sea to the east of Mare Foecunditatis, has its interesting features. The nearby chain, Theophilus, Cyrillus, and Catharina, is indeed the most striking sight at this phase. These three objects are superb, between 65 and 70 miles across. Theophilus is the best preserved, displaying a bright central mountain mass, a depressed floor, and terraced walls rising to 18,000 feet. It is interesting, too, to see how Theophilus has broken into its neighbor Cyrillus, indicating that it is of more recent origin.

A crater chain such as this one—and there are many on the moon— offers eloquent support for the volcanic theory of lunar crater formation. No matter just what igneous process caused these features, it seems clear that they must in some way have been associated with definite lines of weakness in the soft lunar crust. The meteoric theory, which proposes that they are the impact marks of meteors striking the surface and incontinently exploding, cannot account for these chains in anything like so convincing a way. It is probably true to say that the meteoric devotees are mostly laymen in lunar affairs; few active observers who have studied the moon's surface night after night, and made themselves familiar with its crusty features, are prepared to believe that anything other than slow molding over millions of years could have produced the great craters we see today. Of course, many of the smaller pits must have been caused by the impact of small meteors.

Further proof that the moon was once a lava-strewn inferno comes from the nearby crater Fracastorius, on the southern shore of Mare Nectaris. Here, we see that what was once its northern wall has disappeared almost entirely under the molten lava of the mare, which long ago flooded its interior and converted it into a great bay. There are many examples of flooded and partly drowned craters, suggesting that the seas were formed in the later stages of the moon's active history.

At this stage, Mare Tranquillitatis (Sea of Tranquillity) is also coming into view, but the most distinctive feature of the northern part of the crescent is the 62-mile crater Posidonius, on the western shore of Mare Serenitatis. Posidonius has low, rather narrow walls, and a great amount of interior detail. North of Posidonius are the twin craters Atlas and Hercules. Atlas, 55 miles across, is the larger of the two; its floor contains some interesting dark patches which, like the floor of nearby Endymion, seem to vary in tone.

First quarter

Half moon is the most spectacular phase. When the terminator runs like a knife down the central meridian, and the great walled plains are thrown up into plan view, the observer feels convinced that he is hanging in space over this black-and-silver world.

All over the southern hemisphere cluster the sunlit walls and shadow-filled interiors of hundreds of craters. Some immediately catch the eye: the great walled plain Stöfler, which has a smaller crater, Faraday, on its southwestern margin; Aliacensis and Werner to the north; and, north again and near the center of the disk, the 80-mile Albategnius and the 84-mile Hipparchus. Hipparchus must once have been a magnificent object, but it is now sadly reduced; its walls are low, and have been completely breached in the northeast quarter. In fact, near the time of full moon, when Hipparchus is experiencing noon, it is not too easy to make out the crater at all. Similarly, if we now look near the western limb we shall find Vendelinus and Furnerius hard to distinguish from their glaring surroundings, while the mountainous border of the Mare Crisium shows no sign of relief. Only very bright and very dark craters can be distinguished easily when the sun shines vertically upon them.

Mare Vaporum (Sea of Vapors), an ill-defined sea in the center of the disk, contains a small but well-known object. This is the 4-mile crater Hyginus, which lies in the middle of a famous cleft 150 miles long. The cleft is only a mile wide, but it can easily be seen with a 3-inch refractor because it is distinctly lighter than the surrounding surface. The Hyginus cleft is particularly interesting because it is not a true fault at all, but a string of tiny craterlets. A moderate telescope is required to show this well, but there can be no doubt at all of its nature; it is hard to see how these craterlets can be anything but volcanic. Hyginus forms a right-angled triangle with the bright crater Manilius at one corner and the dark-floored Boscovitch at the apex, and these form a convenient guide since they are distinct under all conditions of illumination.

Mare Serenitatis (Sea of Serenity), one of the finest of the large seas, is now well seen. Its southern and eastern borders are marked by the Haemus and Caucasus ranges, while the magnificent Apennine range now leads off into the dark hemisphere. The mare's surface is relatively featureless, except under very low illumination, when a number of ridges become obvious. There is only one distinctive crater, Bessel, which lies on a bright streak that passes centrally across the huge expanse. Farther east, toward the gap between the Caucasus and Apennine ranges, a conspicuous white spot marks the position of the controversial crater Linné.

The Linné furor started in 1866, when Julius Schmidt, who was then working on his famous lunar map, announced that the crater had either disappeared or else changed beyond all recognition. Observing it on October 16 of that year, he found that instead of appearing as a regular crater, it seemed to be just a small bright patch. This flew in the face of observations he himself had made between 1841 and 1843, and of those made by other earlier observers, Johann von Mädler among them. On previous occasions, when Linné lay near the terminator, they had all seen a distinct shadow cast on the crater's floor by the surrounding walls. Yet in 1866, and indeed a century later, this impression was never regained. With powerful instruments, Linné appears as a craterlet about a mile across, surrounded by a whitish patch.

The matter was actually cleared up later by Mädler himself, who stated that he did not consider the crater to have changed its aspect from what it was in the 1830s; but this statement was largely ignored by other observers, and today there are still people who believe that the Linné affair has a basis of reality. Nevertheless, the evidence overwhelmingly supports some sort of optical deception. When conditions are suitable, tiny Linné does give the impression of being larger than it really is; and the fact that observers of the caliber of Mädler and Schmidt could be misled only emphasizes how very careful one must be about jumping to conclusions. The Linné affair is a valuable lesson, and one should not forget it.

To the north of Mare Serenitatis lie two conspicuous craters, Aristotle and Eudoxus. They both have bright floors and are easily seen at full.

Nine days old

It is well worth looking at the moon just a day after the quarter, for at this time a magnificent string of walled plains comes into view. These are Ptolemaeus, Alphonsus, and Arzachel, which lie slightly to the east of the Hipparchus-Albategnius pair. The 90-mile Ptolemaeus must once have been a magnificent object, but it has been somewhat reduced by subsequent activity, although not so drastically as Hipparchus. It is still an imposing sight when caught on the terminator, and there is a conspicuous small crater, Lyot, on the floor.

Its southern companion Alphonsus hit the publicity spotlight in November, 1958, when the Soviet astronomer Nikolai Kozyrev reported detecting an emission of gas, accompanied by a reddish glow, at the base of its central mountain. Kozyrev was using a large telescope—the 50-inch reflector of the Crimea Observatory—but previous observers had also reported seeing faint glows there from time to time. Moreover, the floor contains several dark patches that have been reported as showing variations during the lunation. Although a moderate aperture is necessary for a proper study, a 3-inch will reveal these patches plainly enough. Clearly, Alphonsus is one of the most interesting craters on the moon.

A great number of objects come into view two days after first quarter, but there is no room here to touch on more than a few of them. One of the most remarkable craters on the moon, 54-mile Tycho, lies on the southern region of the terminator. It has a splendid central mountain and is in a good state of preservation; it will already have been noticed that a number of bright streaks crossing the southwestern region of the moon appear to converge on it. These are just some of the far-flung members of Tycho's ray system. It is by far the most extensive on the moon, and by full the whole disk is dominated by these radiating white streaks, some of which extend for more than a thousand miles. They are obscure when near the terminator, but shine out under high illumination.

Tycho's ray system is by no means the only one. Copernicus, a magnificent crater in Oceanus Procellarum (Ocean of Storms), is a prominent ray center, and there are many other examples. The rays are evidently some sort of surface deposit, for they pass over craters and hilltops without deforming them in any way, but their true nature is a mystery that will probably not be solved until astronauts set foot on the surface.

Some distance to the south of Tycho lies Clavius, second largest crater on the moon. This is a colossal walled plain 145 miles across, and the distinctive string of craters across its floor makes it a most conspicuous object. To the north, in the rather ill-defined Mare Nubium (Sea of Clouds), lies the half-drowned Gueriké, which was photographed in close-up by Ranger VII. It is most instructive to compare the amount of detail shown on the photographs with that visible through the telescope. The fine 40-mile crater Bullialdus, also on Mare Nubium, now stands out near the terminator. Nearby lies the curious fault known as the Straight Wall, which is an almost straight ridge some 60 miles long, with the western ground about 800 feet higher than that to the eastern side. It is situated near the prominent crater Thebit, and its southern end runs into a branching group of hills appropriately known as the Stag's Horn Mountains.

To the north of the lunar equator, and near the southern shore of Mare Imbrium (Sea of Showers), the crater Copernicus rears up in magnificent relief. Because of its relatively level surroundings, we see Copernicus undisturbed by later activity. In its superb isolation, it is perhaps the finest crater on the moon. It is 56 miles across, with walls rising to 17,000 feet and bearing on their inner slopes an intricate system of terracing. Impressive, too, is the central mountain mass, which contains three separate peaks. When caught right on the terminator, so that the interior is filled with shadow, Copernicus really seems to jut up toward the observer. The region nearby contains a large number of domes.

Many craters appear impressively deep when seen near the terminator, but it must always be remembered that low sunlight exaggerates. Car headlights can amplify harmless dips into seemingly deep ravines; the same is true of sunrise and sunset conditions on the moon. Relatively speaking, Copernicus and its companions are far shallower than saucers; in a sense, they are more impressive as seen from the earth than they would be from close at hand. For example, someone standing near the center of the walled plain Ptolemaeus would see no mountain border at all, for the peaks would be below the horizon! The moon, being a smaller world than the earth, has a more sharply curving surface, and the horizon is only about two miles away from the observer.

Mare Imbrium is a fine sea, with many interesting features. Its western shore is bounded by the magnificent Apennine range, in which one peak, Mount Huygens, rises to almost 20,000 feet. To the north lie the Alps, whose less impressive appearance is compensated for by the curious valley, as straight as if cut with a knife, that slices its way through the mountains. This can be seen very well immediately after the half phase.

Before the eye crosses Mare Imbrium it is a good idea to look at Eratosthenes, a smaller version of nearby Copernicus, which lies at the southern tip of the Apennines. The floor of Eratosthenes contains some well-known dark patches that give the impression of varying in size during the lunation, although, again, it seems likely to be some sort of optical effect. At all events, it is a mystery worth investigating.

The dark-floored walled plain, Plato, on the northern shore, may well be the most studied object on the moon. It is 60 miles across, with relatively low walls and a level floor, and appears noticeably elliptical because of its closeness to the north pole. Its darkness makes it easily distinguishable at full. What makes Plato so interesting is some of the tiny craterlets scattered about its interior. Figure 21 shows a chart of the major features, and although these craterlets are relatively small, there is no doubt at all of their existence. Yet, on occasions, some or all are strangely difficult to see, when they should, by all accounts, be obvious. On the other hand, as in the case of Linné, it is easy to jump to conclusions; the angle of illumination has so drastic an effect on the appearance of the lunar surface that without a really thorough survey no definite conclusions can be drawn. Proper study of the crater requires a telescope of at least 10 inches aperture, although some of the spots have been made out with a $3\frac{1}{2}$-inch refractor.

A little way south of Plato, on the surface of the mare, is Pico, a bright, isolated mountain. To the east, the impressive Sinus Iridum (Bay of Rainbows) is creeping out of the darkness. It is an unforgettable sight when the terminator passes through it; the semicircular mountain range is lit up like a great gleaming scimitar, while the "bay" itself is still lost in night.

Eleven days old

This is the time for catching two interesting features: the brightest crater on the moon, Aristarchus, and the nearby Schröter's Valley.

In 1783, Herschel made a startling announcement. He had been observing the dark, earthlit portion of the moon, on which, as often happens, the very dark and very light features could be dimly made out, when he noticed the central peak of Aristarchus glowing quite brightly. Moreover, as he reported to the Royal Society, "all the adjacent parts of the volcanic mountain seemed to be faintly illuminated by the eruption, and were gradually more obscure as they lay at a greater distance from the crater."

We know more now than was known in Herschel's day, and the idea of volcanic activity on a scale sufficient to produce such a glow seems distinctly unlikely. On the other hand, an observer of Herschel's experience

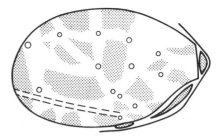

Figure 21. *Plato. This shows some of the more prominent craterlets and light streaks on the floor, as charted by A. Stanley Williams, a famous amateur lunar observer of the last century.*

would not report so remarkable an observation without being sure of his facts, so we are left seeking alternative explanations. One is that the dark side of the moon was illuminated by exceptionally strong conditions of earthshine, causing Aristarchus to glow more brightly than usual.

Aristarchus itself is a normal enough crater, 29 miles across and with a central peak, lying in the rather barren northern reaches of Oceanus Procellarum. It is the center of a small but bright ray system, and the walls and floor are coated with a white deposit that makes it noticeably bright even when it lies on the terminator. The central peak is even brighter than the rest, and by full moon it is so glaring that it is difficult to examine with a large telescope unless a neutral filter is used to cut down the light. Violet hues have been reported in the area, but the most famous observation was made as recently as October 30, 1963, when two United States Air Force lunar mappers were observing from Lowell Observatory in Arizona. They recorded three orange glows in the area, lasting for twenty-five minutes, and were convinced that some form of activity had taken place. However, these observations are made extremely difficult by the great brilliance of the region; the eye is easily deceived, and the fact that a refracting telescope was used makes any color estimates somewhat uncertain.

Aristarchus is also the prototype of a class of lunar features known as *banded craters*. Soon after the sun has risen over Aristarchus, even a small telescope will show two or three bands running from the central mountain toward the eastern wall; these appear to extend and darken during the lunar day, even passing over the wall and onto the outside plain. Once again, we cannot be sure whether or not this is an optical effect, although the development appears definite enough. A 3-inch refractor will show the main bands easily, and they provide an interesting field of investigation.

The much darker crater Herodotus lies closely southeast. It is slightly smaller than Aristarchus, and acts as the terminus for a curious U-shaped valley named after its discoverer, Johann Schröter. Schröter's Valley, which runs north for some 30 miles, then doubles back in a southeasterly direction, is a true fault, with nothing of the crater-chain nature of the Hyginus cleft. It is easily seen with a small telescope, although an instrument of at least 8 to 12 inches aperture is required for a proper investigation. Another interesting crater to be seen at this phase is Gassendi, on the northern border of Mare Humorum (Sea of Moisture). It is 55 miles across, with rather damaged walls, and the floor contains a most intricate system of clefts. Gassendi has recently shown evidence of bursts of activity on its floor, and is one of the regions being watched with colored filters (see page 94).

Thirteen days old

With the moon now moving toward full, the great formations running down the east limb are coming into view; at this phase, depending on the libration conditions, some superb objects become visible. It must, of course, be borne in mind that many of these walled plains are so near the limb that they appear extremely foreshortened.

By far the most conspicuous of these formations is Grimaldi, a colossal walled plain 120 miles across, with a rather low mountain ring and a floor that is even darker than Plato's; parts of it are often cited as exhibiting the deepest tint on the lunar surface. Under low magnifications, the floor appears relatively featureless, but the curve of the lunar surface can be clearly seen. Its companion, Riccioli, is only slightly smaller, and it too has a dark floor. Somewhat to the south, and running right along the limb, are the Rook Mountains, some of whose peaks rise to 20,000 feet. Nearby is the 20-mile crater Sirsalis, through which a prominent cleft runs from north to south.

Farther south still is the immense formation Schickard. This is only slightly smaller than Clavius, but the walls are rather lower. It is chiefly interesting because of nearby Wargentin, which the Reverend T. W. Webb, a well-known observer of the last century, likened to a slice of cheese! Wargentin is a 54-mile crater that for some reason has become filled to the brim with lava, so that it is a true lunar plateau. We occasionally find other instances of the same phenomenon, but on a much smaller scale, so Wargentin is something of a freak.

Between Schickard and Clavius lies an interesting example of two large craters that have virtually coalesced into one. This is Schiller, which is about 110 miles long and only 60 wide, with a slight "neck" where the walls of the two original formations have joined. Another well-known Siamese-twin feature is Palitzsch, near Petavius, best seen a day or two after full.

The northern quadrant of the east limb is rather less spectacular, much of it being taken up with the ill-defined border of Oceanus Procellarum. There is, however, an immense plain named after Otto Struve, the famous Russian astronomer. (It is hardly a true crater, being formed by the confluence of two mountain ranges.) The 85-mile Pythagoras, near Sinus Iridum, would be a noble object were it better placed. At conditions of eastern libration, however, many features creep into view.

Amateur work

This tour of the moon has necessarily been sketchy, but it has at least brought to light some of the characteristic features of the lunar surface. Moreover, the observer will now have a better idea of when certain formations are best placed for observation. The next question is, What lines of research are likely to produce useful results?

It must be admitted at once that the moon is not an easy object to observe—nothing celestial is—and a great deal of the surface has already been well charted, so that an amateur drawing Copernicus with the aid of a 6- or even 8-inch telescope is unlikely to find anything new. On the other hand, there is a certain art in making lunar sketches and plenty of practice is necessary. It would therefore be a good idea for the tyro to select a list of well-known formations for sketching, comparing the detail noted with that shown on published photographs and charts. If these formations are scattered over the surface, one of them is bound to be well placed for viewing on any promising evening.

Making a drawing is by far the best way of exercising the eye. We may scrutinize a feature and imagine that we see all there is to be seen; but the moment details are put down on paper, a host of fresh and finer detail springs into evidence, so that the initial sketch soon turns out to be a mere outline of what is really visible. This happens so frequently that the observer tends to give up in despair; the eye learns faster than the hand can follow, and it pays not to be too ambitious. Certainly, it would be a hopeless task to draw the whole of Copernicus, as suggested. Instead, choose smaller, less complex structures, for they will soon prove to be far more intricate than was originally thought!

A sketchbook of good-quality drawing paper makes the best lunar observation book. Sketches are commonly made too small; a scale of about twenty miles to the inch is a good standard, for the finer features can then be added without complicating the drawing. Some gifted observers have produced really beautiful lunar representations, using ink and pencil, but a simpler outline sketch can be just as useful if written notes are made of intensities and other features that are too subtle to be rendered visually. Each observer has his own method, but it is a good idea to draw in the shadows first, adding the crater walls, peaks, and finer touches as the observation progresses. If the outline of the formation can be traced from a suitable photograph, this will insure basic accuracy. It is necessary to work fairly fast, for when the sun is low the shadows show perceptible movement in the course of an hour.

If atmospheric conditions are good, the highest possible magnification should be used when drawing in the finest features, whereas a somewhat lower power may be better for sketching in the initial outlines. It will be found that high powers can be used on the moon more often than on most of the planets; this is one of those charming idiosyncrasies that so often turn up in amateur astronomy and that are quite unintelligible to the non-observer. Assuming, of course, that conditions are good, both the moon and Saturn show up well under a powerful eyepiece, whereas the other planets tend to give a clearer image with rather less magnîfication (say, × 200 instead of × 300 with a 6-inch). Mars, however, which shows a small disk, requires a powerful eyepiece if its surface markings are to be seen clearly. There is certainly a distinct difference between the telescopic images of Jupiter and Saturn, Jupiter appearing somewhat vague under powers that show Saturn's disk and rings perfectly clear-cut. It is, of course, necessary to experiment with different planets on the same night, so that seeing conditions are comparable, and it must not be forgotten that steadiness improves with altitude. For this reason a formation near the moon's western limb is better observed just after full (i.e., under sunset illumination) than at the crescent stage, since the full moon is visible much higher in the sky. On the other hand, should it be necessary for some reason to make an observation at local sunrise, the inherent difficulties of the observation must be overcome somehow; one way is to observe during the day when the crescent is high, using a deep-red filter to cut down the sky light. When making a thorough survey of any particular feature, it must not be forgotten that high-light observations are just as important as those made under the more spectacular angles of illumination.

The serious amateur, equipped with a telescope of between 6 and 12 inches aperture, will find two main fields of original research open to him. These are, first, the observation of temporary variations of detail; second, examination of the minor features, such as domes, and analysis of crater depths and distribution.

"Variable" regions

Of all lunar research, the observation and confirmation of suspected change is by far the most difficult. During a century and a half of critical examination, there has been only one established case of igneous activity; this was Kozyrev's observation of Alphonsus, and it is worth remembering that it was made with a very big telescope. Any amateur expecting to see a crater spirited away before his eyes is not only highly optimistic, but is also unlikely to make a reliable observer! Moreover, it is impossible to claim any intimate knowledge of a region until it has been observed again and again under every condition of illumination. The Linné affair remains a lesson to everyone.

Of course, some changes are known to be purely optical. The Messier-

Pickering pair presents one such case, and there is another pair of twins, Beer and Feuillé, in Mare Imbrium. There must be a reason for their apparent variations in size, and the best way of finding out is to examine them at every available opportunity. The famous American astronomer W. H. Pickering published several important papers on the subject of temporary variations in the *Annals* of Harvard College Observatory,* and these should be investigated by anyone interested in the problem.

In a similar way, such regions as the floor of Plato, which appears to darken as the sun rises over it, follow behavior that has neither been fully established nor explained. Endymion and Grimaldi are other instances, while the patches in such craters as Eratosthenes and Atlas are worthy of investigation. There is plenty of scope here for observation, and, while a large telescope will give a better view than a small one, it is amazing what can be done with a keen eye and patience.

Banded craters form another field of study. Aristarchus is the most famous example, but many other smaller craters exhibit similar features. Some, like those in Aristarchus, radiate from the center like wheel spokes; Messier, on the other hand, seems to have a single band running across the floor from the west wall towards the east. Anaxagoras (Second Quadrant) and Proclus (First Quadrant) are exceptional in possessing bands that are brighter than the floor.

Amateur observers have charted more than two hundred craters exhibiting bands, but their individual characteristics are not at all well known, and a series of observations made during several lunations would be of great interest. This work is not easy, for the craters are mostly small and high powers must be used. Nevertheless, experience will soon dictate just what features are observable with the aperture at hand. Aristarchus provides a useful testing ground, but others include:

First Quadrant: Aristillus, Burg, Maury, Menelaus, Strabo, Silberschlag, Theaetetus
Second Quadrant: Bode, Kepler, Marco Polo, Pytheas, Timocharis
Third Quadrant: Birt, Moore, Nicollet
Fourth Quadrant: Biot, Messier, Pickering, Rosse

When it comes to the obscuration of local detail and other unusual manifestations, the observer is treading on very shaky ground. There is no use in "expecting" to see something unusual, for the eye will then almost certainly jump to conclusions. An example of the fallibility of even experienced observers was afforded by the impact of Lunik II, when a number of observatories reported seeing flashes or temporary dust clouds; most

*Vol. 32, Part 2 (1900); Vol. 51 (1903); Vol. 53, Part 4 (1905).

unfortunately, they were all in different places! An observation of some anomalous effect is, generally speaking, of much greater value if the observer's attention was elsewhere and suddenly became distracted by the impression of something wrong. However, it may be of interest to list some of the regions in which unusual phenomena have been observed by reliable witnesses on more than one occasion.

MARE CRISIUM. The case of the "quadrangle" in the southwestern corner was undoubtedly due to the oversight of early observers, but the same region is dotted with a great number of tiny craterlets that were also missed, and that are still, on occasions, strangely obscure or even invisible. There are even cases of Graham, the smallest crater on the mare, being missed when it should have been obvious.

ALPHONSUS. There seems to be no doubt at all that some sort of activity occurred here in 1958. The region of eruption lay to the south of the central mountain, and was seen by Kozyrev as a reddish spot. He was, however, using a 50-inch reflector, and it is unlikely that a small instrument could have picked it up. Some observers claim to have seen reddish areas on other parts of the moon; Mädler, for instance, reported reddish tinges near Lichtenberg, a small crater near Aristarchus, and others have made similar observations. Unfortunately, there are many traps for the unwary; the moon is so bright that even the best achromatic eyepieces can sometimes produce false color effects, and it may be significant that the Alphonsus affair heralded an outbreak of color reports.

PLATO. Some of the tiny craterlets in the interior have often been missed under good conditions, but they are so small that a 3-inch refractor will only show them as tiny spots. Plato's floor is covered with streaks of different tint, and these, together with its apparent darkening, make it one of the most interesting areas on the moon.

Obscurations have also been reported in Schickard, Tycho, and around Schröter's Valley, but these are less well documented. In any case, it cannot be emphasized strongly enough that no one should expect to see anything unusual until he has become thoroughly used to lunar observation and has observed the formation in question under all conditions of illumination.

The use of colored filters in lunar observation has recently led to some much-publicized results, and in America and Britain a number of amateur observers have begun to participate in a project known as "Moon-blink." Their purpose is to compare the appearance of a region of the lunar surface as seen in two different colors, red and blue being the most widely used. If, for example, a part of the moon's surface begins to glow with a faint reddish tinge, the color may be too faint to be visible against the white background, but it will appear relatively dark with a blue filter (since the latter, of course, blocks out the red rays). If a simple device is used that permits instantaneous change from one filter to the other, a colored area will appear to "blink."

Since the B.A.A. Lunar Section began this program at the beginning of 1966, a number of members have reported reddish blinks inside certain craters. Not all of these were confirmed, but the classic case occurred inside Gassendi, where independent observers recorded reddish areas during the period April 30–May 2; these were so strong that they were visible without any filters at all. Investigations are still in their early stages, and it would be wrong to draw any conclusions as yet; but it seems clear that the early observers' reports of colored effects may have been more reliable than we once thought.

Suitable filters depend on the aperture of the telescope, since a denser tint can be used with a brighter image. Kodak's Wratten 25 (red) is suitable for moderate apertures, while the other can be a 38 (blue) or a 44 (blue-green). Other filters should also be tried.

Other research

The charting of domes is a field open to those who have moderate apertures. Most of the larger specimens have been noted, but many others need confirmation, and there are probably plenty of small ones still to be found. Lunar observers belonging to the Association of Lunar and Planetary Observers and the British Astronomical Association have joined forces on this project.

There are other useful investigations. Our knowledge of crater depths, especially in the smaller sizes, is not as complete as it might be, and this can obviously have a strong bearing on theories of their formation. Distributional problems have also come to the fore in recent years, particularly concerning ray craters, twin craters, and ridges. All this work is necessary for our improved understanding of the nature of the moon's surface, and there can never be enough good observers to carry it out.

Eclipses of the moon

Just as the moon casts a shadow which at new may fall upon the earth and produce a total eclipse of the sun, so the moon at full sometimes passes through the shadow cast by the earth (figure 22). The most striking observa-

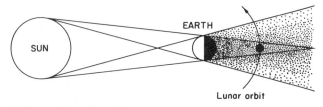

Figure 22. *Eclipse of the moon. (Not to scale.)*

tional difference between the two phenomena is that, whereas a solar eclipse is total over a very restricted region of the earth's surface, a lunar eclipse appears the same wherever the moon is above the horizon. The net result is that, for any particular site, lunar eclipses are rather more common than solar eclipses, and about two hundred times as common as *total* solar eclipses!

Since the sun is larger than the earth, the shadow the earth casts is in the form of a cone. The total length of the cone is about 860,000 miles, and at the average distance of the moon it is about 5,700 miles across. Around this central *umbra* (not to be confused with sunspot terminology) is the *penumbra*, about 6,000 miles wide, the region in which the sun is only partly cut off by the earth. Therefore, as the moon passes into the penumbra it experiences only a very slight darkening until it reaches the edge of the central shadow.

Usually, two full moons a year pass through the earth's shadow.* Not all of these are total, for the moon can simply pass through the north or south edge of the umbra; it may, indeed, just encounter the penumbra, in which case the dimming will be so slight that nothing unusual may be seen. At a total eclipse, the penumbral dimming becomes noticeable about half an hour before the umbra is reached; it takes the moon about an hour to pass fully into the shadow, and it may remain totally eclipsed for up to one and three quarter hours, so that the observable duration of the eclipse may be almost five hours.

Lunar eclipses are of great interest. They have none of the drama of a solar eclipse; but useful observations can be made. One never knows what course the eclipse will take, since the darkness is affected by the earth's meteorological conditions.

It may seem curious that the earth can influence the moon in this way, but the explanation is simple enough. The umbra of the earth's shadow is not perfectly black, because the dense atmosphere, acting as a colossal lens, refracts red light into the shadow. If the earth were airless, a lunar eclipse would be quite dark; but, as things are, the eclipsed moon usually glows with a dull coppery tint; and an observer on the moon would see the earth as a great black ball, with its atmosphere forming a reddish halo. Because the light of the umbra has to pass through the earth's atmosphere, it is clear that meteorological conditions can affect the resultant brightness.

*A list of forthcoming lunar eclipses is given in Appendix I.

96

These conditions change from year to year. The total eclipse of May 13, 1957, was quite normal; but during totality on June 25, 1964, the moon was so dark that it was hard to see without a telescope, although conditions had cleared a little for the second eclipse of that year, on December 19. Searching through the records, we find that the eclipses of 1620 and 1642 were invisible with the naked eye, and the Swedish astronomer Pehr Wilhelm Wargentin reported that he could not see the totally eclipsed moon of 1761 even through a telescope! On other occasions, when the earth's atmosphere has been exceptionally transparent, the moon has been quite bright at mid-eclipse.

It is interesting to try to relate these effects to geophysical events. The explosion of Krakatau in 1883 undoubtedly caused the eclipse of the following year to be unusually dark, for it scattered a huge volume of dust and ash throughout the upper atmosphere, and this would certainly have cut down the transmitted light. Similarly, the eruption of Bali's volcano, Mt. Agung, in 1963 may have contributed to the darkness of the 1964 eclipses.

Quite apart from noting the tone and any curious color effects (some eclipses have been gray-brown instead of coppery), it is interesting to make a closer examination of the surface features. Since the moon has no atmosphere to blanket in the heat, the temperature drops very sharply during an eclipse—from above the temperature of boiling water (for a spot near the equator) to −100°F or less in the course of an hour. This sudden freezing, followed by an equally rapid baking as the shadow moves off the disk, might well produce unusual effects on allegedly "variable" objects, such as the dark patches in Eratosthenes and Endymion, the bands of Aristarchus, and so on. Some observers even claim to have seen the white patch around Linné expand during an eclipse, while others have failed to notice any variations at all. It is certainly only too easy to be deceived by the rapid change of color and illumination, and the greatest care must be taken. Since most craters are either extremely murky or completely invisible during totality, the best way to achieve comparable results is to make a drawing of suspect formations immediately before and just after their eclipse by the shadow.

For observing the progress of an eclipse, a low power should be used so that the whole disk is included in the view. Nothing is gained by using a powerful eyepiece, since the edge of the shadow is far too diffuse to be defined precisely.

Lunar occultations

Since the moon is much closer to us than any other celestial object, it will naturally pass in front of and block out any star or planet that happens to lie in its path. It revolves around the sky in a month, and naked-eye observation reveals its drift; if it is close to a star one night, it will be about 12° east of that star at the same time on the following night. This means that in the course of an hour it appears to move, relative to the stars, across a space equal to its own diameter, so that several of these *occultations*, as they are called, may occur in one night if it is moving across a rich region of the sky.

However, the moon cannot stray over the whole sky. Its orbit is fixed to one plane, which is more or less the same as the plane of the planetary orbits (including the earth's), so that they all keep to a certain band of the sky.* This band is known as the *zodiac*, and it is clear that only stars lying within the zone can be occulted. It is about 18° wide, and runs through the twelve zodiacal constellations: Aries (the Ram); Taurus (the Bull); Gemini (the Twins); Cancer (the Crab); Leo (the Lion); Virgo (the Virgin); Libra (the Scales); Scorpio (the Scorpion); Sagittarius (the Archer); Capricornus (the Goat); Aquarius (the Water Bearer); and Pisces (the Fishes). There is a banal but useful rhyme for remembering the order of the zodiacal constellations:

> *The Ram, the Bull, the Heavenly Twins,*
> *And, next the Crab, the Lion shines,*
> *The Virgin, and the Scales.*
> *Scorpion, Archer, and the Goat;*
> *The Man who pours the Water out,*
> *And Fish with glittering tails.*

Of these, Taurus, Leo, Virgo, and Scorpio each contain a bright star that is occasionally occulted. Even in these cases, however, the glare of the moon (except when a thin crescent) is such that binoculars or a telescope are required for the observation.

Depending on the phase, disappearance, or *immersion*, occurs either at the moon's dark limb (before full) or at the bright limb (after full); conditions for reappearance, or *emersion*, are the opposite. An occultation of a bright star at the moon's dark limb, provided it is not illuminated by earthshine, is startling: One moment it is shining steadily; an instant later, it is blotted out. The very suddenness of disappearance offers one proof that the moon cannot possess a considerable atmosphere, for a depth of air would produce a gradual fading and reddening of the star's light. But nothing like this is ever seen.

Since the positions of the stars are known very accurately, the instant

---

*Because of the large inclination of their orbits, both Mercury and Pluto can sometimes lie outside the recognized limits of the zodiac. The same is true of some of the minor planets.

of occultation offers a clue to the precise position of the moon's limb; if it can be timed to half a second or so, the observation is of use to professional computers. Few amateurs make regular occultation observations, which is a pity; a small telescope is as good as a large one, since low powers are used, and the only other essential is a stop-watch that can be started from some accurate time signal. Occultation predictions are usually given to a tenth of a minute, so there is no need to go to the telescope until ten minutes beforehand. Immersions are easier to observe than emersions, since the sudden flashing out is apt to take the observer by surprise—with the loss of some valuable fractions of a second.

The other essential preliminary is for the observer to find his geographical position to within about a hundred yards. This can be done from a large-scale survey map in the local library, and considerable accuracy is necessary, since each observer has a slightly different view of the moon relative to the stars. The farther east the observer's site, the later the occultation will occur, while latitude also has an effect. To take an extreme case, the moon may pass north of a star as seen from New York, while an observer in Ottawa sees an actual occultation, because of the parallactic effect.

An interesting example of this occurred in 1964, when British amateurs observed the occultation of a faint star on February 20. The star was due to pass behind the moon's south pole, but it was clearly going to be marginal (known as a *graze* occultation), and the occultation limit—the line between a disappearance and near-miss—lay across southern England. Accordingly, one party positioned themselves about 800 yards inside the limit while another observer placed his telescope right on the limit. The results showed that the mathematicians had been only slightly in error, for the marginal observer recorded a miss, and the other party saw the south pole graze the star. In fact, only the peaks projecting from the limb managed to cover it, and four distinct immersions and emersions were noted as the star passed behind these different projections. Such a program naturally takes a certain amount of organization, but it does prove that useful work can be done, for the moon's position could be corrected as a result.

The moon sometimes passes in front of a planet, and planetary occultations can be spectacular, though they are of little scientific interest. Some observers have claimed to see a narrow dark band cross the disk of Jupiter in advance of the lunar limb; and, while such a phenomenon is certainly optical, it is of value in indicating how very easily the eye is deceived. In lunar observation, as with all work involving a telescope, the eye's vagaries must always be borne in mind, and the elimination of its tendency to see what it *expects* to see must be part of the basic education of every good observer.

7

The Sun

The sun is 864,600 miles across, or, as near as makes no difference, a hundred times the diameter of the earth. It is a great sphere of hydrogen gas that is shining at a fiercely hot temperature—about 6,000°C at the surface, and several millions of degrees in the interior. Through atomic reactions, this hydrogen is gradually being converted into helium, so that the sun is really a vast nuclear furnace.

The sun is essentially no different from any of the stars that crowd the night sky, but it appears very different to us because it is so close. It is the center of our solar system, which comprises the planets, comets, and other bodies that revolve around it; and some 5,000 million years ago, so astrophysicists tell us, the sun gave birth to these bodies, including the earth, collecting the material for their formation from a vast cloud of gas and dust far out in space.

In all this time, however, the sun has probably changed very little. The earth itself, which revolves around it once a year at a distance of about 93 million miles, has cooled from its molten state, filled its surface hollows with oceans, seen the development of life from primitive sea creatures to men who have already traveled along the borders of space. During this whole development it has received the sun's steady radiation, and there is no reason to suppose that our star will not continue shining in its present manner for many thousands of millions of years. Its resources are so unimaginably vast that its prodigious emission of light and heat seems to affect it not at all.

Since all the other stars are so far away that we cannot observe their surfaces at all, the sun is of special interest to professional astronomers. Every day, observatories all over the world take photographs of its surface and examine the various features with special equipment that is far beyond the amateur's range, and it must be admitted that there is little chance of the observer making a startling discovery. However, this is no reason for dismissing solar work out of hand, for useful observations can still be made. It is both interesting and instructive to make drawings or take photographs of whatever sunspots may be visible; since they often change rapidly and unpredictably from day to day, one never knows quite what to expect.

Direct observation

It must be re-emphasized that *the sun is a lethal object*. Many a beginner, underestimating its power, has peeped at it through a small telescope and as a result suffered permanent partial blindness. Rumor has it that Galileo's eventual blindness was caused by his unwise solar observations, and the danger is greater now, since telescopes are correspondingly more powerful.

Perhaps the greatest disservice done to astronomers by unthinking opticians has been the invention of the sun cap, a thick, heavily dyed circle of red, blue, or green glass designed to screw over the ocular's eye lens, and intended to make direct observation safe. Unfortunately, the makers have not allowed for the fact that telescopes vary in aperture; thus, while such a filter may (if it is dense enough) provide safety when used for a period of half a minute or so with a 2-inch refractor, it is emphatically *not safe* when used with anything larger. In any case, it is virtually impossible to see anything through a sun cap because of the thickness of the glass and the correspondingly restricted field of view, since the eye cannot get close to the eye lens.

If visual observations of the sun are to be made with any degree of safety, a *solar diagonal* is required. This works on the same principle as a zenith prism, except that an uncoated mirror is used, so that most of the light and heat passes right through. Only a small percentage is reflected into the eyepiece and, with the addition of a light shade glass, the sun can be viewed in complete comfort with apertures of up to 6 inches. The structure of the spots can be observed, and the photosphere is seen to be mottled. Under good conditions, with a magnification of about × 300, a 6-inch telescope will reveal the fine "granulation" of the photosphere, and a large spot group is a magnificent sight. It will be noticed that the best conditions for solar work occur early in the day, before the ground has warmed up sufficiently to produce bad turbulence; good views are rarely to be had around noon, despite the higher altitude.

Projection

While direct observation shows the greatest detail, one of the principal pastimes enjoyed by the amateur is the day-to-day pursuit of the spot groups as they are carried across the disk by the sun's steady rotation. The positions of the spots (noting whether they are north or south of the equator, and in what longitude) are just as interesting as the spots themselves, since at different times different regions of the sun are active. The projection method is the best way of recording them accurately. Figure 23 shows a very simple apparatus that can be made in an hour. Essentially, it consists of a holder that fits over the drawtube, carrying an arm that holds a square board rigidly a foot or so behind the eyepiece. A shield is also needed to protect the projected image from direct solar rays, and a sheet of cardboard or light metal, pierced with a central hole to fit over the object-glass end of the telescope, will serve this function and also help to balance the tube. In the case of a reflector, which is altogether less convenient for solar work because of the heating effects, no shield is required, since the image is not facing the sun. A useful disk diameter is 6 inches, which will require about a $\frac{3}{4}$-inch eyepiece if a 3-inch refractor is being used; it must, of course, include the whole of the sun in the same view. The necessary distance from the eyepiece to the projection board must be found by experiment.

It is worth noting that this distance will not remain unchanged. All the planets in the solar system revolve around the sun in slightly elliptical orbits, so that instead of remaining at a constant distance from the sun, as they would were their orbits perfectly circular, they gradually approach and recede. The planet Mercury, for instance, approaches the sun to within 36 million miles at its closest point, or *perihelion*, but recedes to 48 million miles at *aphelion*. The principle is the same, though much less extreme, in the case of the earth, which is 91,400,000 miles away at the beginning of

Figure 23. *Solar projection apparatus.*

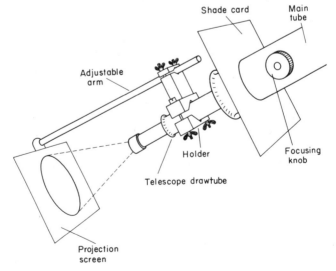

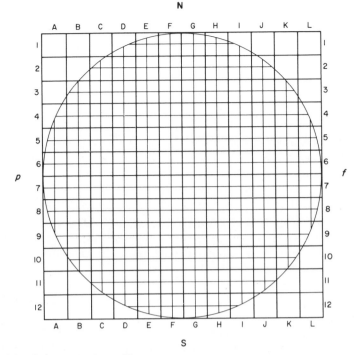

Figure 24. *Solar projection grid.*

January, and 94,600,000 at the beginning of July. In angular terms, the sun's diameter varies from 31′ 31″ to 32′ 38″, a change obvious enough to require a compensating adjustment of about half an inch in the length of the arm.

A piece of clean white paper, bearing a 6-inch circle crossed with a fine grid, is attached to the board, and the solar image is accurately focused on it. This grid (figure 24) must be drawn with a hard, sharp pencil, since coarse lines may obscure some of the finest detail. It is a matter of individual taste just how many lines are drawn in, but $\frac{1}{3}$-inch squares are convenient and allow of considerable accuracy in copying the sunspot positions. Since these are copied onto a sheet of thin paper placed over a similar grid, it is helpful if they can be identified in some way. One good idea is to draw every other line slightly bolder (thus forming larger quartered squares) and marking them with reference letters and numbers, as shown. The second grid should be drawn with ink, so that it shows through the paper.

Before making a drawing, the disk must be orientated. This is done by leaving the telescope stationary and letting the image drift across the screen, twisting the attachment until a sunspot trails along one of the E-W lines. Due to the earth's rotation, the drift is from right to left, with the west limb of the sun leading, or *preceding*, and the east limb *following*—two terms frequently used to describe the apparent motion of a celestial object across the sky. The north and south points are at the top and bottom, respectively. (In the southern hemisphere these directions are reversed.)

Getting accurate positions with an altazimuth mounting is nowhere near as easy as with an equatorial, but it can be done. Very tiny spots, or *pores*, are seen more easily if a sheet of blank paper is placed over the grid so that the disk is seen projected without any confusing lines. Once their general position is established, they can be marked in by reference to the grid. If any bright clouds, or *faculae*, are noticed, these should also be recorded. The main thing to remember is that positions are far more important than details; any attempt to make the result look "realistic" will almost certainly result in exaggerated spot sizes. The secret of accuracy is to wait until the solar disk is exactly central on the screen, and then to memorize the position of a spot in relation to the grid lines. It is then drawn in on the blank.

Heliographic coordinates

We now have a representation of the sun's earth-facing hemisphere, orientated with respect to the earth's cardinal points. This does not mean, unfortunately, that the north pole of the sun is at the top and the south pole at the bottom. From January to June, the sun's north pole is inclined somewhat westwards (i.e., to the left), whereas during the rest of the year it swings out toward the east. Furthermore, from the end of May until the end of December, the north pole is inclined toward the earth, the south pole coming into view during the other months. Figure 25 shows the projected view of the sun at different times of the year.

It is clear that the reduction of the positions to solar latitude and longitude, or *heliographic coordinates*, is not as simple as might appear at first sight. It can, however, be done in a few minutes by a technique devised

Figure 25. *Different views of the sun.*

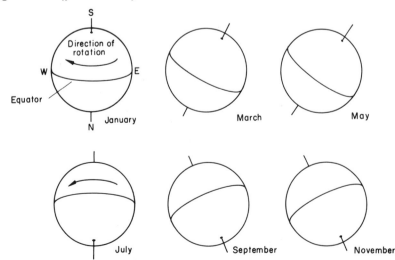

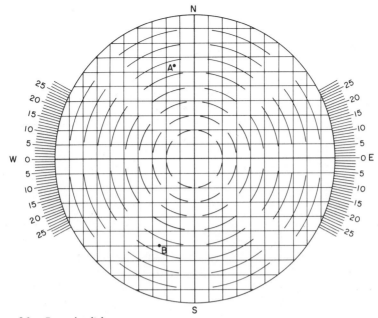

Figure 26. *Porter's disk.*

more than twenty years ago by J. G. Porter, a well-known British astronomer. *Porter's Method* requires the limited use of mathematical tables, but since the formulas are very simple this is no great hardship; it is a great pity that few textbooks give it mention.

A sketch of the projected solar image is made in the usual way, great care being taken to mark the east and west points accurately. This is then laid over a Porter's Disk (see figure 26), which must, of course, have the same diameter. Using the table in the British Astronomical Association *Handbook*, the axial inclination (P) is found and the sketch rotated until the E-W line is inclined at the correct angle. It is worth remembering that the rotation from the zero position is clockwise if the value of P is positive, and counterclockwise if it is negative. For instance, if a drawing were being made in late September, when $P = + 26°$, the east point on the drawing would be turned to coincide with the lower 26° mark at the right-hand side of the disk.

When the sketch is orientated, there only remains the task of estimating the spot's position in terms of horizontal position (x), and vertical position (y). The x factor is reckoned as positive if to the west of the meridian, negative if to the east; whereas y is positive if to the north, and negative if to the south. Each division of the grid corresponds to a value of $0 \cdot 1$. Thus, in the case of spot A, the values would be $x = + 0 \cdot 14$ and $y = + 0 \cdot 64$; for spot B we should have $x = + 0 \cdot 25$ and $y = - 0 \cdot 60$.

It is also necessary to make an estimate of the distance (d) from the center of the disk. This is done with the aid of the concentric lines; in both cases it works out at about 0·65.

When these values are obtained, the *latitude* of the spot (*B*) can be found from the formula

$$\sin B = y + \text{correction}$$

the correction being found by reference to Table I, following. The value of *d* is already known, while B_0, which is the latitude of the center of the disk, can be found in the B.A.A. *Handbook*, or it can be found in Appendix VII.

TABLE I. Correction to the value of y

d	$B_0 =$	0°	1°	2°	3°	4°	5°	6°	7°
0·0		0·00	0·02	0·03	0·05	0·07	0·09	0·10	0·12
0·1		00	02	03	05	07	09	10	12
0·2		00	02	03	05	07	09	10	12
0·3		00	02	03	05	07	08	10	12
0·4		00	02	03	05	06	08	10	11
0·5		00	02	03	05	06	08	09	11
0·6		00	01	03	04	06	07	08	10
0·7		00	01	02	04	05	06	07	09
0·8		00	01	02	03	04	05	06	07
0·9		00	01	02	02	03	04	05	05
1·0		0·00	0·00	0·00	0·00	0·00	0·00	0·00	0·00

The sign of the correction is always the same as that of B_0 (see Appendix VII).

Once the value of *B* is known, the *longitude* of the spot (*L*) can be found from the formula

$$\sin L = x \sec B$$

The value of the secant of *B* can be found in a book of trigonometrical tables, which will also be required for deducing the angles *B* and *L* from their sines. The B.A.A. *Handbook* and the *Astronomical Ephemeris* both give the longitude of the sun's central meridian for every day of the year, and it is simply a matter of adding or subtracting *L* from this value.

Although initially these calculations may appear formidable, no actual algebraic knowledge is called for; it is simply a matter of looking up figures in a set of tables, and taking care in addition and multiplication. Much also depends on the accuracy with which the Porter's Disk is drawn.

Individual sunspots and their characteristics

Some spots, especially the small ones, are quiescent; they either die out as quickly and quietly as they formed, or remain more or less unchanged from day to day. Large groups, however, can be much more active, and may show striking changes in just a few hours. At these times, if the atmosphere is steady enough, it is interesting to make a large-scale drawing of the details of the group, once again by projection.

A large disk is required if the finest details are to be seen, and since the image will appear faint unless protected from the light in some way, the answer is to make a *projection box*. This is made from thin plywood, about 5 inches square and 10 inches long, with the interior painted mat black. The drawtube fits into one end; at the other end is a piece of white paper or Bristol board to act as the screen. The lower half of one of the sides is omitted, so that the image can be examined. Under these conditions, well shielded from daylight, the solar surface is seen with great brilliance. Once the drifting E–W line has been established against the grid drawn on the screen, the details of the group can be copied in the same way as with whole-disk projection. To produce the necessary enlargement, of course, a high-power eyepiece must be used.

The sunspots themselves are titanic disturbances on the visible surface or *photosphere*. Characteristically, a spot consists of a central dark *umbra* surrounded by a lighter *penumbra;* patches of this penumbral matter may also be found scattered over the adjacent photosphere. A complex spot may contain several separate umbrae, and a common sight is that of two spots having roughly the same latitude, one following the other across the disk at a distance of anything up to 50,000 miles.

Although a spot umbra appears dark, it is certainly not black. This is something that can be proved when the moon passes across the disk during a solar eclipse; against the absolutely dark lunar silhouette, a sunspot appears as distinctly brownish. Evidently, then, it is an effect of contrast. The interior of a sunspot, being some 1,100°C cooler than the photosphere, radiates light less efficiently; yet if we could see it divorced from its over-powering surroundings, it would appear as dazzlingly bright!

Sunspot positions are of interest on three counts, and it is worth saying a few words about each of these.

ROTATION PERIOD. The sun, like the giant planets Jupiter and Saturn, does not rotate as a solid body. Instead, its period of rotation relative to a fixed point, or *sidereal period*, varies from about 25 days at the equator to about 27½ days at a latitude of 40°, with more polar regions (if one can imagine "polar" regions on the sun!) rotating even more slowly. Since the published values for the longitude of the central meridian are based on the equatorial period, we find higher-latitude spots gradually dropping behind. It should be remembered, however, the the earth's own revolution around the sun makes it appear to rotate more slowly; the *synodic period*, or period relative to the earth, for the equator is about $27\frac{1}{4}$ days, and about 30 days in the "temperate" regions.

PROPER MOTIONS.   As well as showing a drift according to their latitude, individual spots sometimes have movements of their own. The leading spot of a freshly formed pair frequently gains on its follower at the rate of about 1° a day, but it quickly slows down again to a more orderly rate. These *proper motions*, as they are called, are not always predictable, but they need accurate longitude observations if they are to be made out.

DISTRIBUTION.   Sunspots do not occur erratically all over the solar surface. The main areas of occurrence are the 5° to 40° latitude limits in both hemispheres; only rarely do they appear at the equator, and hardly any have been observed in latitudes higher than 45°.

The lifetimes of spots are exceedingly variable. The majority of groups never get beyond the "pore" stage; these require careful observation to be made out at all, and they die out in a very few days. If two distinct umbrae develop, however, and a major group occurs, it usually reaches its greatest development in about ten days, at which time it is well elongated in longitude. After this, the trailer dies away and the leader becomes small and round, although it may persist for weeks; it will, of course, be temporarily out of view while on the averted hemisphere. In 1943, a spot was followed for almost two hundred days, but this was most exceptional.

The solar cycle

The frequency with which large and small groups form varies greatly. In some years, the sun throws up many groups, while at other times the disk may be spotless for days or weeks on end. The discovery of the *solar cycle*, as it is called, was made by an amateur—a German apothecary of Dessau, Hofrath Schwabe. In 1826, he bought a small telescope and started making daily observations of the sun, drawing whatever spots happened to be visible. By 1843, some sort of periodicity seemed to be emerging, but it was not until 1851 that he considered the fluctuations to be confirmed—an example of devoted persistence that can have few equals. We now know that the cycle has an average period of just over eleven years, and that the rise to maximum is faster than the subsequent decline; but the period is elastic to the extent of several years, while some maxima are much more active than others. The last maximum, which reached its peak in December, 1957, was the most active ever recorded; but the largest sunspot ever seen appeared during the previous maximum, in April, 1947. This group covered an area of about six million square miles, and was easily visible with the naked eye when protected by a dense photographic negative or smoked glass. A group larger than about 25,000 miles can usually be seen without a telescope.

It should not be thought from this that the sun is interesting only around the time of maximum activity. Near minimum the disk is more often blank, but one never knows when a large group may appear; in September, 1963, for example, when the sun was only a year away from minimum activity, I watched a splendid group develop until it could be seen with the naked eye. At the time of writing (1966), the minimum phase has passed, and the sun is now gathering strength for another maximum, due to occur in 1969. This is therefore an excellent time to commence systematic solar work. It is fascinating to watch new spots break out and old ones decay—and one never knows just what is going to appear around the eastern limb! If an exceptionally large group is carried into the averted hemisphere, it is worth keeping a special lookout two weeks later to see if it has reappeared at the eastern limb.

An interesting by-product of the solar cycle is the way it influences sunspot latitudes. The first spots of a new cycle always occur in the higher latitudes, the active regions moving toward the equator as the cycle develops. The sun's recent new phase of activity was heralded by the appearance of a small, high-latitude spot in November, 1964, at the same time that the last spots of the old cycle were appearing in the equatorial regions, so that during this phase there were two distinct spot-zones in each hemisphere. This behavior is known as Spörer's Law, after the nineteenth-century German astronomer who observed it.

The Wilson effect

Some British amateur solar observers have recently been active in investigating a phenomenon known as the *Wilson effect*. This was first noticed in 1769, when Alexander Wilson, Professor of Astronomy at Glasgow, followed a large sunspot as it approached the western limb. He noticed that as it neared the limb, the umbra became steadily more and more displaced toward the center of the sun, as shown schematically in figure 27. Wilson realized the significance of this: The spot must have been shallow, with the umbra lying below the level of the photosphere—rather like a saucer that is viewed from a more and more sharply inclined angle. His supposition was confirmed when the spot, which proved to be a long-

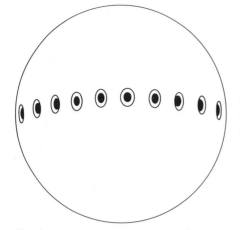

Figure 27. *The Wilson effect. The effect is greatly exaggerated in this diagram.*

lived one, reappeared at the eastern limb with its umbra once more displaced, becoming central as it moved toward the center of the disk.

This was all very well until other observers noticed that only a relatively few spots showed the Wilson effect, whereas a small number produced an umbral deflection in the *opposite* direction, inferring that the spot in question was convex! To investigate this curious state of affairs, members of the Solar Section of the British Astronomical Association, which is an entirely amateur body, took and measured photographs of 79 spots that showed either a positive or negative displacement. The results were most interesting: It was discovered that three times as many spots were concave as convex, and that the degree of depth or elevation of the center was much less than had been widely believed—a spot 20,000 miles across would, on average, show a difference of level of about 500 miles, though larger variations were sometimes found. Moreover, fluctuations occur; one spot was observed to progress from convex to concave. It is clear that a great deal remains to be done before our knowledge of the Wilson effect and its consequences is at all satisfactory. This is a field in which other amateurs may be able to do useful work.

Sunspots and auroras

Sunspots are intensely magnetic, and active groups emit great quantities of what is known as *corpuscular radiation*. These atomic particles are sprayed out almost like water from a hose, and when they reach the vicinity of the earth they trigger off a reaction in the very high-altitude molecules in the earth's atmosphere, which causes them to glow, giving rise to auroral displays. Auroras are seen most frequently in high latitudes, since the earth's own magnetic field usually prevents the disturbing particles from reaching equatorial regions; but just occasionally there are world-wide displays. It is not surprising to find that auroras are closely linked with the solar cycle; although they were common in 1957 and 1958, they are rare at the present time. Nevertheless, the sight of a large group of sunspots passing the sun's meridian is the signal to keep a lookout for an auroral display; it will occur, if at all, about two days after meridian passage, this being the time taken for the slow-moving particles to reach Earth. For regular auroral observation, the observer must have a latitude of at least 50° to 55°, and the higher it is, the better.

Faculae and flares

Closely associated with sunspots are the *faculae*, clouds of glowing vapor that float at an altitude of several hundred miles above the photosphere. In some mysterious way, faculae seem to herald the outbreak of a new spot group; they also linger after the group has decayed—rather like solar vultures! If a group of faculae is seen, it is wise to keep an eye on that particular region and be ready for the appearance of spots.

Faculae can ordinarily be seen only when they are near the limb; this is explained by the extra-effective thickness of the solar atmosphere, or *chromosphere*, at this point. The chromosphere is several thousand miles deep, and acts as a division between the dense photosphere and the tenuous outer atmosphere. The chromosphere itself shines brightly, but its light is overpowered by the brilliance of the photosphere and generally cannot be seen except when the sun is totally eclipsed by the moon. It absorbs so much light from the limb region that the edge of the photosphere appears much dimmer and redder than the center, an effect well seen on the projected image. The faculae are really of about the same luminosity as the photosphere, but since they are floating at a considerable altitude they are less affected by this dimming, and so stand out clearly.

Faculae are quiescent phenomena and rarely spring surprises; but once in a lifetime, if he is attentive, the systematic solar observer may witness something like the following sight:

A very brilliant star of light, much brighter than the sun's surface, most dazzling to the protected eye, illuminating the upper edges of the adjacent spots and streaks, not unlike in effect the edging of the clouds at sunset.

Such was the appearance of the first solar *flare* ever observed, witnessed independently by two British observers, Richard Carrington and Richard Hodgson, on September 1, 1859. Around the time of sunspot maximum, faint flares are often observed photographically, but very rarely is one sufficiently bright to be seen visually, even if an observer happens to be watching at the time. Flares are tremendously powerful outbursts of radiation that last for just a few minutes, but that often produce disastrous effects on terrestrial communications, temporarily upsetting the ionospheric layer high in the atmosphere and interfering with short-wave reception. Not surprisingly, flares and accompanying "fade-outs" are associated with spot groups, a hazard the Apollo astronauts are likely to face when they make their first lunar mission, which is now scheduled to occur at the next period of maximum solar activity. The danger is present because flares also emit certain short-wave radiations that are filtered out by the earth's atmosphere, but that for man out in space might have a destructive effect on unprotected human tissues.

Solar photography

Photography has several applications in amateur astronomy, and the sun is an excellent object on which to experiment, for there is plenty of light available. While with the planets, or even the moon, an exposure of at least half a second is required if a large image is to be obtained, the sun can be photographed in a fraction of a second using even a very small telescope. This means that an ordinary altazimuth instrument is as good as an equatorial. Moreover, excellent results can be obtained, as has been proved by the work of W. M. Baxter, an amateur living in London, who uses a 4-inch refractor. Some of his photographs, of which an example is shown here, have been used by professional workers—again proof that observers living in towns can make themselves useful.

Anyone taking up astronomical photography will certainly be a "terrestrial" amateur in his own right, so there is little point in going into the purely photographic aspects of the matter in great detail. The best solar (or lunar) attachment for the telescope is an old field camera—the type with bellows, designed to take plates—which can probably be picked up for a dollar or so at an optical store. No lens is necessary, but a shutter is, and this is the biggest problem; for even with a large magnification, and using the slowest available emulsion, an exposure of about 1/500th of a second is adequate. The exact exposure must, of course, be found by trial and error. Moreover, the shutter must have metal leaves, for rubber leaves or a cloth blind will be burned. An alternative is to have a focal plane shutter immediately in front of the plate, where the heating effect is negligible.

Whole-disk photographs of the sun are of little value unless they are at least 4 to 6 inches across, which makes them prohibitively expensive; but photography of individual groups can be very useful indeed. The principle is the same as that for projection, using a high-power, well-corrected eyepiece, such as an orthoscopic. A monocentric is not to be recommended, for the intense heat may melt the cementing between the lenses. The end of the drawtube protrudes into the lens aperture—a joint that must naturally be

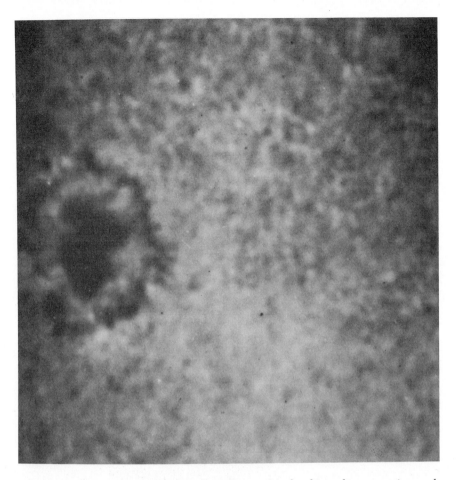

Sunspots. *Two amateur photographs. Above: 3-inch object-glass, negative scale 5½ inches to the sun's diameter, subsequently enlarged. The granulation of the solar surface can be seen clearly. (H. N. D. Wright, London.) Below: 4-inch O.G., negative scale 60 inches to the sun's diameter. This shows the relative contrast between photosphere, penumbra, and umbra. (W. M. Baxter, London.)*

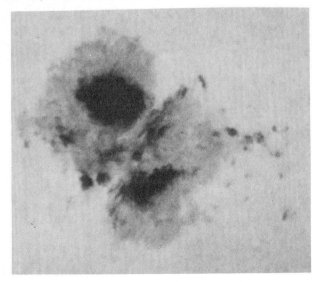

made light-tight—and some sort of bracket will be needed to hold the camera firm. A camera designed for solar work fitted to a 3-inch refractor is shown here.

Anyone taking up astronomical photography must be prepared, at the beginning at least, for a high proportion of failures, and the amateur should not be downhearted because his first pictures are not perfect. One of

Solar camera. *An ordinary plate camera attached to H. N. D. Wright's 3-inch refractor is used to take his solar photographs. The white disk attached to the camera receives the projected solar image from the finder and indicates when the telescope is pointing to the desired region of the sun.*

the main stumbling blocks is accurate focusing. The image in a plate camera is focused on a ground-glass screen, and the first precaution is to make sure that the screen is in the same plane as the sensitive emulsion. Once this is established, there is the difficulty of obtaining critical focus on the relatively rough surface of the screen. One way of solving this problem is to paint a small, clear square in the center of the screen, using varnish. When this is dry, a fine cross is inscribed on the varnish, and an eyepiece mounted behind the screen so that the cross is sharply focused. When the image is seen in the same focus as the cross, the adjustment is accurate.

Once the focusing is correct, there remains the other bugbear of the astronomical photographer: the earth's atmosphere. Ground turbulence is the main trouble here; because of this, it is best to make solar observations early in the morning, before the air has heated up. A photograph taken during a period of boiling will show nothing but hazy outlines, and it is an excellent idea to fit a fair-sized telescope to the main tube and to watch the image with this, exposing when the definition steadies itself. This procedure also has another advantage, for if the second telescope is carefully aligned and fitted with cross-wires, the instrument can be pointed at the right region of the sun without any danger of the spot being out of position when the photograph is taken. Another vital precaution is to insure that at no time before or during the work does the sun shine on the *side* of the tube. Reflector or refractor, the air inside will become turbulent, making it impossible to obtain a good image. When the instrument is actually pointing at the sun, of course, such disastrous heating cannot occur.

It is essential for the astronomical photographer to do his own processing. Quite apart from time and financial considerations, developing and printing techniques play a major part in the success of a photograph. The correct developer will be found by experience; for a slow, yellow-sensitive plate, such as Kodak 0-250 or Ilford 6/30 chromatic, which are suitable for solar work, a vigorous developer is best; but for stellar and planetary photography, in which fast plates are necessary, a speed-increasing developer such as Neofin Blue or Microdol, can give excellent results. Generally speaking, it is unwise to develop plates by inspection. Once a time-and-temperature combination that gives good results has been found, it is best to adhere to it and standardize the processing as much as possible—though, naturally, one should always be on the lookout for improvements.

Since a reflector is perfectly achromatic, it has a certain photographic advantage over the refractor; but for solar work a refractor is to be preferred. A 6-inch reflector, the smallest useful size for visual work, admits far too much light. It is, of course, possible to put a cardboard "stop" over the mirror, so that only a small proportion of the total aperture is used, but this often interferes with the definition, and the alternative, to leave the mirror uncoated, makes it useless for other work. Furthermore, the expansion of the glass caused by the heat can shorten the focal length by a tiny but nevertheless consequential amount, so it is important to watch the focusing very carefully. All things considered, a 3- or 4-inch refractor is the best tool. In this case, the only refinement required is a yellow filter placed just in front of the eyepiece. A dense photographic gelatine filter will serve the purpose excellently, being too thin to have any practical effect on the definition, but great care must be taken not to touch it with the fingers. This filters out the photographic rays that are not accurately focused by the object glass, and insures a sharp image.

Solar eclipses

A total eclipse of the sun, produced when the moon passes directly across the solar disk, blotting out the brilliant photosphere, is the most impressive of all natural phenomena. At such a time, for a few seconds or minutes, the chromosphere and *corona* (the sun's outer atmosphere) glow in the darkened heavens like some cosmic eye, and it requires no special astronomical knowledge to thrill to a spectacle that awed and terrified our ancestors. It is worth journeying many thousands of miles to see such an event, and a journey will almost certainly be necessary, for total eclipses are visible over a very restricted region of the earth's surface.

The reason for this is not hard to understand, for the moon, at its average distance from the earth, is only just large enough to cover the sun's disk. If an eclipse should occur when the moon is at its greatest distance, or *apogee*, it actually appears too small and produces an *annular* eclipse, in which a thin ring of sunlight remains visible at the central phase. Conversely, if the moon is near *perigee*, when it appears largest, the eclipse will last for a longer period. The maximum possible duration, however, is only $7\frac{1}{2}$ minutes, and most eclipses are far briefer.

When the moon passes in front of the sun it casts a small black shadow on the earth's surface. At a favorable eclipse (i.e., one occurring with the moon near perigee), this shadow can be almost 170 miles wide, and would be seen by an interplanetary observer as a black spot. The moon's orbital velocity carries the shadow over the surface at a velocity of more than 1,000 miles per hour, so that when the eclipse is plotted in advance we find out the path of totality. Observers on either side of this path will see only a partial eclipse; care must therefore be taken to establish the equipment on the central line. Also, it is worth remembering that most eclipse paths are considerably less than one hundred miles across.

The standard work on eclipse data is Oppolzer's *Canon der Finsternisse*, giving relevant details of 8,000 solar and 5,000 lunar eclipses from 1205 B.C. to A.D. 2152, and including maps showing the path of each total or annular eclipse. This was first published in 1887, but was reprinted by Dover Books in 1962 under the title *Canon of Eclipses*, translated by O. Gingerich, and so is easily available. Another work, *Canon of Solar Eclipses* by Meens, Grosjean, and Vanderleen, covers eclipses of the sun from 1898 to 2510 with even greater precision than Oppolzer. However, more accurate predictions for the year in question are published in the *Astronomical Ephemeris*, as well as in the B.A.A. *Handbook*, *Sky and Telescope*, and similar publications. A list of forthcoming solar eclipses is given in Appendix II.

A total eclipse of the sun is a superb sight. It begins innocuously enough, an hour before totality is due, when the moon makes a dark nick in the west (right-hand) limb of the sun. It grows rapidly to begin with, then spreads more slowly; but before long the sun is reduced to a thick crescent. The professional astronomers, who have spent months preparing for the vital moments of totality and the last week in anxious anticipation of the weather, make a final examination of their apparatus. The crescent is narrowing, and events happen quickly; there must be no mistakes, for another total eclipse may not come their way for years. Now the tiny fragments of sunlight cast under trees are also crescent-shaped, the gaps in the leaves acting as tiny pinholes. At the same time, some clouds low in the south begin to glow with sunset hues. In the west, from whence the shadow will come, there is the darkness of a thunderstorm.

Only a hairline of sunlight remains. Suddenly, the landscape is covered with trembling, rippling lines, the *shadow bands* that are caused by atmospheric refraction of the vanishing crescent. Now the crescent breaks up into irradiating points of light as the sunlight shines through irregular gaps in the moon's limb. A great wave of darkness sweeps across the ground; the last pinpoint dies; and now, in absolute silence, we see the black lunar disk set in a circle of rosy light—the chromosphere—while, beyond it and far more extensive, the pearly *corona*, or outer atmosphere, glows against the dark sky. The bright planet Venus shines brilliantly; perhaps we also glimpse Mercury or Jupiter or a few bright stars. At three or four points around the moon's limb we see bright spots of red light; these are the *prominences*, masses of glowing gas that surge up from the photosphere for tens of thousands of miles, and that may last for hours before collapsing back again.

But now the western part of the chromosphere is brightening. The moon has almost completed its transit, and totality will soon be over. Suddenly, a blinding spark of light appears, as the first fragment of sunlight shines through a lunar valley; a few seconds more, and the edge of the photosphere flashes into view. Gone are the corona and chromosphere; gone are the planets; the sky rapidly lightens, and the eerie silence is replaced by excited chatter and the return of birdsong. The eclipse has ended, and everyone who watched it carries away his own memories of those unforgettable seconds.

Observing a total eclipse

There is so much to observe during a total eclipse of the sun that no single observer can cover everything. Some of the features are terrestrial as much as astronomical—for instance, the temperature falls through several degrees during the ten minutes around totality—but the more easily observable phenomena occur in the following order:

FLORA AND FAUNA.   Some flowers close during totality, and birdsong is diminished.

THE SHADOW BANDS.   These are seen just before totality; they are more or less distinct depending on the meteorological conditions. They seem to be caused by erratic refraction of the thin crescent in the atmosphere, and the rippling effect makes them extremely difficult to photograph. The distance between the bands—usually a foot or two—varies at different eclipses.

APPEARANCE OF STARS AND PLANETS.   Bright planets, such as Venus and Jupiter, may appear before the onset of totality. It is best, before the eclipse occurs, to work out just where in the sky they will be seen. During totality, if the sky is transparent, fainter objects, such as Mercury and the brighter stars, may be detected if their positions are known beforehand.

THE MOON'S SHADOW.   According to where on the earth's surface the eclipse takes place, the moon's shadow sweeps across the ground at a velocity of from 1,000 to 5,000 miles per hour. When the moon is low in the sky (as during an eclipse occurring near sunrise or sunset), the effective velocity of the shadow will be much higher than if it is overhead. Just before totality occurs, the lunar shadow may be seen in the west as a black veil blotting out the landscape.

BAILY'S BEADS.   Named after the English astronomer who first observed them in 1836, these are the bright fragments of the photosphere left shining through irregularities of the moon's edge after the moon has passed fully onto the sun. These cannot be predicted with much accuracy, since the lunar silhouette is different at every eclipse; their effect is to make true totality occur slightly later than the theoretical time. For the same reason, Baily's Beads may hasten the end of the eclipse. Sometimes one particularly bright bead is left shining after the others have vanished, combining with the already revealed inner chromosphere to give the so-called diamond-ring effect. Although the fragments of light are really very small, they appear large because of irradiation.

CHROMOSPHERE AND PROMINENCES. The chromosphere, when seen shining in its own right, has a characteristic rosy light. Most prominences are relatively small, but just occasionally very large ones are seen, extending for several hundred thousand miles away from the sun. They are really in rapid or even explosive motion, although the brief minutes of totality are insufficient to reveal any movement.

THE CORONA. This is undoubtedly the most beautiful sight of all—the sun's outer atmosphere, extending for millions of miles and glowing with a distinctive pearly hue. Its observed size depends on the clarity of the atmosphere; under exceptionally favorable circumstances, it has been seen to a distance of five or six solar diameters. The form also changes according to the state of the solar cycle. Near maximum, it is more or less evenly distributed all round the limb, while near minimum the polar extensions are short and the equatorial streamers somewhat winged.

When planning to observe an eclipse, it is best to decide on a definite work program. Photography may well prove rewarding; the solar corona shown here is a fine example of amateur work. This was taken by a British observer, H. C. Hunt, who took his 3-inch refractor to Pisa, Italy, to observe the eclipse of February 15, 1961. The photograph was taken at the direct focus of the object glass, using an H.P.3 plate, with an exposure of three

Solar corona. *This photograph was taken at the total eclipse of February 15, 1961, by H. C. Hunt, who carried his 3-inch refractor to Pisa, Italy. An H.P.3 plate was used at the direct focus of the objective; the exposure time was 3 seconds, and the telescope was not driven in any way.*

seconds; the telescope was not guided in any way. Circumstances were favorable, for the eclipse occurred not long after sunrise, and the air was very transparent. The structure of the inner corona can be clearly seen.

If the eclipse lasts long enough, it should be possible to experiment with different exposures. A fraction of a second is enough to record the chromosphere and prominences, but the inner corona requires at least a second, an exposure that will lose the other features in the glare. In recording the tenuous outer corona, a plate-camera lens of about f/6 gives much greater concentration of light and may produce good results. The fields for experiment are many; the time, pitifully short.

There is no need to come away from an eclipse with any tangible result at all. Simply to witness one is an unforgettable experience, and memory is as permanent as the finest photograph; yet the excitement of preparation, and the journey to some unknown region of the earth to see such an event, will make any souvenirs of that expedition even more desirable.

8

The Planets and
Their Movements

Of the nine major planets that form our solar system, only four, Venus, Mars, Jupiter, and Saturn, are really suitable for amateur observation. Venus and Mars, although relatively small—of the same order of size as the earth—are near enough to show disks in a small telescope. Though Jupiter and Saturn are much farther away, they are very large. Of the others, Mercury is extremely difficult to observe because it is always close to the sun in the sky, while the outer planets (Uranus, Neptune, and Pluto) are very remote. Uranus can just barely be seen with the naked eye, and shows only a tiny telescopic disk; Neptune is dimmer still, and Pluto is so faint that it takes a moderate telescope to make it out at all.

There is no room here to discuss any but the most important facts we know about the planets. The writer's *Stars and Planets* covers the field in greater detail. However, before examining each planet from the observational angle, we should look at the solar system as a whole. The major planets (called "major" to distinguish them from the thousands of tiny "minor" planets that lie between the orbits of Mars and Jupiter) are listed in Table II, in order of increasing distance from the sun.

The planets fall neatly into two families. The four inner bodies are relatively small and close to the sun; these are known as the *terrestrial* planets. The next four, the *giant* planets, are all much larger than the earth and so far away from the sun that they are intensely cold. At the frontier of the solar system we find Pluto, a tiny, isolated world that is of no interest to the amateur.

The two planetary groups also differ markedly in their physical makeup. The terrestrial planets are solid and rocky, with a hard crust; we can see the true surfaces of Mercury and Mars, while Venus is enveloped in thick cloud.

TABLE II. The Major Planets

PLANET	DIAMETER (MILES)	MEAN DISTANCE FROM SUN (MILLIONS OF MILES)	LENGTH OF DAY	LENGTH OF YEAR
Mercury	2,900	36	59 days	88 days
Venus	7,700	67	?	224 days
Earth	7,927	93	24 hours	365¼ days
Mars	4,200	141½	24^h 37½^m	687 days
Jupiter	88,700	483	9^h 50^m	12 years
Saturn	75,100	886	10^h 14^m	29½ years
Uranus	29,300	1,783	10^h 48^m	84 years
Neptune	27,600	2,793	15^h 40^m	165 years
Pluto	3,600?	3,666	6^d 9^h	248 years

The giant planets, on the other hand, consist principally of frozen gases, and seem to possess no truly solid surface at all, so that observation is confined to the upper layers of their dense and turbulent atmospheres. We can draw a chart of Mars, but the features visible on Venus and the giant planets are constantly changing.

The planets all revolve around the sun in the same direction (counter-clockwise, if the solar system is viewed from the north), and in more or less the same plane, so that it is possible to draw a plan of their orbits on a sheet of paper. Most of the orbits, too, are almost circular. Mercury and Pluto are the chief exceptions in this respect, and to a lesser extent Mars; but the observer is more concerned with their distance from the earth, since the closer they come, the better the view. This information is embodied in Table III.

TABLE III. The Major Planets

PLANET	DISTANCE FROM THE EARTH (MILLIONS OF MILES)		APPARENT DIAMETER		MAGNIFICATION TO APPEAR SIZE OF MOON (MEAN DIST.)
	Max.	*Min.*	*Max.*	*Min.*	
Mercury	136	50	13″	4½″	× 200
Venus	160	26	66	9½	× 70
Mars	248	35	25½	3½	× 120
Jupiter	413	366	50	30½	× 45
Saturn	1,032	741	21	15	× 100
Uranus	1,961	1,605	3½	3	× 600
Neptune	2,911	2,675	2¼	2	× 900
Pluto	4,660	2,672	¼?		—

The earth, lying third in the sequence from the sun, automatically divides the planets into the *inferior* and *superior* classes. The inferior planets,

Mercury and Venus, always remain near the sun in the sky, whereas the others circle the zodiac quite independently. Figures 28 and 29 explain why this is so.

Figure 28 shows the orbit of an inferior planet. In position *A*, when it lies more or less between the earth and the sun, like the new moon, its night hemisphere is turned toward the earth. This position is known as *inferior conjunction*. Its orbital motion then carries it westward, toward position *B*, so that a narrow crescent becomes visible, swelling until it has become a perfect half. This position is known as *elongation*, because the planet then appears at its maximum angular distance from the sun. In the case of Venus, it can appear up to 48° away from the sun, whereas the greatest possible elongation of Mercury is only 28°.

After elongation (in this case, western elongation), the planet seems to move toward the sun again. The phase becomes gibbous, and at position *C*, when it is lost in the solar rays, the sunlit hemisphere is turned fully toward the earth. At this *superior conjunction*, the planet is shrunken and totally unobservable until it reappears on the eastern side of the sun, passes through eastern elongation and position *D*, and finally returns to inferior conjunction. The inferior planets are therefore alternately visible on either side of the sun, either rising before dawn when west of it, or visible in the evening after sunset when to the east. In the *Iliad*, Homer mentions Hesperus and Phosphorus, the morning and evening stars, which, 2,500 years later, are still visible. They are, in fact, the brilliant planet Venus, seen near one of its elongations, when it appears brighter than any other object in the sky aside from the sun and the moon. At these times, many people notice Venus without realizing what it is.

The two inferior planets, then, present their own observational problems. They can be seen with the naked eye only near sunrise or sunset; and when closest to the earth and therefore largest, they appear as a thin crescent. At this time, Venus appears so large that some people claim to have seen the phase with the naked eye, and it is certainly perceptible with binoculars. But the tiny, full disk it displays near superior conjunction gives little delight to observers with small telescopes.

The superior planets are, in many ways, more convenient for viewing.

Figure 28. *Movements of an inferior planet. (Not to scale.)*

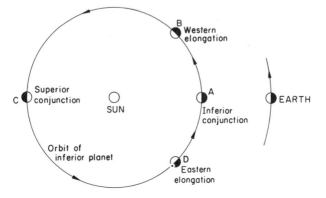

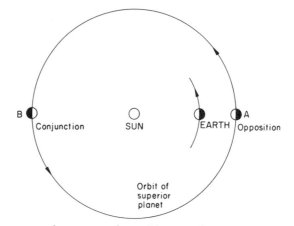

Figure 29. *Movements of a superior planet. (Not to scale.)*

Since the earth lies between the planet and the sun (figure 29), the planet when closest (at position *A*) appears opposite the sun in the sky, a position known as *opposition*. What is more, the disk is fully illuminated, for the case is similar to that of the full moon. The planet then circles in the usual counterclockwise direction until it has found refuge on the opposite side of the sun, at *B*, in the position known as *conjunction*. The disk still appears full, but at this position in its orbit it is clearly more distant from the earth, and its proximity to the sun makes observation impossible for a time. Nevertheless, a superior planet is decidedly more cooperative than the two inferior ones, and presents fewer problems to the observer.

Sidereal and synodic periods

The interval between successive inferior conjunctions or successive oppositions is called the *synodic period*, an important quantity when we wish to find out how regularly a planet will be well placed for observation. To find the synodic period, account must also be taken of the earth's own orbital movement. For example, the period of revolution around the sun, or *sidereal period*, of Venus is a little more than 224 earth-days long, so that if we take inferior conjunction as the starting point (position *A* in figure 28), it will have returned to that point after 224 days. During this interval, however, the earth has completed more than half its own orbit, so that Venus has to travel on for some considerable distance before the three bodies come in line again and another inferior conjunction occurs. This interval, or synodic period, is actually about 584 days, so that Venus is not so regularly placed for observation as might at first appear. Since the earth is moving in the same direction, its effect is to make a planet's apparent movement around the sun seem slower, in the same way that a car traveling at 60 miles per hour seems to be moving much more slowly when we are following it in another car.

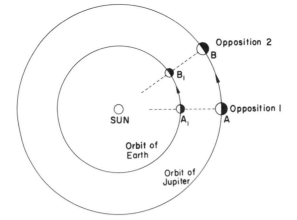

Figure 30. *Successive oppositions of Jupiter. It must be remembered that the earth completes one circuit of its orbit before passing on to B_1. (Not to scale.)*

Since both Venus and Mars are relatively close to the earth and have sidereal periods, or years, comparable with our own, their synodic periods are very long; the average interval between oppositions of Mars is as much as 780 days. But in the case of the giant planets, which move more slowly, the earth does not have to move very far past its starting point to catch up with them again and produce another opposition (figure 30). Jupiter's synodic period is only 13 months, while Pluto moves so slowly that the earth has to travel on for only one and a half days after completing a lap before another opposition is reached. Mercury is convenient for the opposite reason: It moves around the sun so quickly—in 88 days—that it takes little extra time for it to catch up with the earth again. Its synodic period is only 116 days, shorter than that of any other planet.

Northern and southern declinations

We have said that the paths of the planets keep to the zodiac, and this is mainly true, although Mercury and Pluto, because of the exceptional tilts of their orbits, can actually stray beyond its limits. But the zodiac itself is inclined toward the equator, which means that a planet can appear in a more northerly or southerly latitude, or *declination*, depending on its position along the zodiac. The zodiac's tilt is not difficult to understand when we remember that the planets all revolve around the sun in more or less the same plane. Since the earth's axis of rotation is tilted with respect to this plane (it is $23\frac{1}{2}°$ off the vertical), it follows that all the planets' orbits appear as tilted, relative to the equator, by the same amount. It is precisely this tilt of the earth's axis that gives rise to our seasons. Northern midsummer occurs in June, when the sun appears farthest north; southern midsummer occurs in December, when it appears farthest south. The planets follow more or less the same path, so that they too appear to move

125

up and down in the sky. The exact track traced by the sun during its annual revolution around the sky is called the *ecliptic*, and this is centered on the zodiac.

The movements of Mars afford a convenient illustration. Oppositions occur at intervals of somewhat more than two years, and in 1954 and 1956 the planet was well south of the equator and therefore low in the sky for northern observers. Conditions improved in 1958, and the 1961 opposition occurred with it in the most northern part of the ecliptic (in the constellation Taurus), so that to observers in Europe and the United States it appeared at a high altitude. In 1963 and 1965, it had started to sink southwards again, while the opposition of 1969 will show it in its greatest southern declination; after that, conditions will once more improve for northern observers. It is important to observe a star or planet when it is high in the sky, because seeing conditions show marked deterioration at low altitudes.

Orbital eccentricity

It is clear that the planets' movements are not quite so simple as might at first have appeared, and there is yet a third effect to be taken into account before the amateur can know just when is the best time to observe. This is the planet's orbital *eccentricity*, or divergence from a circular path, of which Mars is a striking example.

Figure 31 shows the orbits of the earth and Mars drawn to scale. The earth's orbit is only very slightly eccentric, and for most purposes can be considered as circular; but it will be seen that Mars swings quite appreciably first toward, then away from, the sun. At perihelion, or its closest point, its distance from the sun is only $128\frac{1}{2}$ million miles; at aphelion, or farthest distance from the sun, it is as much as $154\frac{1}{2}$ million. It is clear that oppositions occurring near the time of perihelion are much more favorable for viewing, the minimum distance being about 35 million miles from the earth, as against 63 million miles when they occur near aphelion.

The last perihelic opposition was in 1956, when Mars appeared as a glorious orange object in the night sky; but since then, as the diagram shows, its orbit has been taking it steadily farther away. The opposition of 1965 was aphelic, when the planet glowed dimly in Leo and showed little detail in small instruments. However, this was the worst of the series, and the opposition distances will now shorten until 1971, when the next perihelic one will occur.

Jupiter and Saturn are so far away and their obits are so nearly circular that their eccentricity counts for little. Venus, too, has an almost circular orbit. Mercury's is very eccentric, however, its distance from the sun varying from 29 to 43 million miles. This effect is most noticeable at the time of elongation. Mercury's elongations vary from 18° to 28°, depending on

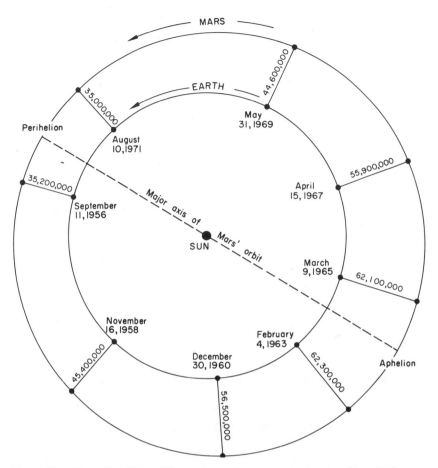

Figure 31. *The orbit of Mars. The earth completes over two circuits of its orbit between successive oppositions. (The orbits of the two planets are to scale.)*

whether they occur near perihelion or aphelion, and the farther Mercury appears from the sun, the better the view.

Retrograde motion

At the beginning of an apparition, a superior planet reappears from conjunction to the west of the sun. This is because the sun, due to the earth's orbital motion, appears to be moving eastward more quickly than the planet, and so leaves it behind. Consequently, the planet appears in the morning sky, rising shortly before dawn. As the weeks pass, it rises earlier and earlier, until by the time opposition is reached, when it appears opposite the sun in the sky, it rises at sunset. After that, it becomes more and more of an evening object until the sun has once more caught up with it, and it disappears in the western glow shortly before conjunction.

All this time, the planet has been moving eastward in front of the stars.

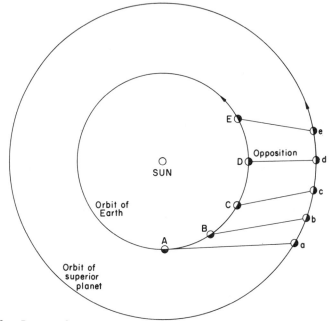

Figure 32. *Retrograde motion.*

But some weeks before opposition is due, a curious phenomenon occurs: The eastward drift slows down, pauses, and then reverses into a westward back-tracking. Opposition passes, and some weeks later still, the backward motion comes to a halt and the planet reverts once more to its orthodox eastward progress. This reversal, which occurs with all the planets, is known as *retrograde motion*.

Figure 32 explains what happens in the case of a superior planet. At position *A*, when opposition is approaching, the earth is moving more or less directly toward the other planet. Since we see the planet's movement not in the three-dimensional aspect, but as a two-dimensional projection against the sky, it appears to be moving eastward at its own orbital velocity.

The earth, because of its smaller orbit and higher orbital velocity (18·5 miles per second), moves through a much greater arc in a given time than the other planet. At position *B*, the planet has reached only *b*, so that the earth is catching up with it quite quickly. Moreover, since the two planets are moving in the same direction, the earth's velocity seems to make the other planet move more slowly than it really does. By the time the earth reaches *C*, with the other planet at *c*, their two velocities are effectively matched and the other planet appears not to be moving at all, just as two cars racing side by side at the same speed show no relative motion. This is called the *stationary point*.

After the earth sweeps past, the other planet appears to be moving backwards, retrograding fastest at opposition (*D* and *d*), when the two planets are moving in parallel paths. Then, as the earth swings away again, its superior velocity is in effect cut down. The retrograding decelerates, another stationary point is reached at E and e; after this, we see the other planet continue its interrupted easterly progress.

Retrograde motion is most obvious in the case of Mars, which moves around the sky more quickly than the outer planets, and so covers a larger arc in a given time. At the opposition of 1965, for instance, Mars reappeared in the morning sky in the constellation Leo, and proceeded to advance into Virgo, reaching its stationary point on January 29. It then retrograded back into Leo, reaching opposition on March 9 and pausing once more on April 21. After that, it drifted back into Virgo, and continued on the zodiacal path through Libra and Scorpio.

Planetary motions are extraordinarily complicated, and it is in no small way a tribute to our mathematicians that the recent planetary probes have been so successful. Fortunately, the demands on the amateur observer are much less stringent. Mercury, Venus, Mars, Jupiter, and Saturn all shine in the sky like well-known friends, and he needs no almanac to identify them. Soon the newcomer to astronomy becomes familiar with their surfaces and their seasons, and the planets become companions of whose faces he never tires.

9

Mercury

Mercury is an intriguing planet, and the fact that we know so little about it makes it more fascinating still. There is obvious reason for its neglect, since it is very small, remains close to the sun in the sky, and is normally only visible for periods of about a fortnight on three or four occasions a year. Few useful observations can be made with a telescope of less than 12 inches aperture. Even so, it is satisfying to glimpse the innermost planet, and a dusky shading or two can be seen, on favorable occasions, with a 3-inch.

That Mercury is an elusive little world is evidenced by the fact that Herschel, a keen follower of planets as well as stars, paid it scant attention. The first systematic observations were made by Johann Schröter, his contemporary, who used one of Herschel's 6-inch reflectors as well as two considerably larger but probably inferior telescopes. He observed Mercury from about 1780 until 1801, managing to make out a few dusky streaks, and to notice that when the planet is in the crescent phase, its south horn appears somewhat blunter than the north. This feature, which has been noticed many times since Schröter's day, is probably caused by a rather dark patch on the disk. Unfortunately, Schröter had a rather wild imagination; he conjectured that it might be the shadow cast by a mountain eleven miles high! From this sensational deduction, he went on to suggest a Mercurian rotation period of about 24 hours 4 minutes. It seems that Schröter had a complex about mountain peaks—perhaps inspired by his lunar work?—since he also bestowed one on cloud-covered Venus, an observation that drew unusually acid comment from his friend Herschel.

With the tragic death of Johann Schröter, three years after the French army occupied Bremen in 1813 and destroyed his observatory, Mercurian observation languished. The next systematic attack was made by an Italian astronomer, Giovanni Schiaparelli, better known for his work on Mars. Using an 8½-inch refractor stationed in Milan, he started observing Mercury in 1882 and came to the conclusion that it keeps the same face to the sun. This announcement caused a good deal of surprise in the astronomical world, but it seemed confirmed by the work of Percival Lowell, also better known for his Martian studies, who observed the planet with the 24-inch refractor of his private observatory at Flagstaff, Arizona. Both observers decided that the dusky patches remained in the same position relative to the terminator. Had Mercury been spinning rapidly, they would be carried out of view into the dark hemisphere and reinstated some time later.

Schiaparelli's observing technique was most interesting: He observed in broad daylight, when the sun (and therefore Mercury) was high in the sky. It is not difficult to find a bright star or planet in daylight, provided the sky is really transparent and the object's position is accurately known. The advantage of observing a bright planet against the blue sky is that the glare is greatly reduced. In the case of Mercury, which is always near the sun, this is the only time when it is high in the sky and the seeing conditions are good.

Schiaparelli had no great difficulty in finding Mercury, for his telescope was mounted equatorially and could be pointed directly to its position as marked in the almanac. Positions in the sky are marked out in terms similar to latitude and longitude, in just the same way as geographical locations. We have the celestial equator and the north and south celestial poles; and the grid is laid down with lines of *declination* (latitude) and right ascension (longitude). (A fuller description of the *celestial sphere*, as it is called, is given on page 241.) It is clear that if the telescope's axis is lined up with that of the earth, it is a simple matter to point it in any given direction. With an instrument on an altazimuth stand, the approximate position must be estimated with the naked eye, and the region swept with a low power.

Schiaparelli found the markings so definite that he was able to draw up a chart. The features he found seemed to be confirmed by the Greek astronomer E. M. Antoniadi, who observed between 1920 and 1940 and issued a revised map. It therefore came as something of a shock to observers of the planet when radar observations, carried out at Cornell University Observatory in April, 1965, suggested that the planet did not keep the same face to the sun at all, but rotated with a period of about 59 days. Despite initial disbelief, it now seems that this result is indeed accurate, and that the conclusions of Schiaparelli and others were drawn much too hastily, making their maps of the planet valueless.

Obviously, the door has now been thrown wide open for a systematic attack on this mysterious world. All that is needed is a large telescope on an equatorial mount, and plenty of patience. Mercury has been shamefully neglected in the past, and it is to be hoped that this recent revision of our knowledge will induce someone to make a long-overdue investigation.

Telescopic appearance

Mercury looks like a tiny moon, its phases changing from almost full to a narrow crescent as it moves around the sun; at the actual times of inferior and superior conjunction, it is totally invisible. It becomes visible in the twilight after it has moved between 10° and 15° away from the sun. Since its synodic period is only 116 days, there are six elongations a year: three in the evening (eastern) and three in the morning (western). Mercury moves very quickly through the sky and its position changes perceptibly from night to night, although its path is not easy to follow because of the lack of comparison stars in the bright sky. Should Venus happen to be near, it affords a helpful guide.

This sounds as though Mercury can be seen regularly every other month, but unfortunately there are two snags. First of all, half the elongations occur with the planet south of the sun in the sky, so that north temperate observers have a very poor view. Secondly, the most favorable elongations, which occur when the planet is near aphelion and so appears about 28° away from the sun, take place when it is in southern declination. Observers in the southern hemisphere clearly have the best of it, and it is perhaps to their discredit that most of the important observations have been made by northern observers. In temperate latitudes (between about 45°N and 55°N) the planet can never be seen with the naked eye on more than fifteen or twenty occasions in the year. Should the enthusiast carry his telescope down to Florida, or the Canary Islands, he would notice a distinct improvement. There the sun rises and sets at a much steeper angle, so that Mercury is carried higher above the horizon and is a far more

Mercury. *A drawing made by R. M. Baum in March 1952. A 6½-inch reflector was used, with a magnification of × 216. The northern cusp is clearly brighter than the southern one.*

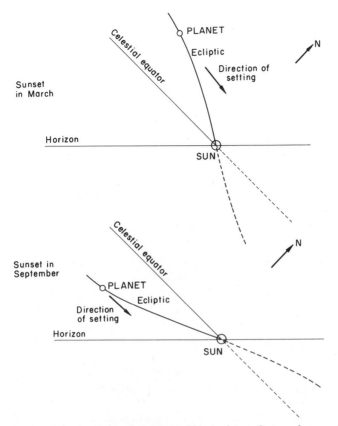

Figure 33. *Spring and autumn elongations. This is drawn for an observer in latitude 45°N. The lower the observer's latitude, the greater the angle the celestial equator makes with the horizon.*

regular visitor to the twilight sky. For all planetary observation, in fact, a low latitude is a considerable advantage, since the zodiac and ecliptic are higher in the sky.

There are definite seasons for morning and evening observation of both Mercury and Venus. Figure 33 explains why. It shows the western sky as seen at sunset in March and September, with an inferior planet at elongation. Both the sun and the planet lie on or near the ecliptic, but at the March elongation the planet is much higher above the horizon than is the case in September, because in spring the ecliptic, which is caused by the inclination of the earth's axis, makes a greater angle with the horizon. On March 21 the sun is exactly on the celestial equator, and is traveling north. Consequently, the ecliptic lying ahead of its present position is inclined to the equator, at an angle of $23\frac{1}{2}°$—the axial tilt of the earth. This means that the planet is situated well north of the celestial equator. But in September, when the sun is once more on the equator but traveling southwards, the ecliptic is passing down toward its midwinter position, so that the planet now appears very low in the sky. An evening elongation is therefore best observed when occurring in the spring, while a morning elongation is most favorable in the autumn. Conditions are reversed, of course, for observers in the southern hemisphere.

Observing Mercury

A high magnification is essential for observing Mercury. A power of at least × 100 is required to make out the phase, while nothing less than × 250 will show a reasonable disk, and × 350 is better still. Denning, in a series of observations made eighty years ago, used powers of × 250 and × 312 on his 10-inch reflector. It is optimistic to expect to see much with smaller apertures, although the blunting of the southern cusp can be glimpsed with a 3-inch. Daylight observation requires moderate apertures, but the tube must be protected from the direct sunlight, or the air inside it will become so turbulent that nothing can be seen. A great deal, too, depends on the transparency of the sky; the slightest haze will produce so much glare around the sun that the planet is lost from view even in a large telescope, and the success of Schiaparelli in seeing markings with an 8½-inch refractor is testimony not only to his own eyesight, but also to the clarity of the Italian sky.

Many textbooks say that the disk appears pinkish. Certainly, the planet appears distinctly warm-colored when viewed with the naked eye close to the horizon (though on these occasions the seeing will be far too unsteady for serious work); but this tint may be due, in part at least, to the twilight glow. Denning saw it as leaden in hue; and I once observed it with a 3½-inch refractor when it appeared so close to Venus in the sky that both planets were included in the same high-power field. On this occasion, Venus shone with a brilliant, pure white luster, and Mercury appeared to be a dull reddish-gray. Mercury's bare surface is a poor reflector of sunlight and the cloud-covered Venus dazzles, so it is not surprising that the one over-powers the other. Mercury appears brightest as an evening star between 10 and 14 days before elongation, and during the same period after elongation, when it is a morning star. At such a time, its phase is about 80 per cent.

Reflection investigations have suggested that Mercury has a rough surface. This would explain why the disk appears to darken near the terminator, so that the phase often seems less than it actually should. There is no doubt at all that this is an optical effect, since the predictions of phase cannot possibly be in error; but a series of observations of Mercury's apparent phase, carried out over several elongations, would be of great interest. This is work that could be performed with a 6-inch refractor or an 8- to 10-inch reflector, provided it is equatorially mounted so that the planet can be picked up in daylight.

Mercury is a difficult object for study. Its minute disk reveals few secrets, yet the secrets are undoubtedly there.

Transits

Just occasionally, when the line-up is perfect, the planet at inferior conjunction passes across the solar disk and can be seen as a tiny black spot. This is known as a *transit*; the last one occurred on November 6, 1960; the next is due on May 9, 1970. The only other three that will occur this century will be on November 9, 1973; November 12, 1986; and November 14, 1999. The path of the 1960 transit is shown in figure 34.

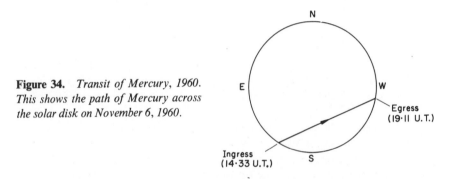

Figure 34. *Transit of Mercury, 1960. This shows the path of Mercury across the solar disk on November 6, 1960.*

Transits of Mercury are interesting phenomena, but it must be emphasized that unless a proper solar eyepiece (not a sun cap) is used, the only safe way of observing one is by projection. The planet appears as a tiny black spot, like a sunspot without a penumbra, as it takes about five hours to cross the disk. Some observers, using direct vision, have noticed curious effects of light and color around the disk as it moves on to the sun, but these are certainly caused by contrast.

10

Venus

Venus is a most suitable object for study with a small telescope. Like Mercury, it is an inferior planet and shows phases, but its disk is usually much larger, and it is so bright that it cannot possibly be missed. Not only has it been seen in daylight with the naked eye, but there are records of its casting a shadow on those occasions when it can be seen against a dark sky.

Yet Venus, despite its shining visibility, is far from easy to observe; in fact, it is precisely its brilliance that makes it so easy to be deceived by false effects. The only answer is to observe it either during broad daylight or around the time of sunrise or sunset. It is easy to find even with an altazimuth mounting, and, apart from the time spent near superior conjunction, when its disk is not much larger than Mercury's, it can be followed almost continuously. Systematic work is essential, for the features are so vague and changing that they must be observed as consistently as possible.

The true surface of Venus can never be seen. It is the earth's twin in size, with a diameter of 7,550 miles, but it seems unlikely that there are any other great resemblances. The results of the Mariner probes, which recorded close-up measurements in 1963 and 1967, have caused a good deal of comment, but we can at least be sure that the true surface is extremely hot. Swathed in thick clouds, and covered with a dense atmosphere that probably consists principally of carbon dioxide, the heat rays are blanketed in so efficiently that a surface temperature of 600°F seems quite likely. Venus may well prove to be as inhospitable a world as barren Mercury.

The impervious atmosphere conceals other secrets also; our knowledge of the rotation period is still vague. On the whole, visual and photographic work has suggested a rotation period of a few days or weeks. Recent radar

136

results, indicating a period of from 240 to 250 days, are in obvious conflict with earlier estimates, and more experiments must be carried out before they are confirmed. It does seem, however, that visual investigations into the rotation period are doomed to failure, whereas radar techniques are much more promising.

The markings of Venus

The first reliable observations of markings on Venus were made just three centuries ago by the Italian observer J. D. Cassini, who also discovered the main division in Saturn's rings and made other observations of note. Later, other observers, not all of them as reputable, reported seeing dusky features that seemed to be moving across the disk, and the popular view was that Venus' day is of about the same length as the earth's. However, the fact that Giovanni Schiaparelli's work in 1877–78 suggested to him that Venus keeps the same face toward the sun shows just how unreliable such estimates are. The occasional shadings are hopelessly faint and ill-defined, and it is worth noting that Johann Schröter, a model of honesty and patience if not of observational skill, watched the planet for *nine years* before he felt convinced that he had observed a definite marking! This should be remembered when considering sketches made by observers using small telescopes who record features each time they examine the planet.

However, the situation offers some hope. Although the disk often appears blank, apart from a perceptible falling-off of light toward the terminator, most elongations produce one or two shadings that have an element of reality. Of these, the most frequently seen are the *cusp caps*, which can appear during either the gibbous or crescent stage. These are bright areas near the apparent poles of the planet. Sometimes they even appear to have a dark border, or collar, although this is probably the result of a contrast effect. There are two cusp caps that have been widely recorded in recent years. Some observers put them down to optical deception, but the fact that they are not always visible seems to disprove this, and most regular students of the planet consider them to be real phenomena.

The caps usually stay visible for several days or weeks, appearing and fading out so slowly that it is impossible to establish any definite term of appearance that might give a clue to the rotation period. It is not even certain that they mark the poles, for we do not know where the axis lies; but since bright regions are rarely seen at other points on the disk, it seems possible that they indicate some anomalous cloud formation over the polar zone.

Yet we must not be over-hasty in drawing conclusions, for some recent photographic investigations have been of great interest. One of the world's leading planetary authorities, Gerard Kuiper, has taken photographs of Venus with the 82-inch reflector at the McDonald Observatory, Texas, using plates sensitive to ultraviolet light. These have revealed streaky markings, lying parallel to each other, that are quite different from the vague patches usually observed telescopically. Pioneer work in this field was carried out at Mount Wilson in 1927 by F. E. Ross, who used his photographs to deduce a rotation period of about thirty days, the value at which Kuiper arrived. Moreover, if these elongated markings suggest the angle at which Venus spins, it would mean that the axis may be tilted as much as 85° from the vertical, which immediately dismisses the cusp caps as true polar phenomena.

What makes these observations so interesting is that a few amateurs have recorded similar streaks that are quite invisible to the majority of observers. Lowell was one, and he had abuse hurled at his head when other workers, using even better telescopes, failed to confirm his findings. Barnard, using the 36-inch refractor, could glimpse only the faintest shadings; Dawes, using smaller telescopes, always found the disk feature-less. The fact that both these observers had magnificent records for glimps-ing very faint stars indicates that the human eye is a more specialized instrument than many people suppose.

There is one other point: Experiments have proved that some people's eyes are slightly sensitive to ultraviolet light, whereas most eyes respond only to the normal visible spectrum, from red to blue. Clearly, the slightest differences in visual sensitivity may have far-reaching consequences when we observe features as elusive as the Venusian shadings. Perhaps some amateur could devise an experiment to measure the ultraviolet response of various observers of the planet, then examine their observations to see if there is any correlation.

Apart from the cusp caps and the occasional dark shadings, Venus sometimes shows slight irregularities in the smooth curve of the terminator, particularly when it is in the crescent phase. These, like the shadings, have been recorded for three centuries, but it would be rash to call all the obser-vations reliable. On many occasions of poor seeing, the limb of a planet appears irregular or serrated; under such conditions an unreliable observer might well record nonexistent deformities. A bad observation of any planet will, to a very large extent, prejudice the value of the good ones that have preceded it, and it is far better to leave the telescope covered and to wait for another more favorable occasion. Bad seeing is particularly treacherous in the case of Venus. With such planets as Mars and Jupiter, its effect is to erase detail; with Venus, it seems to inspire markings. "The better, the blanker" might well be the slogan of regular observers of the planet.

Terminator deformities, which certainly seem to occur from time to time, are probably contrast effects. A dark shading near the terminator can give the impression of an indentation at that point, while a bright cusp cap can seem to project slightly due to irradiation. If·such an effect is noticed, it should be followed most carefully to see if there is any change of position from day to day, or even from hour to hour. A steady shifting of some easily identified detail is the only means the visual observer has of getting a clue to the rotation period and the tilt of the axis. Little of a definite nature has emerged from three centuries of telescopic work, but observers of Venus, like the warriors gathered outside the walls of Troy, are nothing if not persistent. There is always the very remote chance that this infuriating dense cover will produce some exceptionally dark or brilliant cloud to give us a lead. Such a feature was seen on August 21, 1956, when a bright cloud appeared near the northeastern limb; but most unfortunately it soon lost its definite nature and no information was forthcoming.

If any additional proof were needed that Venus has a dense atmosphere, it occurs when the planet is visible as a very thin crescent either just before or just after inferior conjunction. At this time, the horns can be seen not terminating sharply at the cusps, but extending in a vague, glimmering arc that may almost completely encircle the planet. This twilight arc can be seen with a 3-inch refractor, since at this time the planet, being closest to the earth, appears very large. But since it is also within a very few degrees of the sun, it must naturally be observed in broad daylight. If its position relative to the sun is known, it can be found easily enough if a low-power, wide-field eyepiece is used, but the greatest care must be taken not to accidentally sweep across the sun itself. Venus is furthest from the sun at inferior conjunction when it occurs in March or September.

Phase effects

It has been known for many years that the theoretical and observed instants of half-phase, or *dichotomy*, do not agree. Schröter was the first observer to point this out, and it has been referred to as *Schröter's effect*. It is caused by the considerable falling off of brightness at the terminator, with the result that, like Mercury's, the observed phase of Venus appears always less than computed.

Dichotomy offers the most convenient moment for checking the phase, since it is not too difficult to time the instant at which the terminator appears perfectly straight—although there may well be an uncertainty of two or three days. Thus, dichotomy is always early during an evening apparition, since the phase is lessening, and late during a morning one, when the planet is waxing. Strangely enough, the discrepancy seems to be greater at evening apparitions, when dichotomy may occur as much as 8 to 10 days early, while at morning elongation it is about 4 to 6 days late. Making estimates of these discrepancies is interesting, since the difference seems to vary somewhat.

The Ashen Light

A phenomenon which has given rise to much dispute, even though its occurrence seems established by the weight of observation, is the occasional very faint luminosity of the dark side, aptly termed the *Ashen Light*. Some good observers, using large telescopes, have never seen a trace of it and so remain skeptical; but many regular observers of Venus have occasionally recorded it with instruments ranging from 3 to 12 inches in aperture. This tenuous gray veil, spread between the horns, is far too elusive to photograph, so the evidence rests almost entirely on the work of amateurs who have patiently followed the planet during its crescent phases. On the whole, independent confirmation is good; for instance, many British observers recorded the Ashen Light during the first half of January, 1958, whereas sightings since that time have been sparse. The first observation was made as long ago as 1643, by Riccioli; since that time it has been reported by many observers of repute. One of them, the Reverend T. W. Webb, the famous nineteenth-century amateur observer, made his first observation on January 31, 1878:

> *Though a frequent observer of the planet Venus through a long series of years, I have never till yesterday evening seen the unilluminated side, which presented itself rather unexpectedly, as I had not been thinking particularly about it, and was not making it an object of special examination. The air was frosty and hazy, and definition tremulous, and the planet low; my beautiful 9½-inch With reflector brought nevertheless the horns to sharp points. I had noticed nothing remarkable with a low Kellner eyepiece, but on changing it for 212 I perceived the phenomenon pretty distinctly at intervals; it was much overpowered by the splendid light of the planet, but came out occasionally rather paler and browner than the background of the twilight sky . . . and was equally perceptible when the planet was hidden by a bar in the field.*

What is the Ashen Light? We do not know and can therefore only theorize, but it seems possible that it could be caused by intense auroras in Venus' atmosphere. We must remember that Venus is relatively close to the sun, and so receives much more radiation than does the earth. If Ashen Light sightings could be tied in with solar activity, the evidence would be conclusive.

It is treacherously easy to imagine seeing the dark side, for some ocular effect makes the area between the horns appear lighter in tone than the outside sky, and a careless observer might well record this as a "sighting." The only way of vindicating the observation is to get rid of the bright crescent by using an *occulting bar*. A very simple one, which has been found to give good service, can be produced in five minutes by gluing a scrap of paper across the field stop of the eyepiece. With most types (apart from the Huygenian and Ramsden, which are useless for Venusian observation because of the glare), the stop lies just in front of the field lens, and it is an easy matter to fix the strip of paper so that it appears sharply in focus. This allows the crescent to be hidden behind the bar, so that if the dark side is seen projecting, it is clearly real. An extra refinement is to cut a scoop out of the bar to match the curve of the terminator, but this is a delicate operation. Good results are also obtained by using 15-amp fuse-wire, with an induced kink to block out the crescent.

Because of its faintness, the Light is usually best seen when the sky is fairly dark. Some observers have reported seeing the entire disk by day, appearing *darker* than the sky, but this is most probably an optical deception, although some observers believe it may be due to silhouetting of the planet against the sun's outer corona.

Observing Venus

Venus rarely behaves according to form, if, indeed, it may be said to have any form at all, and its unpredictability demands an open mind. The planet's cloudy surface can efface itself in a strange way; one evening some feature is recorded with fair certainty, and the next evening the disk appears totally blank. A reliable observer has to perform a difficult task: He must eliminate from his thinking all expectation of seeing a dark marking, a cusp cap, or the Ashen Light, and come to the telescope with an open mind. If reason says that a feature *ought* to be there because it was there the previous night, it has an uncanny habit of appearing!

The planet is also demanding in an instrumental sense. Because of the great brilliancy of the disk, it shows up telescopic flaws that seem of negligible account for other work. Both object glass and eyepiece suffer a severe test of achromatism when Venus shines in the sky. The best object glass is not perfect; no matter how carefully computed and figured, there is always a very slight bluish halo remaining, known as the *secondary spectrum*; and a bright object naturally exaggerates this halo. However, since it is usually most unwise to observe Venus in a dark sky, when it produces flares and false color effects, the secondary spectrum does not present any serious problem. Generally speaking, the best time to observe the planet is either when the sun is above the horizon, or else just below it. If it is easily visible with the naked eye, then the sky is too dark.

Eyepieces must be carefully selected. The nonachromatic types are quite useless, and a Barlow amplifier is bound to be suspect because of the extra color it may introduce. Any "haunted" oculars will also prove troublesome; the legend of Venus' ghost satellite undoubtedly arose from this cause. The choice probably lies between a Monocentric and a Tolles. High magnifications are not necessary; for routine work, powers of between × 150 and × 200 are satisfactory, although a powerful eyepiece may be of use when the planet is near superior conjunction and so appears exceptionally small. This part of the orbit is grossly underobserved, an extra pity because during these months a large proportion of the illuminated hemisphere is presented.

Refractors and reflectors each offer their particular benefits. A reflector is perfectly achromatic, provided the eyepiece is good, but, as we know, its open tube is much more sensitive than the refractor's enclosed tube to changing air temperature; this happens quite quickly at sunset, when most of the work on Venus is done. For this reason, a refractor may give somewhat steadier images.

When observing Venus, it is most important to be consistent. If a 3-inch refractor is used on one occasion and a 12-inch reflector on the next, one cannot expect the observations to fit into a comparable sequence. Since the eyepieces also have an effect on the view, it is wise to use the same ocular on all occasions. Furthermore, the planet's aspect differs slightly by daylight and by twilight; so, if the time of observation can also be standardized, so much the better. Of course, this is not always practicable, but any departure from routine should be noted in the observing book so that allowance can be made. It is most instructive to compare the views obtained under various conditions of sky brightness. At night, the horns of the crescent appear in brilliant contrast against the sky, while in daylight the terminator merges almost indefinably into the blue sky, making the phase seem reduced. (One obvious by-product of this is that Schröter's effect is even more marked for daylight observations.)

Finding a planet by daylight

Venus appears brightest when about 27 per cent of the disk is illuminated. Therefore, when near elongation, and as a thick crescent, it can easily be spotted during the day, using an altazimuth stand. Once the approximate position is known—and this can be worked out from the positions of Venus and the sun as given in the almanac—the region is searched with the finder or with a low-power eyepiece. Indeed, if the sky is a deep blue, it should be visible with the naked eye. An equatorial telescope, if its axes are graduated, can be set at once on the position. However, when Venus is near the sun in the sky, around the time of inferior or superior conjunction, the glare makes it difficult for an altazimuth telescope to sweep it up at random, and so a rather more scientific approach is desirable.

Let us consider first a simpler case, when a planet is east of the sun and follows it across the sky as the day progresses. First of all, the difference between their right ascensions is found from the almanac. This is always reckoned in hours rather than degrees, since the sky appears to revolve once in twenty-four hours. One hour of right ascension (R.A.) is equal to 15° at the celestial equator, so if we point a telescope to a star that lies on or near the equator, and leave it untouched for an hour, another star will be found in the field of view that lies 15° of R.A. to the east of the first one.

Let us now suppose that an observation of Venus was being made on May 20, 1964. At that time, the planet's phase was only 22 per cent, and it was moving in toward the sun, with inferior conjunction due on June 19. The sun's R.A. on the day in question was 3 hours 49 minutes; that of Venus, 6 hours 23½ minutes. The difference between these values, which is all that matters, is 2 hours 35½ minutes.

Like any other celestial object, the sun is highest when on the *meridian*, an imaginary line running from the north to the south horizon and passing directly overhead. Since observing conditions improve as altitude increases, it is clearly advantageous to catch Venus at this point. Accordingly, the telescope is pointed to the sun at around the time of local noon, the exact time being noted. Just over 2½ hours later (assuming that no clouds have materialized) Venus should be seen in the vicinity.

Now, if Venus and the sun had exactly the same declination, the planet would obviously drift right through the field after the interval of 2 hours 35½ minutes. But this is rarely the case. On the day in question, the sun's declination was 20° north of the celestial equator (written + 20°, south declinations being negative), while that of Venus was + 27°. It therefore follows that the telescope must be raised 7° before Venus will appear in the field. Great care should be taken not to disturb the azimuth axis as the telescope is slowly swept up and down. The planet should be picked up without any difficulty.

In this particular case, Venus was so far from the sun that it could certainly have been found by random sweeping. A difference of R.A. of 2½ hours suggests an angular separation of about 37°, and if we remember that an outstretched hand seen at arm's length subtends an angle of roughly 20°, the approximate vicinity of the planet can easily be estimated. However, the principle is clear enough, and this drifting method can be used very successfully when Mercury or Venus is east of the sun. Unfortunately, it is quite useless when the planet is a morning star, since it crosses the meridian before the sun; under these conditions, the best way is to time the moment at which it will cross the meridian. To do this we must consider the concept of *sidereal time*.

For most civil purposes, the sun is an effective clock. In the northern hemisphere, it is due south at approximately noon, and it takes just 24 hours to make one circuit of the sky—an apparent motion provided by the earth's rotation on its axis. It is thus convenient to suppose that the earth actually rotates on its axis in 24 hours; and so it does, relative to the sun. But its actual, or *sidereal*, rotation, relative to a fixed object such as a star, is accomplished in only 23 hours 56 minutes. This is called the *sidereal day*, because it is a rotation of the earth with respect to the stars rather than the sun (*solar day*).

Figure 35 explains why we have the discrepancy of four minutes. On the first day, point *A* on the earth's surface is turned toward the sun at exactly 12 o'clock noon. By the time the second day is reached, the earth has traveled some way along its orbit (the effect is greatly exaggerated for clarity's sake). Consequently, after the elapse of one sidereal day, when point *A* is facing the same direction in space, the sun is no longer there! The angle has changed, and the earth has to spin on for another four minutes before noon occurs again.

The important thing to realize is that distant objects, such as planets and stars, return to the same position in the sky not after one solar day, but after one sidereal day. It is here that the concept of right ascension makes life easy for the astronomer. The longitudes on the celestial sphere are divided into 24 hours, and sidereal time is so arranged that *the R.A. of an object on the meridian is equal to the sidereal time.* The R.A. of Venus on May 20, 1964, was 6 hours 23½ minutes. If we had a sidereal clock, we could know the moment at which Venus was due south without having to refer to the sun at all. Fortunately, there is no need for one, since Appendix VIII gives the conversion from ordinary Universal Time (U.T.) to sidereal

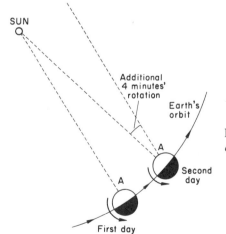

Figure 35. *The sidereal day. The effect of the earth's orbital motion is exaggerated.*

time. On the other hand, it is not difficult to make a clock by giving an ordinary clock a gaining rate of about four minutes per day.

This method is universally used by professional astronomers for finding celestial objects. A telescope on an altazimuth mount can be used only for objects on the meridian. An equatorial telescope, however, can find objects anywhere in the sky, provided its axes are graduated accurately. For amateur purposes, however, the equatorial is something of a two-edged weapon. It is undoubtedly convenient for finding objects by daylight, when there are no reference points except the sun; but one learns nothing of the night sky by always setting the telescope by circles. Like an engine in a sailing yacht, it is useful in emergencies, but it should not develop into a habit.

With an altazimuth telescope, the only necessary adjunct is a meridian mark, to insure that the telescope is pointing due south. Some distant and easily defined object, such as a tree or a house (television aerials are particularly useful), are excellent for the purpose, provided the telescope is always used from the same position. Care must also be taken to insure that the telescope's vertical axis really is vertical; otherwise, the telescope will veer off the meridian during sweeping.

Filter observation

A number of amateurs have recently been experimenting with colored filters for planetary observation. The results, particularly in the case of Venus, have caused tremendous controversy; and three groups of observers have emerged. There are those who find that filters can bring out otherwise invisible features; the second, more extensive group has found that they improve contrast but show nothing new; those in Group III have merely found that Venus appears blue through a blue filter and red through a red filter—one of the few unanimous opinions ever voiced by observers of the planet!

Since it has now been proved that some eyes are sensitive to wave lengths of light not responded to by others, it is to be expected that results when using colored filters will vary from observer to observer, just as drawings made in white, or "integrated," light rarely agree with one another. However, some facts are generally proved: Red increases the planet's contrast against the sky, since it absorbs the blue light (for this reason, a red filter can be useful in spotting a planet during the day); whereas blue reduces the contrast, tending to blunt the horns of the crescent and to make the phase appear rather less than it really is. Not surprisingly, "red" and "blue" dichotomy dates differ by several days.

The effect of filters on planet/sky contrast is predictable enough. What is more interesting is that the Group I observers, and to a lesser extent those in Group II, have also found that the dusky shadings appear rather more definite in blue light, and that the cusp caps are also emphasized. There have even been reports that the Ashen Light is best seen with a red filter, though it is hard to say whether this is because the light really is reddish, or merely because of the improved contrast with the sky.

Color filters have not yet led to any conclusive results, and we must await further experiments before anything definite emerges. Venus is undoubtedly the most tricky planet of all to observe, and eyestraining can produce quite remarkable effects, as can the observer's own expectations of what he ought to see. Some of the success claimed for filters may be due to the reduction of glare, so a reflector with a heavily tarnished mirror may be found to give a much improved view, although its performance on dimmer objects may not be as satisfactory. At all events, any experimenting is welcome—provided it is performed with an open mind.

11

Mars

Mars, perhaps the only planet in the solar system besides the earth to have borne life, is a strange little world. Absolute proof is still lacking, but even a small telescope reveals grayish-green shadings against an ocher background that seem to undergo seasonal changes of form; and some lowly type of plant-life would answer the observations well. The fact that we can see the solid surface—a surface proved by Mariner IV to be unexpectedly rugged—comes as a relief after attempting to unravel the veiled mysteries of Venus.

In compensation, Mars puts other obstacles in our way. It is only 4,220 miles across, and since it can never approach the earth as closely as can Venus (its minimum distance is 34½ million miles, as against 26 million in the case of Venus), the disk appears relatively small. Moreover, this minimum distance is attained only once every fifteen years or so, when the planet comes into opposition at perihelion. At other times, the gap between the planets is even greater.

Mars is the first of the superior planets; so, instead of confining itself to the twilight sky, it roams right around the zodiac. It takes more than two years to pass from one opposition to the next; and since observations can be usefully made for only two or three months on either side of opposition, opportunities to study it are only fleeting. The distance increases enormously when Mars moves toward conjunction. At its farthest point from the earth, it appears even smaller than the remote planet Uranus, and observations are in any case impossible because it lies in a bright sky. Only Mercury, Venus, and Jupiter can be observed satisfactorily during the day with small or moderate instruments.

At opposition, Mars appears as a small reddish-ocher disk, slightly lighter at the perimeter than at the center due to its atmospheric haze; usually, it bears a white cap at its north or south pole, depending on which hemisphere is tilted toward Earth. On the disk itself, the eye first suspects, then sees with certainty, dark markings that appear of about the same intensity as the lunar maria when seen with the naked eye. As with all planetary work, the first view is a disappointment; the disk appears so small, and the markings so elusive, that it seems a hopeless task to identify even the main features. But perception comes with practice, and with acclimatizing the eye to the object under observation. A 3-inch refractor is quite capable of revealing the better-known dark areas, although to make useful observations even at a favorable opposition an 8-inch reflector is about the minimum aperture required, and a 12-inch is much better. Since opposition distances are now decreasing—the next perihelic view is in 1971—this is a good time to start observing the planet and to plan the bigger and better telescope that is always at the back of every amateur's mind. A season of negotiation with a small instrument will pave the way for a more effective siege when a larger aperture is available.

If the Martians have finally been abolished from the scene, Mars itself has lost little of its romance, for here we have an essentially earthlike world—the only planet in our solar system even remotely to resemble our own. Millions of years ago, the resemblance may have been much closer, for Mars is running through its evolution and decay much faster than the earth. Its small mass is responsible for this. A once considerable atmosphere is now desperately thin, since the molecules have slowly leaked away into space, and the only homely features are the two small caps at the poles that melt away almost completely in the summer. With even a small telescope it is not difficult to watch the shrinkage of the cap that happens to be turned toward the earth and the sun.

The results of the Mariner IV probe, which transmitted its sensational photographs to the earth in July, 1965, hardly come within the scope of amateur observation—but they are too important to overlook. The unconscious assumption that the Martian surface is relatively smooth has received a severe jolt; craterlike depressions similar to those on the moon have been recorded, and it seems likely that they were formed in the same manner. However, atmospheric erosion has probably worn them down over the aeons since their formation, so that the Martian topography, spectacular though it may be, cannot rival the lunar grandeur.

Mars' crucial water problem, together with the question of whether or not its atmosphere contains any free oxygen, must dictate the possibility of a terrestrial type of life on its surface. At present, there seems no reason why lichens, which belong to the lowest type of plant form known on the earth, should not be able to cope with the severe conditions. If we suppose that certain regions of the planet are somewhat more hospitable than others, the plants would tend to mass there, which would produce the well-known dark markings first observed in 1659 by Christian Huygens. The feature he saw then (shown on the chart in figure 36) is still identifiable. It is a distinctive wedge-shaped marking called the Syrtis Major, following the nomenclature introduced by Schiaparelli, who started observing Mars at the very favorable opposition of 1877 and began the "canal" furor. It is ironic that the canals (which, as such, do not exist) have perhaps done more to promote Martian observation than anything else!

The dark areas

The sketches made by Huygens and others, who depended on crude aerial telescopes, could not be expected to show much, and the first really revealing observations were made by Schröter. Unfortunately, he held the curious opinion that the Martian markings are only temporary and due to cloud formations. Clouds certainly occur on Mars from time to time, but they are light, not dark; and it is hard to understand how the German observer was misled. His contemporary, William Herschel, was under no such delusion, and by watching the regular progress of the features he was able to announce, in 1784, a rotation period of 24 hours 37 minutes 27 seconds (the modern accepted value is 24 hours 37 minutes 22·7 seconds). The markings are so far from being cloudlike that it is a relatively easy matter to time the return of any particular feature to the planet's central meridian, and if the observations are maintained over a period of weeks, the error is cut down to a few seconds.

So far as is known, Herschel never produced a formal chart of the planet; this task was left to the lunar observers Mädler and Beer, who in 1840 published a map based on observations made with their 3¾-inch refractor. Although necessarily crude by comparison with more modern charts, it is a remarkable piece of work considering the aperture used. The detail shown, which proves how much can be seen by a keen eye, was amplified by later observers, all of whom believed that the dark areas were seas and the ocher expanses dry land. In the latter belief, they were correct; but they were certainly mistaken in believing that there are any great areas of water on Mars. Whatever these patches actually are, they must be almost as dry as the rest of the surface.

Many observers have claimed that these markings go through seasonal color changes—from greenish-blue to brown—that coincide with local spring and autumn and suggest the flourishing and decay of plants. However, when making such observations the transparency of the earth's atmosphere must be borne in mind. Changes can occur daily, and the

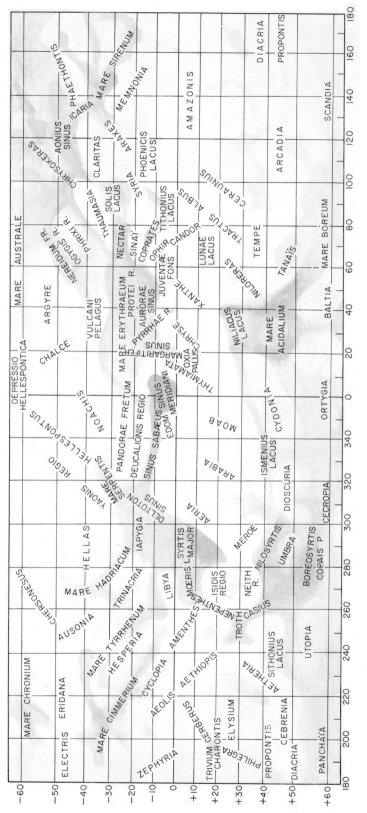

Figure 36. *Map of Mars.*

slightest haze immediately imparts a yellowish tinge to a planet's surface. Jupiter is often referred to as cream-colored, but under conditions of exceptional transparency the disk is almost as silver as that of Venus; similarly, Mercury often appears pinkish but is really more gray. In the same way, the Martian markings may appear a dull gray-brown one night and an unmistakable green the next, of a tint sometimes approaching turquoise.

The undisputed fact about the dark areas is that they change in form. Some transformations seem to be seasonal, while others occur from month to month. For instance, the elliptical area known as the Solis Lacus, which lies in the southern hemisphere, in the Argyre Desert, completely changed its shape between 1926 and 1930, and underwent further transformations in 1939. Some features are totally absent at one opposition and prominent the next. Another widely observed event of recent interest was the sudden darkening of the Aethiopis–Mare Cimmerium region in 1958; by 1963 it had again returned to its normal intensity. There is no doubt at all that these effects are real; the main task of the Mars observer is to keep track of such changes and note whether any pattern of behavior emerges.

The short-term changes are of equal interest, for here we seem to have definite evidence of seasonal development. A good example is the distinctive Syrtis Major, which seems to spread eastward during local spring, encroaching on the Libya Desert; to the west, the Pandorae Fretum is well known for its seasonal darkening. This is certainly good evidence for the plant theory, and it shows that the planet's economy is very largely dictated by the behavior of the polar caps.

The polar caps

On the earth, the seasons are caused by the tilt of the planet's axis. In March and September, the equator appears edge-on to an observer on the sun, neither hemisphere receiving preference. In June and December, however, the north and south poles, respectively, are inclined at the maximum angle of $23\frac{1}{2}°$ toward the sun, bringing extra sunlight and heat to the appropriate hemisphere.

The same state of affairs holds true for Mars. The tilt of its axis, or the angle between orbit plane and equator, is 25° 12′, hardly different from our own, so that the sun's annual rise and fall in the Martian sky is about the same. There are, however, two other differences: Its year is 687 earth-days long, and its orbit is much more eccentric than the earth's. This means that Mars is appreciably hotter when the planet is near perihelion than when at aphelion (on the earth the difference is negligible); and, since southern midsummer occurs near the perihelion point and southern midwinter occurs near aphelion, this hemisphere suffers much greater extremes of temperature. To earthbound observers, a more important consequence is that the south pole, with its glittering cap, is always presented at the favorable perihelic oppositions. As a result, we know the southern hemisphere of Mars in considerably greater detail than the northern.

At their maximum extent, the caps are visible in a very small telescope; but for critical work during the interesting stages of their shrinking, a moderate instrument is necessary. The southern cap, which can extend down to latitude 55° in midwinter and has been known to disappear completely during Martian July, has a large fragment called the Novissima Thyle, which breaks off and leads a short independent existence. The explanation seems to be that Novissima Thyle is a huge plateau elevated several thousand feet above the surrounding surface, so that the frozen material takes longer to melt in the cooler air. The northern cap has a similar offshoot called the Rima Borealis, and sometimes other deformities appear along the edge of the caps. These must be watched for carefully.

It is clear that the caps cannot be thick. They are probably no more than a few inches deep, for the weekly shrinkage during the melting season can be very obvious. Sometimes the gleaming white seems framed by a dark border, known as *Lowell's band*, after the famous American amateur observer of Mars. This is often too distinct to be dismissed as a mere optical illusion, as in the case of the Venusian "caps," and must be due to the temporary darkening of the surface by the melted water.

The re-formation of the caps cannot, unfortunately, be seen as clearly. As winter approaches, Mars swings away from the sun; and the southern polar region becomes obscured by a hazy white cloud at the very time that its northern counterpart melts and brings spring to the other hemisphere.

Clouds

The Martian air, which consists mainly of the inert gas nitrogen, has probably only about 1 % of the ground pressure of our own; it would be far too thin to breathe even if it consisted of pure oxygen.* Nevertheless, it is dense enough to support clouds, and few apparitions of the planet pass without a couple becoming prominent, even though they are nowhere near as thick as the rain clouds of our own world. Besides these white clouds, there are occasional yellow obscurations that are probably caused by desert dust being blown up into hazy veils. No observer of the favorable 1956 opposition is likely to forget these "yellow" clouds.

---

* Our knowledge of the density of the Martian atmosphere is still not conclusive. Although the Mariner IV probe suggests a small ground pressure, equal to that on the earth at 100,000 feet, this may not be the true ground pressure but that of an elevation several miles high.

Several white clouds were seen during the 1964–65 opposition, but before this the last really distinctive ones were seen in 1952, when several well-known features were hidden beneath the opaque layer. Just occasionally, as happened over Hellas in 1967, they can become bright enough to resemble a polar cap. This effect is even more striking when they happen to lie near the limb. Bright clouds usually last for at least a couple of days before fading away, and they should be watched closely to see if there is any sign of movement from night to night. This would give a key to the direction and strength of the wind.

Blue filters aid observation of cloud, for they diminish the background intensity and so improve the contrast. Some clouds, indeed, are so tenuous that they are visible only when a filter is used; for this reason, they are known as "blue" clouds, although they are really white. These are very high-altitude features, probably lying fifty miles or more above the surface, whereas the ordinary white clouds are much lower. A blue filter also emphasizes the atmospheric whiteness at the edge of the disk, caused by our viewing the surface through an augmented thickness of air, so it is important not to be misled when making these observations. A Kodak photographic filter, Wratten 47B, has been found to give good results.

The yellow clouds, the Martian dust storms, are less visible in themselves than in the surface features they obscure, for they have the same color as the ocher surface. The favorable oppositions of 1909 and 1911 were to a large extent mitigated by the blotting out of large areas of the surface; and in May, 1956, soon after the planet had appeared in the morning sky and was moving in toward opposition in September, the dark markings were seen to be unusually diffuse. By the end of August, a great yellow haze had developed over the region of Noachis and Argyre, and on August 30 the shrinking polar cap itself was obscured, not to reappear until September 7. On this occasion the Martian atmosphere was unusually turbulent, and even at the succeeding opposition, that of 1958, the hazy veil was still noticeable.

Observing Mars

All planetary observation demands an open mind; and in the case of Mars, after one has studied charts and become intimate with the major surface markings, it is extremely difficult to avoid prejudice. The tendency to sketch in features because they *should* be there has contributed largely to the "canal" controversy. It is significant that no observer ever recorded a thin straight line on Mars until Schiaparelli announced his observations in 1877!

Mars rotates slightly more slowly than the earth. If the Syrtis Major is seen on the planet's meridian on one night, it will reach the same point 37 minutes later on the following night. Conversely, since the planet seems to rotate from right to left, it will be slightly to the right of the meridian at the same hour of observation. As the days pass, the region is carried farther and farther out of view until it remains entirely on the far side during the night's work, returning to the meridian at the former time after an interval of about five weeks. This means that different areas of the planet gradually come under scrutiny, and, depending on the inclination of the weather, one can hope to observe three or four complete cycles of the planet during the time in which it presents a reasonably large disk. Since these opportunities come at intervals of more than two years, every favorable night must be exploited to the full—though this is superfluous advice to the keen observer who has awaited the return of the elusive visitor for many months.

Mars requires the use of high magnifications, since its disk can never be more than 25" in diameter (at an aphelic opposition it is only 14"), and for guiding under these powers efficient slow-motions are necessary. The earth's rotation quickly carries it out of the field of view, and unless the tube is easily adjustable the observer will consume most of his time and temper in simply keeping the planet in view. With an altazimuth telescope, the best way is to adjust the position so that the planet drifts right across the view. By the time it has reached the central region, where definition is best, any residual tremors will have died down and the observer can concentrate on the scraps of detail that appear and fade away. For viewing the general features, a power as low as × 200 is often useful, since the tube has to be shifted less frequently, but the finer details demand × 300 or × 350 if they are to be seen well. A single-lens eyepiece, if it is well made, can give excellent results, but the field of good definition is so small that an equatorial mounting is almost a necessity.

The focusing requires great attention. This may sound self-evident, but Mars is an extremely difficult object to focus properly, because of the glare at the limb and because not all of the surface markings are well defined. The polar cap is useful, should it be visible; if not, a nearby star offers the best means of achieving a perfect focus. It pays dividends to refocus carefully every five minutes or so until the eye has been taught to remain relaxed.

Some observers adopt a definite scale for their sketches, varying the size of the drawing according to the planet's apparent diameter. There are arguments for and against this practice, but at any rate the disk should never be less than an inch across, and around the time of opposition a 2-inch disk is the most suitable size. The advantage of a standard diameter is that a local printer can run off a supply of blank disks with a blacked-in back-

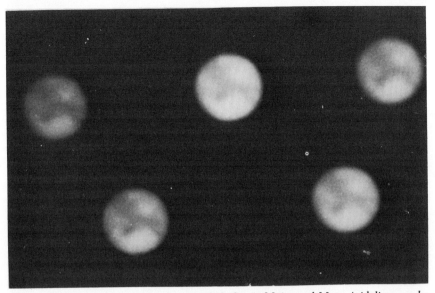

Mars. *Photographed on November 13, 1958. Syrtis Major and Mars Acidalium can be seen quite clearly. The photographer used a 12·5-inch reflector with eyepiece projection and orthoscopic oculars; focal length, 141 feet; exposure time, 1·5 seconds. (Jack Eastman, Jr., Manhattan Beach, California.)*

ground, and these can be pasted in the observing book. They are useful for Mars and Jupiter, but not so convenient for Venus because of the phase effect and the fact that the planet is usually observed against a light sky.

Mars, too, can show a slight phase. This is most noticeable when it forms nearly a right angle with the sun, a position known as *quadrature*, occurring about three months before and after opposition. At this time, the phase is about 88 per cent, and allowance must be made for this when sketching the disk. It is remarkable that Galileo was able to make out the phase with his tiny telescope, although the polar cap and dark markings eluded him.

The rotation of Mars, while considerably slower than that of the giant planets, is nevertheless sufficient to be noticeable after a period of ten minutes. Since it can take easily half an hour to make a drawing and note down the various details—such as the relative intensities of different regions, any unusual development of the dark areas, the state of the polar cap, and the possible presence of clouds—allowance must be made for the spin. The best way of doing this is to sketch only those features fairly near the central meridian, since the western border will be carried out of view, and the right-hand side will be considerably displaced by fresh detail arriving from beyond the limb. A 2B pencil, if used skillfully, will allow both dark and diffuse shadings to be rendered. Some amateurs color their drawings, but it is difficult to achieve really accurate representations, and the best answer is to record all the finer details in the written notes so that there can be no subsequent error in interpretation.

The satellites

Mars has two moons, but they both appear very faint. The larger one, Phobos, is probably about 12 miles across, and circles Mars in a sidereal period of only 7 hours 39 minutes, at a distance of 3,700 miles from the surface. Deimos, probably half the size of Phobos, is 12,500 miles away and has a sidereal period of 30 hours 21 minutes. Both moons are brighter than the 13th magnitude, so that technically they are visible with a 6-inch telescope; however, the glare around Mars is so great that they are hard to see with a 12-inch, even under the most favorable conditions.

The "canals"

The story of the canals, fascinating though it is, belongs more properly to a history of astronomy than a handbook of observation; yet, as with so many other telescopic myths, it is of value in proving just how easily the eye is deceived, and how effortlessly the subconscious takes over the task of recording detail. Schiaparelli, observing in Milan with an 8½-inch refractor at the opposition of 1877, observed a number of streaky markings that had, in fact, been seen by previous observers of the caliber of Mädler, Lockyer, and Dawes. They had given no hint of artificiality and aroused no special comment. But at the return of 1879, and at succeeding oppositions, the streaks became narrower and straighter, and the mistranslation of the Italian word *canali* (channels) into "canals" simply hastened the unfolding deception. Lowell took up the work at Flagstaff, Arizona, when the Italian retired after the opposition of 1890, not only extending the network of "canals," which he really thought they were, but publishing the evidence for a highly-organized, Mars-wide civilization in his famous book *Mars and Its Canals* in 1906.

We can never know just how Schiaparelli and Lowell were deceived, although there are some suggestive facts. Schiaparelli had to give up observing through failing sight, which ended in blindness; and this handicap, coupled with the strain of observing with a relatively small telescope, might well be expected to produce false effects. Lowell, observing with his fine 24-inch refractor, often worked with it diaphragmed down to only 18 inches. Under conditions of poor seeing, it sometimes helps to reduce the aperture; but Lowell Observatory enjoys conditions as good as anywhere in the world, and in any case it is most unwise to make observations when the seeing is poor. Furthermore, he also drew sharply-defined streaks on Venus, which is notorious for its ghostly shadings!

Whatever the cause, the "canal" observations had a predictable effect: some amateur astronomers using 6-inch telescopes started drawing linear streaks where their similarly equipped predecessors had merely seen detached markings, and the hangover is still with us today, despite the conclusive failure of reliable and well-equipped observers, working in good conditions, to confirm the results of Schiaparelli and Lowell.

Some of the features are certainly streaky, but there is nothing extraordinary in this; and the new knowledge that much of the surface is apparently rugged rather than smooth should be enough in itself to dispose of the possibility of any canaliform network. It is high time that the myth was buried; and the amateur would do well to devote his attention to matters of established reality. The glittering polar caps, the fleeting clouds, and the mysteriously variable patches offer fascination enough for those who turn their telescopes to this strange and tantalizing world.

12

Jupiter

The first and largest of the giant planets, Jupiter, is perhaps the finest object on the solar system for observation with a small telescope. Like Venus, it shows a large disk; but it never shrinks inconveniently small, is always fully illuminated, and exhibits far more in the way of definite detail. Moreover, this detail is changing all the time, so that there is always something new and unexpected happening.

Jupiter, Saturn, Uranus, and Neptune are formed on an entirely different pattern from the terrestrial planets. They are nowhere near as dense, since they consist mainly of gas (principally ammonia and methane) that has been frozen into crystalline or liquid form by the intense cold, swathing their surfaces in dense clouds. It seems doubtful that any of them contains a true rocky core; at all events, our observation is confined to the upper layers of their atmospheres. Luckily, Jupiter's cloud features are so definite that there is no serious disagreement over the main details to be seen.

The belts and zones

The basic hue of the disk is silvery-cream, darkening a little at the limbs, where we see the "sunrise" and "sunset" regions. Across the disk, dividing it into various zones, are a number of dark belts lying parallel to the equator. The wider and more prominent of the belts often display a reddish-brown tint, so that Jupiter, despite its surface temperature of $-220°F$,* has a distinctly warm appearance when seen through a telescope of moderate aperture.

*The word "surface" refers to the top of the cloud layer.

158

The belts, which form the framework against which the finer features appear, develop and fade from year to year, and each apparition of the planet has its special characteristics. Usually the North and South Equatorial belts are very conspicuous; so is the North Temperate Belt, with the South Temperate Belt and the high-latitude features somewhat fainter. However, the South Temperate Belt has attained prominence in recent years, while the North Temperate Belt has gone into a temporary decline. The Equatorial Zone, which normally appears as a bright band across the center of the disk, turned yellowish for a time in 1959 and in 1960 began to darken, an appearance that was maintained for the next four years. Jupiter's refusal to become habit-ridden is just one of its fascinations; the observer never knows quite what to expect.

The diagram in figure 37 gives a very schematic view of the main belts and zones, and it must be emphasized that Jupiter never looks anything like this. Quite apart from individual fluctuations, some belts often appear double (the two equatorial belts especially), while the regions near the equator are replete with complex detail. Dark wisps, bright ovals, gaps—all these features pay tribute to the immense turbulence that must be going on in Jupiter's atmosphere. When we remember that the planet's equatorial diameter is 88,700 miles, it is obvious that some of the larger "clouds" are considerably bigger than the earth!

Jupiter's belts and zones are referred to by the following standard abbreviations:

South Polar Region   S.P.R.
South South Temperate Zone   S.S.T.Z.
South South Temperate Belt   S.S.T.B.
South Temperate Zone   S.T.Z.
South Temperate Belt   S.T.B.
South Tropical Zone   S.Tr.Z.
South Equatorial Belt   S.E.B.
Equatorial Zone   E.Z.

Figure 37. *The principal features of Jupiter.*

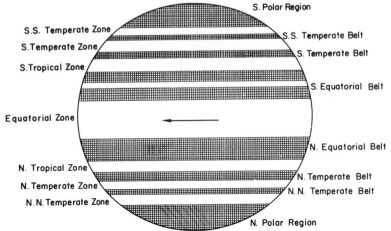

There are corresponding abbreviations for the northern hemisphere. The belts have no defined latitudes; sometimes they also appear in even higher latitudes than the normal position of the second temperate belt, in which case another directional letter would be added; an N.N.N.T.B. is fairly common. When a belt appears double, the components are given north and south subscripts (e.g., S.T.B.$_s$ and S.T.B.$_n$). Two other useful abbreviations—used when describing the longitude of one feature relative to another —are p (preceding) and f (following). Jupiter spins so quickly from right to left that an experienced eye can notice the difference in just two or three minutes, and the use of the p and f terms is obvious.

Rotation periods

The main object of Jovian observation is to find out as much as possible about the planet's atmospheric currents, which cause the various features to drift in longitude by different amounts. Most of these are impermanent, lasting for a few weeks or even less, but while they survive they give us valuable clues about the forces at work. Some regions rotate faster than others, while many individual spots have their own periods, and it is by timing these that the amateur can make his greatest contribution to the study of the planet. This is carried out by noting the instant at which they cross the planet's central meridian; and while the taking of *transits*, as they are called, may sound a dull business, the fascination increases as skill and experience are gained.

Jupiter has two main rotation periods. The main portion of the disk rotates in about 9 hours 55 minutes, but the Equatorial Zone, bounded by the north edge of the S.E.B. and the south edge of the N.E.B., takes about five minutes less. As a result, features in the Equatorial Zone seem to advance steadily relative to the rest of the globe, taking about six weeks to achieve one "lap"—if they survive long enough. Jupiter's rapid spin is demonstrated by the flattening of the disk, which is caused by the extension of the equatorial regions by centrifugal force. Jupiter's polar diameter is only 82,800 miles, and this flattening must be allowed for when making a sketch. The best procedure is to have a blank disk prepared, then have a stock run off by the local printer.

Because the planet rotates so quickly, it is not difficult to time the instant at which a feature crosses the meridian. To begin with, there may be an error of five minutes, but with experience a transit can be timed to the nearest minute, and the longitude of the feature can be worked out from tables. If it then survives for several rotations, its drift can be followed. Occasionally, spots are observed with rotation periods two or three minutes different from that of the surrounding region, so that they move steadily past adjacent features. If a spot gains in longitude, it is said to be *advancing*; if it moves backward, it *retrogrades*.

The *Astronomical Ephemeris* and B.A.A. *Handbook* give longitude tables for the central meridian of the two main zones: System I is for the equatorial region; System II is for the rest of the disk. These work for synodic rotation periods of 9 hours 50 minutes 30·003 seconds and 9 hours 55 minutes 40·632 seconds, respectively. These periods are quite arbitrary, but are close to the average periods of revolution of features in the two regions. However, when we examine the records more closely we find that different latitudes have their own rotation periods, differing by several seconds from those nearby. Altogether, some twenty different currents have been found to exist, carrying along at their own individual rate any features that happen to lie in them. On top of these, there are occasional short-lived spots with special drifts of their own. Few features show much drifting in latitude.

Much of our knowledge of the behavior of the features and currents of Jupiter is owed to the work of amateur observers. Systematic observation began with A. Stanley Williams, who devised the simple transit system of longitude determination and announced the discovery of nine individual currents in a paper published in 1896. This work coincided with the foundation of the British Astronomical Association, whose Jupiter Section has now amassed records extending back over seventy years; and the work of the Association of Lunar and Planetary Observers in New Mexico has reinforced Jovian observation since its foundation after World War II. Much is known, but much is also still mysterious, and there is a great need for more observers to keep track of the planet's caprices.

The Great Red Spot

Among the intricate but evanescent features that decorate the silvery disk of this great world, one object in particular catches the imagination through its great size, and, still more startling, its persistence. If we can trust a drawing made in 1664, by the British physicist Robert Hooke, it has survived throughout the era of telescopic observation of the planet. This is the Great Red Spot, which Hooke represented as a large elliptical feature in the southern hemisphere. Cassini is said to have drawn a similar feature in 1665. It also figured in a drawing made in 1713 by J. P. Maraldi, and on September 5, 1831, it was drawn by Schwabe, of sunspot fame. But the redness for which it has become so famous did not appear until 1877, and during the period 1879–82, its color was often referred to as "brick-red," a vague term, but certainly descriptive enough to suggest definite activity. Thereafter it faded, becoming gray and occasionally invisible among the other detail of the S.Tr.Z., in which it lies; but occasional revivals have occurred: in 1957, when it assumed an obvious pink hue and could be seen with a small telescope; in 1961; and prominently again in 1966. The Spot measures some 20,000 miles in longitude, by about 8,000 miles in latitude, and it sometimes overlaps the S.E.B.s and produces an indentation in the belt known as the Red Spot Hollow.

The Spot may be a solid body (though a recent theory suggests that it may be the top of a "standing current" in Jupiter's atmosphere, produced by the planet's rotation); but it cannot be fixed to the core. This is proved by its erratic rotation period, which has varied from as little as 9 hours 55 minutes 32 seconds in some years to as much as 9 hours 55 minutes 44 seconds in others. A variation of 12 seconds may seem a small amount, but the mind reels at the thought of the colossal forces required to perturb this vast object.

The Spot is so large that it is not too easy to judge just when the center is on the planet's meridian. The best method is to take three transits, for the p and f ends as well as the middle.

Periodic disturbances

Fresh spots and detail may break out in any region of the disk; but the S.E.B. is the seat of two well-known disturbances. One has not appeared for some years, and may well be periodic; the other is a frequent phenomenon of the planet.

THE SOUTH TROPICAL DISTURBANCE. This was first recorded as such in 1901, although earlier records suggest that it was not a new feature. It took the form of turbulence occurring on the southern edge of the S.E.B. and so extending into the S.Tr.Z. The main characteristic was its relatively short rotation period of about 9 hours 55 minutes 20 seconds, considerably shorter than the mean System II period. The site of turbulence became extended in longitude, and because of its shorter rotation period it began to catch up with the Red Spot, which it did in 1902. When this occurred, there was apparently some mutual attraction, for the Spot was pulled forward from its resting place and suffered a distinct acceleration of several seconds before the Disturbance had passed by!

The same pattern of events was repeated whenever the Disturbance passed the Spot, as it did no fewer than nine times between 1901 and about 1935. After that, it suffered a decline and, apart from a brief revival in 1940, it has not been seen since, although some observers reported a characteristic darkening of the S.Tr.Z. soon after it reappeared from conjunction with the sun in 1966.

S.E.B. ERUPTIONS. The S.E.B. is the most active region on the planet. In some years it is almost invisible; in other years one can observe almost cataclysmic revivals. The first recorded eruption of this sort was in 1919–20; the second was in 1928–29. More recent disturbances, lasting for several months, occurred in 1943, 1949, 1952, and 1958, with a minor outbreak as recently as 1962. Clearly, some sort of periodicity is involved, and another eruption may occur at any time. Characteristically, a number of light and dark spots develop, which organize themselves into two zones. Those on the south edge of the S.E.B. have a long rotation period that may be two or three minutes more than the average for System II. The others, on the north edge of the Belt, may have a period as short as 9 hours 52 minutes, and occasionally even less. The active regions therefore drift steadily apart in longitude, and during a severe outbreak they may completely girdle the planet. The Red Spot, which lies near the S.E.B., may disappear for a time during one of these eruptions, as happened in 1958, just after its recent revival to prominence.

Other disturbances are seen from time to time. Between 1930 and 1934 a "circulating current" was observed in the S.Tr.Z., where a number of dark spots were seen to retrograde along one line of latitude and then, apparently, to jump a few degrees southward and advance in the direction from which they had come. It is these apparently inexplicable currents, combined with periodic outbreaks of light and dark markings, that make Jupiter a source of such constant fascination.

Observing Jupiter

Even when Jupiter is near conjunction with the sun, its image has a diameter of about 30″. This is larger than the disk of Mars at a perihelic opposition, so the planet can be observed profitably whenever it is visible in the sky. In temperate latitudes, it is lost from view about six weeks before conjunction, reappearing in the morning sky after the same interval, so that an enthusiastic observer can follow it for about three-quarters of the apparition. Low-latitude observers are even more favored, for it sets at a greater angle to the horizon and so stays visible for even longer. Because of the difficulty of observation, any views obtained near conjunction are of special value, since they act as a link between the bulk of the work done around the time of opposition.

Jupiter does not have as sharp a limb as the other planets. This may well be due to the falling-off of illumination at the edge of the disk, which is usually the easiest part of a planet on which to focus properly. Consequently, medium powers usually work best, which is no disadvantage since the disk appears so large. A good view is given by × 150 on a 3-inch or

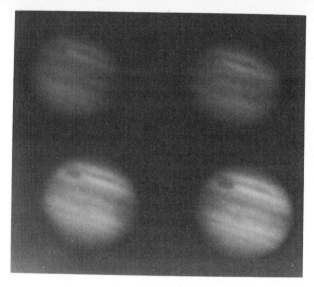

Jupiter. *Photographed on July 28, 1961, through a 12½-inch aperture; focal length, 113 feet; exposure time, 3·5 seconds. Film used was contrast process Pan. The Red Spot is discernible. (Jack Eastman, Jr., Manhattan Beach, California.)*

× 200 on a 6-inch reflector. Even with a 12-inch reflector, powers between × 200 and × 300 give excellent results. A 3-inch refractor will show sufficient detail to allow transits to be taken, but a larger aperture naturally reveals more delicate features and increases the scope of the work.

Disk drawings are of secondary importance to transit work. If some unusual features are seen, it is worth making a "finished" sketch, but normally the main importance of a drawing is as a guide to the features observed in transit. The best way to start is to spend a couple of minutes surveying the planet, looking for any unusual markings and taking note of the spots and streaks that are likely to transit during the session. It is not advisable to make a sketch until the planet has been under observation for an hour or so; in this time, the first features seen to transit will have moved on to the *p* part of the disk, and room is now left on the sketch for the fresh features that have come into view on the *f* part. Once the outlines are drawn in, the finer details can be inserted as their transits are taken, using a watch correct to the nearest minute. If the session is a long one, it will be necessary to make another sketch to cover the new area of surface that the planet's rapid spin brings into view.

The Galilean satellites

This is the name given to the four bright satellites discovered by Galileo. The other eight in Jupiter's family of twelve moons are too faint for amateur observation, but the Galileans form one of the best-known sights in the sky. Indeed, they are so bright that some sharp-eyed observers claim to have seen them without optical aid, and binoculars will certainly give a good view. Because of their interest, it is worth giving their details in full.

TABLE IV.   The Galilean Satellites

NAME	MEAN DISTANCE FROM JUPITER (MILES)	ANGULAR DISTANCE AT ELONGATION	DIAMETER (MILES)	ORBITAL PERIOD			MEAN MAG.
Io	262,000	2¼′	2,000	1^d	18^h	28^m	5·5
Europa	417,000	3¾	1,750	3	13	14	6·1
Ganymede	666,000	6	3,000	7	3	43	5·1
Callisto	1,170,000	10¼	2,800	16	16	32	6·2

The satellites being of the 6th magnitude or above, they would be naked-eye objects were they not masked by the planet's glare. A low-power eyepiece gives a wonderful view of the four moons, their positions changing perceptibly from hour to hour as they revolve around the planet. While observing this charming sight, the colossal size and mass of Jupiter are brought home to the observer by the realization that Ganymede is probably slightly larger than the planet Mercury!

Jupiter's axial tilt is only 3° 05′; thus, unlike the case of Mars and Saturn, we always see the equator virtually edge-on. What is more, the Galilean satellites revolve almost exactly in the plane of Jupiter's equator, so that to our view they are strung out more or less in a straight line. Their nightly positions around the planet are listed in the almanacs, but with a little practice it is easy to distinguish them. Io moves the fastest, and is never far away from Jupiter. Europa has a rather dull, grayish tint. Ganymede is easily identified because of its brilliance, and even a 6-inch reflector will reveal a definite disk, although surface details cannot be made out except with very large telescopes. Callisto is the slowest moving and faintest of the four. It is worth keeping an eye on the satellites' relative magnitudes, for Callisto has sometimes been recorded as having almost the same brightness as Ganymede, and Io also shows fluctuations. These variations may be due to irregular light and dark patches on their surfaces, but they are not well understood.

These moons are often eclipsed in Jupiter's shadow. Their eclipses occur more frequently than those of our own moon because Jupiter's shadow is much larger than the earth's. At other times, they pass in front of the disk, a phenomenon known by that adaptable word *transit*. As figure 38 shows, the ease with which eclipses can be observed depends on the position of the earth. When our vantage point is at C, as it is at opposition, the shadow lies directly behind the planet and so cannot be seen; at quadrature, we are angled to the greatest advantage and the shadow leads away to one side of the disk: to the p side before opposition (A), to the f side thereafter (B). Io is so close to Jupiter that its eclipses occur very near the limb; the same is usually true of Europa, but Ganymede and Callisto can pass

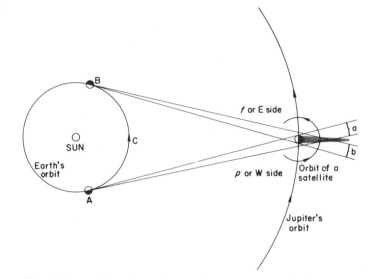

Figure 38. *Eclipses of Jupiter's satellites: Before opposition, when the earth is near A and Jupiter is a morning star, a satellite vanishes in its shadow before it reaches the W side, or limb, and reappears at the bright limb, being invisible through the range a. After opposition, when Jupiter is seen from B and is an evening star, a satellite vanishes at the W limb and passes into the shadow behind the planet, reappearing from eclipse at some distance from the E limb. At opposition (C), the shadow is directly behind the planet and both disappearance and reappearance take place at the limb. Due to the slight inclination of Jupiter's axis, it is sometimes possible for the outer satellite, Callisto, to pass north or south of Jupiter's shadow and avoid eclipse altogether.*

right through the shadow before being occulted by Jupiter itself. Callisto is so far away that the slight tilt of its orbit sometimes makes it miss eclipse altogether.

Transits are well worth observing. The satellite approaches the disk from the *f* side, appearing as a gleaming spot as it passes onto the shaded limb but quickly becoming lost in the planet's brilliance (although it may reappear during transit as it crosses in front of some unusually dark feature). The satellites also cast shadows, keeping Jupiter well supplied with solar eclipses. These shadows, like the satellites, move across the disk from east to west; they can be seen very easily with a 3-inch telescope, appearing as sharply defined black spots. Just occasionally, one satellite may pass through the shadow cast by another, while mutual occultations can also take place. Unfortunately, the adequate observation of such phenomena requires large apertures.

13

Saturn

Saturn reveals its loveliness in a very small telescope. When the rings are well presented and lie at their maximum inclination towards the earth, as happens every fifteen years or so, good binoculars can show a distinctly oval outline. A 2-inch telescope and a magnification of × 20 are enough to show the rings, and a 3-inch refractor gives a splendid and unforgettable view. On the other hand, though Saturn is a noble showpiece of the heavens, it is a much less convenient object for study than Jupiter. For really useful work, a telescope of at least 10 inches aperture is desirable, although occasional spots have been discovered with smaller instruments.

Galileo's simple telescope revealed to him something protruding from Saturn's outline, but its definition was too poor for him to solve the problem. Succeeding efforts were not much more successful, and it was not until 1659 that Huygens solved the mystery. As a result of patient efforts with a $2\frac{1}{3}$-inch refractor of 23 feet focal length and a magnification of × 100, he was able to announce the planet's amazing ring system. He also managed to see some markings on the disk itself, which, although fainter than those on Jupiter, seem to be essentially similar. This indicates that the two worlds are constructed on the same pattern, with thick, freezing ammonia and methane clouds. However, Saturn's temperature of −250°F has doubtless produced a more quiescent world, and fewer than a dozen really conspicuous features have been observed during the present century, although minor irregularities are common enough. Saturn has its equivalents of the Jovian equatorial and temperate belts, with the accompanying bright zones, but certainly has no permanent features to rival the Red Spot.

Rotation and markings

Saturn's equatorial regions rotate in about 10 hours 14 minutes. This is slightly longer than Jupiter's period, but despite its smaller diameter (75,100 miles), Saturn is actually more flattened at the poles. Clearly, its make-up must be even less substantial, since the more solid a body, the less its tendency to deform; and we arrive at the surprising conclusion that Saturn is actually less dense than water. The image of a planet floating in some colossal ocean is enough to show that its solid core, if any, must be very small. It is a world composed principally of freezing, evil-smelling atmosphere.

As with Jupiter, different parts of the globe rotate at different rates. Exact knowledge of the different regions is frustrated by the paucity of distinctive markings in high latitudes, which only goes to show how vital it is for amateurs with adequate optical means to keep a watch on the planet; a few transits of an identifiable feature would add immensely to our knowledge of these regions. The evidence so far amassed suggests that instead of the planet's being divided into two main rotational zones, the period of rotation steadily increases with latitude, being about 30 minutes longer at a latitude of 60°. Any prominent spot appearing on Saturn counts as a major astronomical event, and must be observed to the full.

As seen with the naked eye, the planet has a characteristic yellowish hue. Telescopically, the disk is seen to be scored by a bright, almost white equatorial zone, with the temperate regions a somewhat darker tint and the belts themselves darker again, often with rather vague edges that seem to melt into the adjacent zone. The polar regions are usually dark, but undergo occasional brightenings. In 1963, for example, the south polar region became almost as light as the equatorial zone, which itself turned unusually dark in 1964. With moderate and large instruments, fine belts can often be seen in quite high latitudes; but they are almost always featureless. Most of the activity occurs in the two equatorial belts, which frequently exhibit a somewhat fluted border with the equatorial zone.

Easily recognizable spots are rare. Cassini is said to have seen a couple of streaks in 1683, but even William Herschel, who paid more attention to Saturn than to any other planet, recorded a conspicuous spot only once, in 1780; this took the form of a large dusky spot on the equator. Nearer the present time, there was a major outbreak of small white spots close to the equator between 1891 and 1894, and again in 1932; all of these gave a rotation period of about 10 hours 14 minutes for the equator. However, the most prominent spot ever recorded was seen a year later, in 1933, being discovered on August 3 from England by an amateur who was rather better known to the public in another sphere—the British stage and screen comedian Will Hay. Hay's white spot was easily visible with a 3-inch refractor, but it quickly extended in longitude and faded away, having been visible for only a few weeks.

Saturn turned active once again during the appearance of 1960, this time in the north temperate regions. Several white spots were seen by amateur observers between March and September, and one in particular, followed from March 31 until May 14, was almost as bright as Hay's. After it had disappeared, several other spots were sighted, the whole zone being in a state of unusual turbulence. They all lay at a latitude of about 60°S, and had a rotation period of about 10 hours 39 minutes, so that they added considerably to our slender knowledge of these regions. These isolated outbreaks, which usually uncover features that are visible in quite a small telescope, prove that persistent observation is essential if we are to make the most of these scraps of evidence.

The rings

Saturn's ring system is one of the wonders of the visible universe. With a diameter of 169,000 miles, and a thickness of about 10, the rings have been called "the thinnest things in existence"; and they are so slender that when the earth passes through their plane they are invisible, for a day or so, even in large observatory instruments. The rings look solid enough, but they are really very insubstantial, being composed of millions of tiny moonlets just a few inches across. We do not know how they came to be formed, but Saturn's gravitational influence must in some way be responsible. It could be that a former satellite approached injudiciously close and achieved an unexpected immortality, but it is more likely that the rings form the proto-particles of a moon that never coalesced into a solid body.

The system is divided into three distinct rings, termed A, B, and C as one progresses inward; they are shown diagrammatically in figure 39. Ring A is 10,000 miles wide; it has a yellowish tint, rather like the temperate regions of the planet, and is separated from the brighter Ring B by a dark line

Figure 39. *The rings of Saturn.*

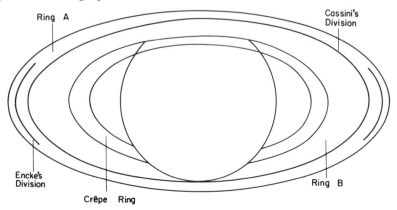

known as *Cassini's division*, named in honour of J. D. Cassini, who discovered it in 1675. Cassini's division is obvious with a 3-inch refractor when the rings are at their maximum presentation, but is naturally invisible through foreshortening when they are almost edge-on.

Ring B is 16,500 miles wide, of a clear cream color that is usually brighter than the planet's equatorial zone, so that it acts as a useful photometer for estimating the zone's occasional brightenings. The interior part of the ring is somewhat shaded, and between its inner border and the planet lies the much fainter Ring C, or *Crêpe Ring*. This is so dim that it was not discovered until 1850, by W. C. and G. P. Bond, using the 15-inch refractor of the Harvard Observatory, and, independently two weeks later, by the Reverend W. R. Dawes in England, using a refractor of only 6¼ inches aperture. It is worth remembering that observers of the caliber of Herschel, Schröter, and Struve all studied Saturn with instruments of considerable power, and yet *missed the Crêpe Ring*, not because it was invisible with the equipment at their command, but because they were not aware of its existence—a proof of Sir John Herschel's dictum:

When an object is once discovered by a superior power, an inferior one will suffice to see it afterwards.

Even so, when we consider that the Crêpe Ring requires an aperture of about 8 inches if it is to be well seen, Dawes' discovery with a 6¼-inch refractor is certainly a remarkable feat. The ring is about 10,000 miles wide, leaving a gap of 9,000 miles between the inner edge and the outer reaches of Saturn's disk. The different intensities of the rings are explained by the particle density in different regions; Ring B is very closely packed, with the particles perhaps more pulverized and so better reflectors of light, whereas the Crêpe Ring is tenuous and Cassini's division is almost devoid of moonlets.

From time to time, observers have reported fresh refinements in the ring system, but the only confirmed feature is *Encke's division*, a very faint line about three-fifths of the way toward the outer rim of Ring A. This has been glimpsed with a 9-inch, but a proper study requires a much larger aperture, and so do other reported "divisions," of which there is one in Ring A, two in Ring B, and one in the Crêpe Ring. Another unconfirmed feature is the *dusky ring* exterior to Ring A. Records of this go back to the nineteenth century, but it was reported independently in 1907–8 by French and Swiss observers. E. E. Barnard, however, was unable to see a trace of it with the 40-inch Yerkes refractor, and the evidence is too inconclusive to allow any definite deductions to be made. A. F. O'D. Alexander, in his book *The Planet Saturn*, has aptly described it as a sort of "Loch Ness monster."

Presentation of the rings

Luckily, Saturn's axis is not as erect as that of Jupiter. If this were the case, our view of the rings would always be very oblique, since they revolve exactly in the plane of the planet's equator. But the axis is tilted from the vertical to the orbit plane at an angle of 26° 45', so that when one of the poles is turned to its fullest extent toward the earth, we have a reasonably good view of the rings' surface. This phase happens twice during Saturn's sidereal period of 29½ years; the north pole was presented in 1958, while the southern regions will be well displayed in 1973. In the intermediate position (1966), the earth passed exactly through the plane of the rings. These phases are shown in figure 40.

The edge-on stage is most interesting. To an observer in the position of the sun, there would be only one phase—when he passed through the plane of the rings, and the opposite side came into view. But since the earth and sun make slightly different angles with Saturn, there are actually three definite phases.

EDGE-ON TO THE EARTH.   Depending on the position of the earth relative to Saturn, it can pass either once or three times through the plane of the

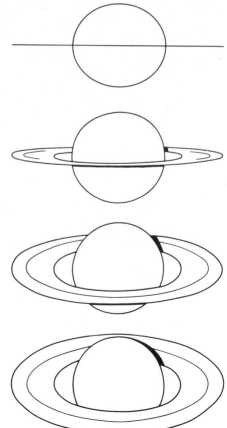

Figure 40. *Presentation of Saturn's rings.*

rings. If it is only once, as happened in 1951, the planet is always near conjunction and is unobservable; when it occurs three times, as it did in 1966, one occasion is near conjunction but the other two occur around the time of opposition. The rings are so thin that they are lost from view, even in a large telescope, for a few days. For instance, when the earth passed through the ring plane in 1920, Barnard, using the 40-inch Yerkes refractor, could see no sign of the rings between November 8 and 13; amateurs had to wait another week before the rings returned to visibility.

EDGE-ON TO THE SUN. This means that although the surface of the ring system is slightly inclined to our view, the sunlight is striking it horizontally. When this happens it appears very dim, but it is visible in apertures greater than about 4 inches.

EARTH AND SUN ON OPPOSITE SIDES. This is the most interesting stage of all. It may be that the sun is shining on the north surface, while we view them from the south; in this case, they are seen by light transmitted *through* the rings, instead of being reflected off the surface. Consequently, regions such as the Crêpe Ring and Cassini's division, which contain few particles, transmit the most light and appear bright, while the denser Ring B is almost invisible. These observations are of great delicacy and require at least moderate apertures. During this phase in 1966, which lasted from October 29 until December 18, the rings were glimpsed by some observers using 12-inch reflectors, but there were few reports of their visibility with smaller apertures. They were easily seen with a 3-inch refractor only two days after the earth passed through the ring plane for the third time, on December 18, bringing the sunlit surface once more into view.

The years around the period of ring-plane passage are also the only time when we have a good view of the whole of Saturn's disk. During the rest of its appearance, one hemisphere is more or less obscured by the rings.

Shadows

The ball of Saturn casts a shadow on the part of the rings that is directly away from the sun. At opposition, when the earth is exactly in line with the planet, the shadow is hidden by the disk; but on either side of opposition it is partly visible as a dark line between the rear portion of the rings and the planet's limb. This shadow lies on the *p* side of the rings before opposition, and on the *f* side afterwards. Furthermore, the part of the rings which is in front of the planet casts a shadow on the disk, which may appear on either the polar or equatorial side of the rings, as illustrated here. When it appears on the equatorial side, it appears rather like a very dark belt on the planet,

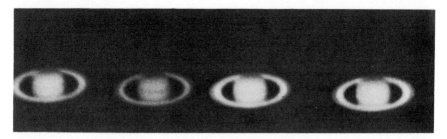

Saturn. *A fine example of an amateur planetary photograph, taken through a 12½-inch aperture; focal length, 109 feet; exposure time, 4 seconds. (Jack Eastman, Jr., Manhattan Beach, California.)*

and the shadow has often been reported as such by unwary observers. The Crêpe Ring sometimes gives the illusion of another belt where it crosses in front of the planet, appearing as a faint shading where the light shines through it. This effect is heightened if the Crêpe Ring is invisible against the black sky beyond the disk.

Occultations by the ring system

Some of the most important observations ever made of Saturn's ring system were secured by two amateurs, J. Knight and M. A. Ainslie, half a century ago. Observing independently from southern England, on February 9, 1917, they watched Saturn pass so near a 7th-magnitude star that the star was occulted by the outer portion of the rings. The star was considerably dimmed when seen through Ring A, but it could be made out clearly enough with a 9-inch reflector and a 5-inch refractor; and twice it brightened spontaneously for a few seconds. One brightening was evidently its visibility through the faint Encke's division, while the other must be taken as evidence of another gap in—or at least a thinning of—the ring particles. When the star reached Cassini's division, it shone out normally. It did not pass behind Ring B, but another occultation occurred on March 14, 1920, when observers in South Africa saw the star shining distinctly through the bright ring.

Saturn quite frequently occults a star—about once every other year—but usually these are too faint to shine distinctly through the rings, and in recent years no stars have been as obliging as those of 1917 and 1920. Occultation predictions are given in the B.A.A. *Handbook*, however, and every effort should be made to observe those that do occur.

Observing Saturn

Although spasmodic white spots can be seen with small telescopes, routine work on Saturn requires at least a 6-inch refractor or an 8-inch

173

reflector, and larger apertures are of course preferable. Nothing less will show the minor irregularities of the belts and such fine features as Encke's division; neither will it allow sufficiently high magnifying powers to be used, for the disk appears almost as small as that of Mars when seen at an aphelic opposition.

Saturn is an infuriating object to draw, and it is not worth making regular "finished" sketches unless unusual markings are seen. Written notes are normally adequate, especially if they concentrate on the color and intensity of different regions. Some observers have gone so far as to draw up a brightness scale, ranging from 0 (brilliant white) to 10 (the blackness of the sky); but it is extremely difficult to make estimates of such accuracy. A better method is to use Rings A and B as standards for estimating the zones, belts, and polar regions. The great drawback of numerical scales is that they *appear* to be highly accurate, whereas eye-estimates are not very stringent, particularly where color is concerned. An entry such as "Equatorial zone perceptibly brighter than Ring B" really means much more than its evaluation on a 0–10 scale.

The satellites

Saturn's family of ten moons is of great interest. Four or five are visible with a 6-inch reflector, and seven with a 12-inch. Their details are given in Table V.

TABLE V.   Saturn's Satellites

Name	Mean Distance from Saturn (miles)	Angular Distance at Elongation	Diameter (miles)	Orbital Period			Mean Mag.
Janus	98,000	26″	250?		18^h		13?
Mimas	113,300	30	350		22	37^m	12·1
Enceladus	148,700	38	450	1^d	8	53	11·8
Tethys	183,200	48	750	1	21	18	10·3
Dione	234,600	1′	900	2	17	41	10·4
Rhea	327,600	$1\frac{1}{2}$	1,100	4	12	25	9·8
Titan	759,500	$3\frac{1}{4}$	3,000	15	22	41	8·4
Hyperion	920,100	4	200	21	6	38	13·0
Iapetus	2,213,200	$9\frac{1}{2}$	1,000	79	7	56	9–12
Phoebe	8,053,400	35	100	$550\frac{1}{2}$			16·5

(The diameters of the smaller satellites are most uncertain.)

With the exception of the two outer satellites, all the moons revolve almost exactly in the plane of the equator and the rings. This means that when we have an equatorial view, as in 1966, the moons are strung out in a line—as with Jupiter's family—while at other times they are distributed much more irregularly. When the rings are almost edge-on, a large telescope will show the satellites apparently threading their way along the sliver of light, like pearls on a wire: a sight that delighted William Herschel when he viewed the planet in August and September, 1789, with his immense new 48-inch reflector. It was on these occasions that he discovered two inner satellites, Mimas and Enceladus. Mimas is extremely hard to see, not simply because it is faint, but because it is always very near the planet. At its greatest elongations, it has been glimpsed with a 10-inch refractor, but this is an exceptional feat, and many first-class observers have failed with apertures of less than 18 inches. It is actually slightly brighter than Enceladus, but the latter appears more distinct because it is further from the planet, and has been detected with a 6-inch reflector, although an unpracticed eye will naturally require greater optical assistance.

Titan, which is probably the largest satellite in the solar system, although some authorities consider Ganymede to be larger, is so bright that it can be seen with a very small telescope; it was first recognised as a satellite by Huygens in 1655, although there is a curious legend that Sir Christopher Wren, whom one associates more with cathedrals than observatories, saw it independently at the same time. The other bright four (Tethys, Dione, Rhea, and Iapetus) were all discovered by Cassini; Hyperion was found in 1848, and Phoebe was discovered photographically in 1898. The rough order of visibility is: Titan, Rhea, Tethys, Dione, Hyperion, Enceladus, Mimas, Phoebe; Iapetus varies so in brightness that it cannot be included in a list. Rhea is usually visible with a 3-inch, while a 4-inch should pick up Tethys and Dione; Hyperion requires at least a 6-inch refractor. However, so much depends on the state of the air, the condition of the instrument, the nearness of the satellite to Saturn, the presentation of the rings (since when they are open, the glare around the planet is increased), and the observer's keenness of vision, that it is misleading to be dogmatic. Just one of many examples of how eyes differ is revealed in this account by the Reverend T. E. Espin, a well-known amateur observer of past years, of an observing session with the author of the classic *Celestial Objects for Common Telescopes*:

A curious instance of difference of vision was well illustrated one superb evening, when Mr. Webb and the writer were observing Saturn with the 9½-inch reflector at Hardwick. Mr. Webb saw distinctly the division in the outer ring [Encke's division] which the writer could not see a trace of, while the writer picked up a faint point of light, which afterwards turned out to be Enceladus, which Mr. Webb could not see.

Iapetus is exceptional in this family of satellites, because it varies greatly in brightness. When near its eastern elongation, it is about as difficult to see as Enceladus, but at western elongation it is actually brighter than Rhea, and can easily be seen in a 3-inch. The explanation seems to be that it keeps the same face toward Saturn, and that opposite hemispheres differ markedly in reflecting power.

Neither are the other moons of constant magnitude. Rhea has been found to vary by about half a magnitude, and Titan too may show slight fluctuations. Estimates are extremely difficult to make, since they appear fainter when near the planet and so suffer an apparent variation on top of the real one; even so, it is a problem that can be tackled with modest equipment.

A new innermost satellite, Janus, discovered in December, 1966, by A. Dollfus, of the Paris Observatory, seems likely to be moving in the same plane as the other moons, and is so close to the rings that it will be far harder to see than Mimas. It is significant that it was discovered on photographs taken when the rings' dark side was turned towards the earth, thus reducing the glare around the planet.

14

The Outer Planets: Uranus, Neptune, and Pluto

The three remotest planets were all discovered telescopically. Uranus was found more or less accidentally by William Herschel in 1781; and Neptune and Pluto were tracked down in 1846 and 1930, their existence being established by their gravitational pulling on Uranus. Uranus and Neptune are both built on the "giant planet" pattern, although they are considerably smaller than Jupiter and Saturn; but they are too far away to show much of a disk, even in a large telescope, and amateur study of their surface markings is out of the question.

Uranus

Uranus is far bigger than the earth, with a diameter of 29,000 miles, and its freezing gas-clouds seem to reflect light well. But, at 1,775 million miles from the sun, it is so far away that it appears very dim. The naked eye can follow its ambling along the ecliptic without a telescope at all, but the ancient astronomers can hardly be blamed for not noticing it. At the time of writing (1966) it lies in the southeastern part of Leo, but it will soon pass into Virgo. The movement is very slow, since it takes 84 years for Uranus to circle the sky once.

When its position is known, Uranus can be picked up telescopically as a bright, bluish "star"; careful attention reveals a disk with a power as low as × 40, and anything higher expands it very obviously. However, using a powerful eyepiece also dims the planet so seriously that no detail can be seen. This explains why a large telescope that collects plenty of light is necessary for examination. The only well-established feature of the planet is a bright equatorial zone, with somewhat dusky poles, and there is little chance of anyone adding to our knowledge of its surface features without using a gigantic telescope.

On the other hand, interesting variations seem to occur in its magnitude, and amateurs have been tackling the problem on and off for the past seventy years. The first task is to identify what we might call "natural" effects. Thus, the planet will appear brighter at opposition than near conjunction (a variation of about 0·4 of a magnitude); it will appear brighter when at perihelion than at aphelion (about 0·2 of a magnitude); while the brightness also fluctuates in a period corresponding to its rotation time of 10¾ hours, due to the passage of lighter and darker features across the disk (about 0·1 of a magnitude). We have also to consider the curious tilt of the axis—98°. This means that we sometimes see the pole of the planet in the center of the disk, as happened in 1943, whereas in 1965 the planet presented the normal equatorial view. Since Uranus is appreciably flattened at the poles, its disk shows a slightly larger area when pole-on, an increase that might be expected to augment the magnitude by about 0·3. Clearly, these effects must be weeded out; but even so, discrepancies seem to remain. A German authority, W. Becker of Münster, claimed in 1933 to have discovered a roughly eight-year period extending over about 0·3 of a magnitude, although this was denied by Kuiper and D. L. Harris in 1961. Nevertheless, B.A.A. members investigated the brightness of Uranus between 1952 and 1955, and discovered that it was appreciably brighter than the "official" magnitude of 5·8. This work, done with the simplest of equipment, revised the magnitude of Uranus to about 5·5.

Fluctuations probably do occur, since the outbreak of bright or dark features will affect the reflectivity, and regular estimates of the brightness would be of value. The method is the same as that described for variable stars (in Chap. 20), where the planet's brightness is compared with that of stars of known magnitude, known as *comparison stars*. In the case of variable stars, the comparison objects are always the same; but Uranus is on the move all the time, so fresh comparison stars must be found and their magnitudes obtained from a reliable catalogue. A very low power must be used, so that Uranus will look like a star rather than a disk, and it will probably be found that binoculars are of far more service than a regular astronomical telescope. It is hopeless to expect quick results, but at least there is nothing complex about the method or equipment.

Uranus has five satellites. The two inner ones, Ariel and Umbriel, are so close to the disk that they are lost in the glare, and it takes a very large telescope to show them. The next two, Titania and Oberon, both of about the 14th magnitude, have been glimpsed with a 6-inch refractor when Uranus itself was hidden by a field bar; but most observers would do well to catch them with a 12-inch. The fifth moon, Miranda, is so close and faint that it has never been seen visually, although it can be photographed.

Neptune

Found in 1846 by Johann Galle, after predictions issued independently by two mathematicians, J. C. Adams and U. Le Verrier, Neptune is slightly smaller than Uranus, and a thousand million miles farther away from the sun. It can be seen as a "star" of about magnitude 7·7 with a pair of binoculars. At the time of writing (1966), it lies in the constellation Libra, and since its orbital period is 165 years it seems to move across the sky at only half the speed of Uranus. The B.A.A. *Handbook* publishes annual charts showing the positions of Uranus and Neptune.

Neptune's somewhat greenish disk can just be distinguished with a 4-inch refractor, and its satellite Triton, which is probably a little smaller than Saturn's Titan, is somewhat easier to see than the outer satellites of Uranus. The other moon, Nereid, appears very minute. It may be that Neptune shows magnitude fluctuations of the same kind as Uranus; the matter has not been fully investigated, and it may provide a promising field of investigation.

Pluto

Pluto was found from the Lowell Observatory, Flagstaff, by Clyde Tombaugh in 1930, after independent calculations had been made by Lowell himself and W. H. Pickering. It then lay in Gemini, and so slowly does it move across the sky that even now it has only reached Leo, two "doors" along the zodiac.

It is of no interest to the amateur, since a telescope of about 10 inches aperture is needed to show it at all, and it simply looks like a faint star. However, it is satisfying to glimpse the point of light that marks this frozen, almost forgotten world.

15

The Minor Planets

The small, rocky bodies circling more or less between the orbits of Mars and Jupiter are often referred to as *asteroids*, a word meaning "starlike," although, like all the other members of the sun's family, they shine by its reflected light. But the term is reasonable enough, for only the greatest telescopes can show even the largest and nearest minor planets as definite disks, and the amateur's task of identification might appear hopeless. Luckily, there is a very easy way of distinguishing one from the other, for the stars have retained the same patterns in the sky for thousands of years, whereas an asteroid moves appreciably from night to night.

All the planets, in their orbital movement around the sun, appear from the earth to creep along the zodiac. When Mars, for instance, passes close to a naked-eye star, its movement over the course of a day can be detectable without optical aid. Jupiter, more remote and therefore slower-moving, takes longer to reveal its drift, since it takes 12 years to circle the zodiac, whereas Saturn takes 29½ and the outer planets even longer. Nevertheless, the earliest astronomers noticed this movement and termed them "planets," or "wanderers." So, to identify an asteroid once its approximate position is known, the observer simply draws the star field and reexamines it a couple of nights later. One of the "stars" will have shifted slightly, proving its planetary nature.

Discovery of the asteroids

This process is all very well once it is known which region of the sky contains the asteroid; but the original asteroid-hunters, affectionately known at the time as the "celestial police," were faced with an immense task. In the early nineteenth century, when interest was at its height, there were no accurate maps of the fainter stars; each observer had to plot and "patrol" his own allotted fields along the zodiac, watching for any suspicious shifting of a "star." The vagaries of weather and moonlight made this process alone difficult enough; but the detection of a wanderer was only the beginning. Its movement then had to be measured so that an orbit could be worked out, and it had to be done immediately and accurately, for the tiny body could easily be lost again among the myriads of stars. But the job was done, and done well. By 1847, eight asteroids were known; by 1891, 323. After that, photography provided a quicker, more convenient way of recording faint stars, and the discoveries snowballed into the thousands.

One asteroid, Vesta, sometimes reaches magnitude 5½ and is readily visible with the naked eye. Another, Pallas, can reach magnitude 6·3 at a favorable opposition. Both have diameters of between 250 and 300 miles. The largest asteroid, Ceres, first to be discovered, is about 480 miles across but can never exceed the 7th magnitude, which suggests that it is composed of rather darker substance than the highly reflective Vesta. Altogether, about forty asteroids can exceed magnitude 9·0 at opposition, and are therefore visible with 2-inch binoculars, while hundreds are brighter than the limiting magnitude of a 3-inch refractor, which usually lies somewhere between the 10th and 11th magnitudes.

Location and plotting

Since the B.A.A. *Handbook* and *Astronomical Ephemeris* give ephemerides for the brighter minor planets visible during each year, it may sound a simple matter to find them. If the observer is lucky enough to possess a copy of the *Atlas Elipticalis*, or Webb's *Star Atlas*, or one of the other maps showing stars as faint as the 9th magnitude, the asteroid's position can be plotted directly, and the star field compared with the low-power telescopic view. If the asteroid is of the 7th or 8th magnitude, it should immediately be obvious as an extra "star" shining where none is marked in the chart.

One precaution is necessary when adopting this line of attack. The stars' positions, in terms of right ascension and declination, are changing steadily as the years pass, and it is necessary to adjust the asteroid's published position to correspond with the epoch of the chart. This can be done by using the precessional table in Appendix VI. If, for instance, an asteroid's position was being plotted in 1965, it would have been necessary to subtract the precessional difference for 110 years to fit it accurately into the coordinates of the *Atlas Elipticalis*, drawn up for the year 1855.

Most amateurs, however, depend on *Norton's*, which shows stars down to the 6th magnitude only. In this case, a good deal more work is involved, but the challenge is greater and the final identification more satisfying. The method here is to plot the minor planet's position on the atlas, and to draw a map of all the telescopic stars visible within an area of perhaps two degrees square around the critical position. We can be reasonably sure that one of these "stars" is, in fact, the minor planet; but there is no direct way of identifying it except by its motion. On the following night, therefore, either the field is redrawn, or the chart is compared with the telescopic view to see if the visitor has betrayed itself by shifting its position. This procedure is not as easy as it sounds, for a slight inaccuracy in the original map may conceal the motion, or the planet may lie outside the region plotted.

Even when the asteroid is found, there is no guarantee that it will remain within reach. A sequence of cloudy nights can mask its motion into a new and unknown region of the sky, so that fresh charting is necessary before it can be identified again. But there is always the challenge of following it over a long period, watching it brighten as it approaches opposition and dim again as it swings away from the earth and toward conjunction.

It must be admitted that study of the minor planets is hardly a profitable branch of amateur astronomy. Physical observation of their surfaces is clearly out of the question; even Ceres shows only the minutest disk when viewed with the largest telescopes in the world. Moreover, study of their color and of their light variation, which can be taken as evidence of rotation, has been undertaken by professional astronomers using more accurate equipment than the amateur usually commands; Appendix V lists some details of the more important minor planets. But, because of the rather large eccentricities of many of the orbits, we sometimes find a normally dim and inaccessible asteroid approaching the earth sufficiently close to be visible with modest equipment. Under these conditions useful observations of magnitude and light variation can be made. The technique, comparing their brightness with that of nearby stars whose magnitudes are known, is the same as that used in variable star work (see Chap. 20). It must be remembered, however, that these little planets are moving across the sky all the time, so the star field is changing and fresh comparison stars must be found.

The greatest chance for an amateur to make a really important contribution comes when a minor planet passes in front of a star. These occultations are, however, excessively rare. The B.A.A. *Handbook* publishes predictions for "appulses," or close approaches to stars; but the diameters of even the larger planets are so small that the chances of a perfect line-up are remote. There is, nevertheless, an air of excitement about awaiting a very close approach, since our knowledge of their motions is not perfect, and an error of even a second of arc in the ephemeris may make all the difference between a hit and a miss. Neither must we forget the parallactic effect, minute but still present, which could mean that an observer in, say, Peru sees an actual occultation, whereas another in Canada records a near-miss. If an occultation ever occurs, the time during which the star is invisible affords a direct clue to the diameter of the minor planet concerned.

16

Lunar and Planetary Photography

Visual observation is by far the most potent way of detecting lunar and planetary detail. A study of some of the finest telescopic photographs ever taken of the moon—with, for instance, the 40-inch Yerkes refractor or the 100-inch Mount Wilson reflector—will reveal little detail that is beyond the range of a small or moderate telescope. On the other hand, if these giant instruments were used visually they would far outstrip smaller apertures.

Why is this so? The explanation lies neither in the telescope nor in the photographic plate, but in the atmosphere. To take a large-scale photograph of the moon or a bright planet requires an exposure of appreciable duration—perhaps one or two seconds—and the chances of the air being perfectly still throughout this interval are very small. Almost inevitably, the image will give a tremor or two. This is enough to blur the photograph, and lose the finest details. On the other hand, the eye reacts swiftly enough to grasp the moments of best seeing and to remember the most delicate features that are obliterated until the air steadies itself again.

A really fast film, requiring an exposure of only a fraction of a second, might solve the problem. Such films are available today, but unfortunately their great speed introduces a fresh drawback. The sensitive emulsion consists of millions of tiny "grains," and the faster the film is, the coarser these grains must be. So, if a very fast emulsion is used, the graininess destroys the definition as efficiently as the turbulent atmosphere.

If this were all, there would be little point in investigating the matter further. But photography possesses an advantage over the eye in another way: it is *impersonal*. It is unaffected by the factors that influence the observer's vision, and it is free from preconception. If a photograph of the moon or a planet shows far less detail than a visual observation made through the same telescope, it does at least reveal the outlines with unimpeachable accuracy. This is especially valuable in the case of lunar work. An instance was cited recently in the *Journal* of the British Astronomical Association, in which a photograph taken by an amateur of the region around the crater Caramuel—which is so near the northeast limb that it can be studied only on rare occasions—indicated considerable inaccuracies in the official chart being compiled by the U.S. Air Force. Although it shows no more than can be seen with a 3-inch telescope, the correctness of the general outlines and positions of the craters is above suspicion, and it can be used as a basis for an accurate chart of the area.

Compared with lunar work, photography of the planets can be interesting, but it is of little use with any instrument of less than 12 inches aperture. Only two, Venus and Jupiter, show reasonably large disks, and Venus is featureless in ordinary white light, although ultraviolet photographs have been taken with more success. The more prominent belts of Jupiter can be recorded with a 6-inch reflector, but without a large aperture there is no hope of photographing fine detail. The amateur who wants his photographs to be of real value will find the moon the most encouraging subject.

Telescope and mounting

The earth's rotation makes every celestial object appear to circuit the sky once in 23 hours 56 minutes—the sidereal day. The actual distance each object has to travel depends on its declination; a star near the north or south celestial pole (+ or −90°) moves in a small circle right around the

Caramuel. *The crater Caramuel, which is situated on the averted hemisphere. Only at rare instances of extreme eastern libration, as occurred when this photograph was taken, can the crater be seen even reasonably well. Taken with 6-inch reflector at f/29, 1/5 sec., Ilford Zenith plate, on October 20, 1964. (H. R. Hatfield.)*

pole, whereas an object near the celestial equator ($0°$) has to travel right around the sky, and so moves much faster—at around $15°$ per hour. Since the moon and planets always lie fairly near the equator, there clearly must be some means of "freezing" this motion if the photograph is not to be hopelessly blurred.

The moon's apparent diameter is about $\frac{1}{2}°$, so it advances by this amount in two minutes. If it appears to move across its own diameter in two minutes, and its diameter is 2,163 miles, then $2163/120$ gives 18 miles per second, its rate of drift. So, if we wish to record fine detail only two or three miles across, which is perfectly possible with a 6-inch reflector, the exposure with a stationary telescope must not be longer than about 1/10th of a second. So short an exposure time demands a very fast film, and therefore coarse, obtrusive grain. Clearly, then, the telescope must be mounted equatorially, with some means of guiding it during the exposure so that the image remains stationary. Although crude "snapshots" can be taken through an altazimuth instrument, an equatorial is essential for serious work.

One of the secrets of successful lunar photography is to keep the exposure as short as possible. As long as the shutter is open, the bad influences of atmospheric turbulence and inaccurate guiding are at work. If the telescope has a smooth drive to the polar axis, guiding errors should be negligible during an exposure of a few seconds, but the image can still be wrecked by a sudden burst of bad seeing. The atmosphere is very rarely perfectly steady, even for a second, and the aim must be to expose the plate during one of these favored intervals. The advantage of, say, a 10-inch reflector over a 6-inch is less a matter of improved resolving power than of increased light-gathering power. The larger instrument, gathering three times as much light, allows the exposure time to be cut to a third, with better chances of enjoying a period of good seeing.

When it comes to visual observation of the moon, the question of light-gathering power is probably less important than that of definition and resolving power, which means that a 3- or 4-inch refractor can be as effective as a 6-inch reflector. But for photographic work, the latter is far superior. Not only does it give a brighter image; the mirror is also perfectly free from traces of color. A yellow filter placed just in front of the field lens of the eyepiece is necessary for photographic work with a refractor, since the object glass does not correctly focus the blue rays; and because this absorbs some of the light, the disadvantage is even more marked.

The camera

Excellent lunar photographs can be taken with an ordinary 35mm camera, or even a simple box camera, and this is the best way of beginning.

Central region of the moon. *A photograph of the region from the cleft of Hyginus (lower) to Arzachel (top right). On the original negative, which was taken with a 6-inch reflector, the lunar image was 1½ inches across. The photograph was taken by Cmdr. H. Hatfield, R.N., who made the telescope and mirror himself.*

This method has the advantage of requiring no special accessories, apart from some sort of bracket to hold the camera firmly in place at the end of the drawtube; and a few trial exposures will teach far more than pages of notes.

This technique employs an eyepiece as well as the camera lens to focus the image onto the sensitive emulsion, and the principle is simple enough. When using a telescope for visual purposes, the eye is kept relaxed (i.e., focused on infinity). It follows from this that if the eyepiece is adjusted so that the view is sharp, and the camera lens is focused for infinity, the image will be in focus on the film.

Unfortunately, not all eyes can focus on infinity; if the observer is nearsighted and normally wears glasses, his "relaxed" distance may be just a few feet. One way of overcoming this and securing critical definition is, first of all, to take a small hand telescope, or a pair of binoculars, and to focus on a star. Then look through the main instrument via the telescope and adjust the eyepiece accordingly. This means, incidentally, that we are multiplying the nominal power by the magnification of the second telescope, a product that may come to about × 1,000 and that should cure the most ardent magnification enthusiast! Of course, if the camera has reflex focusing, where the image formed by the lens is examined on a screen or through a special viewfinder, the adjustment of the eyepiece can be carried out directly.

The size of the image on the film depends on the magnification of the telescope, and also on the focal length of the camera lens. With the usual type of miniature camera, a magnification of × 100 will give an image about $2\frac{1}{2}$ inches across, so that only a portion of the lunar surface can be included at any one time—in any case, the marginal aberrations of the eyepiece will preclude sharp definition over the whole area. Unless a reflex camera is used, it is necessary to align the finder very accurately so that the telescope can be pointed to the region to be photographed.

Image size, film, exposure

All these factors are closely related, and most of the preliminary work will be concerned with finding the best compromise. Using any given telescope, a large image reveals more detail than a small one, but it also requires a longer exposure—if the moon is twice the diameter, the intensity is reduced to a quarter (ratio of areas) and the exposure must be four times as long. A slow, fine-grain film also shows finer detail, but it too requires a longer exposure. Either extreme is bad, and a middle course must be found. Some amateurs have been experimenting with Polaroid film, which is extremely fast, has very fine grain, and can be developed within seconds. It is, however, much more expensive than ordinary film.

Film emulsions vary enormously, from the slow and very fine-grain type like Kodak's Panatomic-X, through the middle range, such as Ilford's FP3, or KB34, manufactured by Adox, to the fast, rather coarse emulsions like Ilford's HPS or Kodak's Royal Pan. Generally speaking, superfast films do not pay off in terms of image quality; with small or moderate apertures the choice lies between a 3- or 4-inch image on medium-speed film, or an even smaller image on fine-grain stock. Both these methods will require about the same exposure time, probably somewhere between $\frac{1}{2}$ and 2 seconds for a 6-inch reflector, depending on the phase and other conditions, so that the ultimate result depends upon both the focusing and guiding, and the darkroom technique. Developing and printing is an enormous field on its own, and cannot be detailed here. Obviously, a fine-grain developer must be used if the image is to hold all its original details, and Kodak's Promicrol has been found to give good results.

Trial and error will soon show that different parts of the moon, and different phases, require their own exposure. The full moon reflects fully four times as much light as the quarters, while the crescent is dimmer yet. Moreover, the part of the surface under a high illumination is much brighter than the terminator region, where the sunlight is oblique. This is not so noticeable visually, but it manifests itself very obviously in a photograph, where the extreme edge of the terminator may be almost invisible. The only way of getting over this disparity of brightness is to "dodge" the final print, shading the terminator during enlargement so that it appears as bright as the rest of the surface. It is, incidentally, very difficult to do this without leaving an obtrusive line, so once again practice pays dividends.

Venus and Jupiter can be photographed in the same manner. Fortunately, their disks are considerably brighter, area for area, than the moon's surface (although the moon naturally sends us far more *total* light), so a higher magnifying power can be used. Alternatively, one can settle for film of finer grain. There should be no great difficulty in recording the phase of Venus or the equatorial belts of Jupiter, though such photographs are of little real use.

The guiding of the telescope plays a large part in the success of the photograph. If the telescope has a smooth automatic drive, there should be no great problem; provided the gears mesh smoothly, the tube should turn without jarring. Hand-guiding, where the movement has to be supplied manually, raises greater problems, but dexterity comes with experience. It is in any case an excellent idea to attach a powerful guiding telescope to the tube. This need not be of good optical quality, but it must be fitted with a high-power eyepiece bearing cross wires, so that any displacement of the image becomes obvious. Another advantage of such an auxiliary is that the exposure can be delayed until a patch of good seeing presents itself, thereby saving otherwise wasted film.

Vibration is another problem. No observer needs to be told that an

Ptolemaeus, the central region of the moon. *Seen soon after first quarter. Ptolemaeus is at bottom right; to the south is Alphonsus, with a conspicuous dark patch inside its eastern wall. The Straight Wall is visible as a dark line in the upper right-hand part of the picture. Photographed with a 12-inch reflector at f/30, 1 sec., Ilford G-30 plate, on May 28, 1966. (H. R. Hatfield.)*

astronomical telescope is a wonderful seismic lever, and with most mountings the slightest contact results in a minute tremor. Operating the camera shutter can give rise to serious vibration and is probably responsible for much of the lack of sharpness in amateur photographs. The best answer is to dispense with the camera mechanism and to use some other way of effecting the exposure. A very crude method that in practice works surprisingly well is to use a hand-held cardboard "shutter" over the mouth of the tube. The camera is set on the time, or T, position with the cardboard shutter in place so that no light reaches the objective. The shutter is then eased slightly away from the rim of the tube, and a few moments are allowed to elapse so that all vibration is stilled. The cardboard is then whisked away and back again, and finally the camera shutter is closed. The exposure can be judged quite easily to within about half a second. If the camera has only a "B" setting, the trigger can be held open with a small rubber band. Needless to say, a solid tube is necessary if a reflecting telescope is being used, so that no stray light can make its way into the drawtube. Operating the slow-motion handle with one hand, working the shutter with the other, and tracking through the guiding telescope at the same time may sound a hazardous business—but it can be done.

The first results may not be perfect, but they will probably be much better than expected; it is quite a thrill to find even a few craters showing on the negative when one realizes how little detail can be seen with the naked eye. Perseverance is necessary, and, after a few trials, it is a good idea, to decide on a certain combination of film and developer and to keep to it, concentrating thereafter on the technique of actually taking the photograph. Different eyepieces, image sizes, and exposures should be tried until photographs can be taken with little fuss and with fairly predictable results. Once this stage is reached, they can be incorporated into the observing program instead of serving as an end in themselves.

A lunar camera

While surprisingly good results can be attained with the simple "attached camera" method, a special camera is needed to take the best possible photographs. Plates are preferable to film, partly because they can be developed individually, and also because they are perfectly flat and allow for more critical focusing. For the finest definition, the camera lens itself should be dispensed with; an eyepiece or a Barlow lens will serve to form the image. Not only does the camera lens interfere with the definition, but it also absorbs a certain amount of light and necessitates a slightly longer exposure.

The camera itself can be built along the lines of the solar camera described in Chapter 7. Focusing is performed through a clear patch in the ground-glass screen, while a very simple manual shutter can be made to leave the plate ready for exposure by the hand-held shutter. The enlarging eyepiece must, of course, be achromatic. An orthoscopic gives good results, but a Barlow lens is the best, since it gives a "flatter" image and hence provides sharp definition over a wider area.

As an example of what can be done with simple means, the photograph of the Hipparchus-Ptolemaeus region of the lunar surface was made with a 12-inch reflector. An Ilford G-30 plate was used, with a 1-second exposure. The image was $1\frac{1}{2}$ inches across and formed by a Barlow lens, and the plate was developed in Promicrol; the telescope mirror, mounting, and clock-drive were all homemade. The result speaks for itself, since the smallest craters visible are only about $2\frac{1}{4}$ miles across.

One precaution needs to be taken when photographing the moon: because of its orbital motion around the earth, it has an appreciable drift of its own along the ecliptic, moving the distance of its own diameter in an easterly direction in the space of about an hour. This means that its diurnal

Northeastern limb. *A view near the crater Plato. Photographed with a 6-inch reflector at f/29, 1/5 sec., on Kodak 0–250 plate, on October 9, 1965. (H. R. Hatfield.)*

westerly motion is slightly less than that of the stars and planets; and, while the difference is small, the drive speed must be adjusted to the lunar rate if the best results are to be obtained. Roughly speaking, the moon appears to move at about 18 miles per second from east to west, due to the earth's rotation, and about half a mile per second in a roughly easterly direction, due to motion along its own orbit.

Other investigations can also be tried, such as photography through filters; while the earthlit night hemisphere affords an interesting challenge. A long exposure is required on account of its dimness, and so the bright crescent will be badly overexposed, but this can be compensated to some extent when printing the photograph. A great deal of detail can sometimes be made out, such as the maria and the light and dark craters. Lunar eclipses, too, can provide an interesting series of photographs. In short, telescopic photography constitutes a method of observation that can be both fascinating and useful.

17

Comets and Comet-hunting

A bright comet is one of the finest of all natural phenomena. Like a total eclipse of the sun, it is as impressive to the layman as to the fully trained astronomer. No scientific knowledge is required to appreciate the spectacle of a milky tail stretched across the sky, and it is perhaps for this reason that more misconception surrounds the subject of comets than any other branch of astronomy.

A comet is a mass of gas, dust, and icy particles, that revolves, like a planet, under the sun's gravitational influence. There is, however, one important difference: its orbit is very eccentric, so that whereas at perihelion it may be only a few million miles away from the sun, at aphelion it recedes far out into the depths of interplanetary space. Only around the time of perihelion do comets glow brightly; throughout the rest of their orbits, almost all the known specimens are so faint that no telescope can pick them up, although mathematicians can calculate approximately where they are.

The size of the cloud composing a comet may be anything from a few hundred thousand miles across to a million or more, but in terms of actual mass there is less matter in the greatest comet than in a small asteroid. The *nucleus*, which is the central collection of solid particles, is rarely more than a few miles across, and the surrounding aura of gas and dust is inconceivably tenuous. On several occasions during recorded history, the earth has passed through these shadowy regions with no noticeable effect; although a collision with the nucleus itself might have serious consequences, the chances of such an encounter are extremely small. For all their fire and fury, comets are ethereal bodies.

193

Life cycle and movements

A comet usually brightens up into telescopic visibility at about the distance of Mars. If it is a known body, certain observatories that specialize in this work (e.g., the United States Naval Observatory, Flagstaff station) will be carefully photographing the region of the sky where it is expected to appear, until finally a tiny smudge of light signals the return. Although these predictions, known as ephemerides, are usually remarkably accurate, there are always slight errors, or *residuals*. One of the first tasks of the astronomer is to measure accurately its position relative to the stars, so that the ephemeris can be corrected. At the same time, a circular is issued announcing the recovery. The clearinghouse for cometary information is Harvard Observatory, Oak Ridge, Mass., which issues Announcement Cards; and the British Astronomical Association issues circulars to its members. Ephemerides are listed annually in the B.A.A. *Handbook*, and notes on current returns are included in the monthly *Sky & Telescope*.

The comet continues to brighten as it approaches the sun. This occurs partly because of the increased illumination, but also because, as the temperature rises, the material composing the head of the comet is vaporized and starts to glow, so that it emits light as well as shining by reflected sunlight. The fuzzy *coma*, the matter surrounding the nucleus, begins to expand, while the force of the atomic particles that are flying away from the sun—known as the *solar wind*—brushes some of the coma backwards to form the *tail*. Generally speaking, the closer the comet approaches to the sun, the longer and more spectacular the tail becomes; the coma and nucleus also glow more brightly. Greatest brilliance is reached at perihelion, but at this time the comet is often so close to the sun in the sky that it is quite invisible; so it is best observed just before and after perihelion, when it is still bright but can be seen against a dark sky.

It must not be thought that all comets reach the "sword-in-the-sky" stage. Relatively few do, but these are the ones likely to be acclaimed in the popular press. Of the six or eight comets that are observed every year (which includes new ones discovered as well as known ones recovered), by far the greater number are telescopic objects, approaching the sun no closer than about a hundred million miles, and perhaps not even growing a tail. About one a year brightens sufficiently to be visible with the unaided eye from some part of the world; once every five years or so, the sun is visited by a comet bright enough to attract general attention; and perhaps five really brilliant ones may be seen in a century. The last really spectacular comet appeared as long ago as 1910, in the same year as the less brilliant but rightly famous Halley's comet made its periodical return. The comet discovered in September, 1965, seemed likely to put up a splendid show, but it passed so close to the sun that it probably disintegrated, and it faded out soon after its perihelion passage.

More than 500 comets, bright and faint, have been discovered since the invention of the telescope. There are records of naked-eye sightings going back to ancient times, so they are clearly plentiful; the solar system probably contains hundreds of thousands. Every year, two or three new ones are discovered (no fewer than 11 were found in 1948), and many faint ones doubtless slip past perihelion unseen. Comets do not keep to the zodiac as do the planets, since their orbits can lie in any plane; because there is no way of telling just where a new comet is likely to appear, comet-hunters need both immense perseverance and luck. It is therefore not surprising that a good proportion of discoveries have been made by a line of dedicated amateurs.

The popular idea of comets "flashing across the sky" is wildly mistaken. When they are far away from the sun they seem to move among the stars at planetary speed; even when they are near perihelion, and therefore moving fastest, they stay in the same region of the sky from night to night. Halley's comet, at its last return, was visible with the naked eye for about two months, and was followed telescopically from September, 1909, until April, 1911. The great comet of 1882 was a naked-eye object for five months and could actually be seen in broad daylight when it was only a few degrees away from the sun. Of course, few comets are as brazen as these, but even the less spectacular examples, such as the two naked-eye comets of April and August, 1957, could be followed with a small telescope for several weeks.

Known comets are generally sighted when they are far away from the sun and several months from perihelion; but new discoveries are usually made when they are close to the sun and so appear much brighter. When a new comet is found and its movement investigated, its image can often be made out on routine sky photographs taken several weeks previously by professional observatories. It would be far too great a task to examine every photograph for such tiny features; for this reason, many new comets slip through the initial net and avoid discovery until they are quite bright. The second of the two conspicuous comets of 1957 was discovered when it was a naked-eye object, and many have been visible with binoculars when first picked up.

Comet-hunters

Historical literature contains many references to bright comets. Halley's comet, which returns to the sun every 76 years, has been periodically recorded, back to 239 B.C., and other bright comets have appeared from time to time. Naturally, the recent records are more complete, especially since the invention of the telescope; indeed, the age of modern observation can be taken as dating from 1758, the year in which it was proved that comets revolve around the sun, and are therefore true members of the solar system.

This was a posthumous triumph for Edmund Halley, the British Astronomer Royal who in September, 1682, observed a bright comet and carefully tracked its path across the sky. Its general similarity to the comets of 1531 and 1607 made him suspect that they were actually the same body; accordingly, he predicted a return for 1758, expressing the hope that others would search for it. Halley died in 1742, but in 1758 his hope was fulfilled: Charles Messier, the French "ferret of comets," and Johann Palitzsch, an amateur astronomer living near Dresden, both swept the sky at the appointed time, Palitzsch first spotting it on Christmas night, 1758. This was a sensational achievement, for it not only proved the nature of a comet's movements, but also established the telescope as a powerful weapon of discovery. The comet was named after Halley not because he discovered it, which is the usual method of nomenclature, but because of his remarkable prediction.

Palitzsch made no further discoveries, but Messier, no doubt both inflamed by his own failure and inspired by his rival's success, undertook regular comet-hunting with a 2-inch refractor, using a power of only × 5 and therefore having a very wide field of view. By his death in 1817 he had discovered 13 comets in the period 1759–1801; but he was closely challenged by the French observer Pierre Méchain, who discovered 10 between 1781 and 1802, while five were found between 1786 and 1797 by Caroline Herschel, William Herschel's sister and assistant. Her brother had made her a special "comet-sweeper"—a 4-inch Newtonian reflector of 27 inches focal length, with a magnification of × 20 and a field of just over 2°—with which she made her discoveries.

However, of all these comets, not one is likely to return to the sun's vicinity for many generations; their orbits are so extensive, probably reaching out to Pluto and farther, that one course will take hundreds or even thousands of years. The majority of comets, including all the really brilliant ones, belong to this "once-only" class, which explains why a new one may appear unannounced at any time.

Another notable comet-astronomer of the time was the German physician Heinrich Olbers, who for forty years observed and swept the sky for comets from his house in Bremen; he found one with a period of 73 years, which last returned in 1956. He also used his considerable mathematical talents to devise a system of orbit computation known as *Olbers' method.* This period also saw the king of comet-hunters, Jean Louis Pons, of Marseille, at work. He began his career as doorkeeper at the local observatory, receiving casual instruction from the director, but he discovered 27 comets between 1801 and 1827—a record for a single observer. One of these, discovered in 1812, returns to the sun every 72 years. In 1884, at its next return, it was found quite independently by the well-known American observer W. R. Brooks, and is now known as Comet Pons-Brooks. Brooks himself, observing from near New York, discovered 22 comets between 1883 and 1911, and his contemporary, E. E. Barnard, who worked at the Lick and Yerkes observatories and spent his spare time observing and photographing the night sky, found 16 between 1881 and 1892.

Brooks and Barnard were both associated with large observatories, and it might be argued that they had equipment superior to that of most amateurs, and so had a better chance of success; but no matter what the equipment, it must be used with patience and enthusiasm. As we have noted, many comets are quite bright at discovery, and it does not require a large telescope to show them. Indeed, a small and maneuverable instrument is more or less essential, both from the point of view of easy manipulation and because of the wide field. Great telescopes have very restricted fields of view, and an aperture of between about 4 and 10 inches is best for cometary work.

Amateur achievements have declined in recent years, but there is little doubt that this is largely due to lack of effort. The great planetary and meteor observer W. F. Denning used to hunt for comets with his 10-inch reflector when he had no other observing program on hand, and he discovered five in thirteen years. Anyone showing similar persistence today might well be equally successful. Between 1925 and 1939 the American amateur Louis Peltier discovered five comets with his 5-inch short-focus refractor; but nowadays the initiative seems to have moved southward, and most new comets are being reported by observers in South America and Japan. One of Japan's keenest comet-hunters is Kaoru Ikeya, who was nineteen when he found his first comet in 1963, after 109 negative nights.

Since Denning's time there was almost no systematic work in the British Isles until G. E. D. Alcock began his comet-sweeps in 1953, using high-power binoculars. His discovery of two comets in August, 1959, has acted as a local stimulus, and about half a dozen British amateurs are known to be making regular sweeps. In 1960, M. P. Candy discovered a bright comet in the constellation Cepheus, well away from the sun, and Alcock brought his total up to four with discoveries in 1963 and 1965.

Nomenclature and ephemerides

When a comet is first sighted, whether it be new or periodic, it is given a provisional designation consisting of the year followed by an italic letter signifying the order of detection. It is also known popularly after its discoverer, or, in the case of independent detection, co-discoverers. In November, 1956, for instance, two Belgian astronomers named Arend and Roland found the eighth comet of that year. Since it was new and not periodic, it was titled Comet Arend-Roland; it was also known as 1956*h*. Comet Pons-Brooks, at its third return since discovery, was the third comet to be sighted in 1953; it was therefore designated 1953*c*. This provisional identification is used during the apparition of the comet, but is subsequently replaced by the permanent designation: the year and order of perihelion passage, given in Roman numerals. Since Arend-Roland reached perihelion in April, 1957, the third comet to do so in that year, it has become known as 1957 III. The name itself is not always definitive, since one observer may discover a number of different comets.

Comet ephemerides give the position of the comet, in terms of right ascension and declination, at intervals of a week or ten days, so that its path may be plotted on a star chart. Terms used in ephemerides include these:

T—Date of perihelion passage, usually given to decimals of a day.

i—Angle, or *inclination*, of its orbit with respect to that of the earth.

q—Distance of the comet from the sun at perihelion.

e—Eccentricity of the orbit. If *e* is less than 1, the orbit is elliptical. If it is 1·0 or greater, the comet will probably never return to the sun, since its path is parabolic or hyperbolic and does not close on itself.

P—Period between perihelion passages. This refers only to comets with elliptical orbits. If the period is less than about 200 years, the comet is referred to by the symbol P/; thus, P/Pons-Brooks, P/Halley, and so on.

r—Distance of the comet from the sun on any given date.

p—Distance of the comet from the earth on any given date. All distances are given, not in millions of miles, but in *astronomical units* (A.U.). One A.U., which is the mean distance of the earth from the sun, is 93,000,000 miles.

Equipment

Most visual comet discoveries, as against photographic ones, have been made with telescopes of between 4 and 6 inches aperture, with magnifications varying from × 25 to × 40. Low magnifications are essential, for comets are diffuse bodies, very difficult to detect under a powerful magnifier; moreover, a low magnification provides a large field of view, so that a given area of sky can be covered in fewer sweeps. These requirements are very convenient, for low-power work is relaxing to the eye and carries incidental advantages: the mounting need not be perfect, since vibration is less noticeable than with high-power work, and the objective can possess appreciable flaws and still be serviceable, since perfect definition is not necessary when it comes to distinguishing a fuzzy patch of light from a star. The important characteristics of a comet-sweeper are good light-gathering power and a wide field of view—between 1° and 3°.

Refractors are definitely in vogue for this kind of work. Caroline Herschel and Denning were almost alone in using reflectors; the most successful American observers, Brooks, Barnard, Swift, and Peltier, all used refractors, while 4- or 5-inch aperture binoculars are used by some modern observers, including Alcock. They are also in vogue at the Skalnaté Pleso Observatory, Czechoslovakia, from where an observing team discovered 19 comets between 1948 and 1960. It is probable that the Japanese observers are also using either binoculars or wide-field refractors.

Of course, giant binoculars are expensive and difficult to obtain, and a suitable refractor will cost as much or even more. An ordinary instrument is not very suitable, since it is difficult enough to get a field of view of even 1° with a 4-inch refractor. This is because the focal length of such an object glass is commonly about 60 inches, giving an image scale of about

Armchair mounting. *Dr. Henry E. Paul demonstrates his armchair mounting for a pair of binoculars and short-focus refractor. Mounting is controlled by convenient hand cranks. This "Sky Sweeper" chair was originally designed and built by Dr. Edgar Everhart, who used it in his discovery of the comet 1964h, which now bears his name. (Sky Map Publications, St. Louis, Missouri.)*

1°/inch. Since the internal diameter of the drawtube is only 1¼ inches, the preferable field of 1½° or even 2° is quite out of the question.

To overcome this difficulty, some enterprising telescope manufacturers have designed special telescopes for comet-hunting, often called *rich-field* telescopes. By having an object glass with a relatively short focal length, they embrace a very wide field of view. For instance, if the 4-inch lens mentioned above had a focal length of only 30 inches, the image scale would be halved; using the same eyepieces would give a field of view twice as big. Such an object-glass would not be convenient for high-power work, since eyepieces of a very short focal length would be required; but they are ideal for comet-sweeping. Unfortunately, it is difficult to correct object glasses of short relative focal length, since errors of figuring are enhanced, and they are rather expensive.

In the light of these facts, it seems curious that short-focus reflectors have not come into vogue. This involves using a telescope with a mirror not of the usual f/8 variety, but of f/4 or f/5, giving a smaller focal image and a wider field of view with standard eyepieces. Anyone who has ground himself an orthodox mirror will be able to make a satisfactory short-focus type; the finish need not be perfect, since the instrument will be used with low powers. A mirror of 6 or 8 inches diameter, with a focal length of between two and three feet, could form the basis of an inexpensive and most powerful astronomical tool. For instance, a 6-inch mirror with a focal length of 30 inches (f/5), used in conjunction with a low-power eyepiece, could give a field of view of over 1½° and show stars down to the 12th magnitude. Since most comets are of 8th or 10th magnitude when discovered, the opportunities afforded by such an instrument are clear enough.

But, however desirable a special instrument may be, an ordinary reflector of moderate aperture should not be looked down on. Denning discovered his five comets with the 10-inch telescope he used for planetary work, using a power of × 32 or × 40; and he rightly instanced a point that is often overlooked, namely, that many telescopic comets are so small, almost starlike, that too low a magnification will result in some being missed. He usually swept with × 40, keeping a × 60 eyepiece at hand with which to examine any small, suspicious objects.

Predicted comets

Let us now come down to earth and examine the business of sweeping up and following known comets. This can be almost as exciting as finding a new one, since comets rarely behave exactly as predicted by the mathematicians.

In addition to a suitable telescope, the other necessity is a good star atlas, such as *Norton's*, which is clearly marked with lines of right ascension and declination, so that the path of the comet can be drawn in lightly in pencil. It is then a matter of sweeping the appropriate region of the sky, which is commenced when the comet is judged bright enough to be visible with the equipment available. If it is a well-known and regular visitor to the sun, its ephemeris will have been published well in advance. Ephemerides usually give its likely magnitude, but the comet may differ from the prediction by several magnitudes. There is also the difficulty of assigning an accurate value to a diffuse object, so that brightness classification is inevitably somewhat vague.

Three factors are likely to hinder the observer as he searches: If the comet is low in the sky, it will appear faint through horizon haze; if too close to the sun, it will be drowned in twilight; if the moon is up, the sky may be too light. Generally, only a very bright comet can be seen within about 15° of the sun, since this is the limit of the main twilight arc; and remnants of twilight linger on for another 10° or so. In short, to be seen against a dark sky a comet should be about 30° away from the sun; even then, it will be low in the sky and dimmed by haze. If it is likely to be faint, therefore, it must be sought some time before and after perihelion, unless its perihelion distance happens to be unusually large. This point is often not appreciated, for a light sky will drown a quite considerable comet, and many beginners search hopefully in the bright twilight and are disappointed. As for moonlight conditions, these change from night to night and opportunities must be seized as they occur.

Sweeping must be done with scrupulous care. To allow for possible errors in position, it is best to cover an area 2° or 3° square around the predicted point. Move the telescope very slowly in horizontal sweeps; at the end of each traverse, slightly raise or lower the instrument and make an *overlapping* return sweep, so that every part of the region is covered two or even three times. For this work, an altazimuth telescope is much more convenient than an equatorial. If no suspicious hazy object is seen in the region, then the comet is too faint for the aperture and another sweep must be made under more favorable conditions.

An invaluable technique when trying to glimpse faint objects is the trick of *averted vision*, in which the observer directs his gaze at one part of the field while concentrating his attention elsewhere. Often a very dim star or nebulous object that has been invisible to the direct gaze becomes relatively conspicuous when sighted out of the corner of the eye! Also, since a moving object attracts the eye more powerfully than a stationary one, a gentle side-to-side motion of the telescope may amplify a half-suspected hazy patch into clear visibility.

Efficient dark-adaptation of the eye is obviously of the greatest importance. About half an hour is required to bring the retina to full sensitivity; once this is gained, it must not be destroyed by shining a bright flashlight onto the star chart. A dim red light, just sufficient to allow reference without straining the eye, is an essential adjunct. It is also a good idea to protect the idle eye from stray light. Closing it while observing through the other puts a strain on the ocular system; a better answer is to wear an old pair of spectacle frames, one rim holding a patch over the idle eye, and the other left empty to admit the eyepiece.

When the comet has been sighted, the most important observations concern its magnitude, the appearance of the coma and nucleus, and whether or not it has a tail. One good way to estimate the magnitude is to memorize the appearance of the coma—which will probably be a faint, spherical haze 2′ or 3′ (minutes of arc) across, then to rack out the eyepiece until the extrafocal images of the stars have the same diameter, noting the magnitude of the one whose brightness most closely matches that of the comet. It is quite possible to estimate the magnitude of a comet to within about 0·5, once the observer is used to the appearance of stars of different brightness in his instrument. If more accurate results are required—and they are probably not justified by the crudeness of the method—two or three different comparison stars can be used, their exact magnitudes being found from a catalogue; but few observers are likely to have a sufficiently comprehensive catalogue at hand, since the comet may be as faint as the 9th or 10th magnitude.

By this technique, the total, or *integrated*, magnitude of the comet is found (i.e., the magnitude of the starlike point that would be produced if its coma were compressed), and this value can be of use to computers in correcting the predicted magnitude. At the same time, notes should be made of the diameter of the coma (in minutes of arc), and the appearance of the nucleus. Some comets have an almost stellar center, while others are either weakly condensed or have no noticeable nucleus at all; the latter is frequently the case when they are far from the sun. The tail, if any is visible, will be best seen with the lowest available power; and, because of the better light-concentration provided by instruments of very low power, it may be seen better in the finder or with a pair of binoculars.

Some comets have changed markedly in appearance from night to night. Fluctuations sometimes occur in their total light, while the tail may develop or decay. Neither must it be assumed that because a comet is conspicuous before perihelion, it will be equally noteworthy afterward. Alcock's second discovery, 1959 VI, was never recovered after it disappeared into the sun's rays; and the hopes raised by Comet Ikeya-Seki, discovered by Japanese observers on September 18, 1965, as it was moving in towards perihelion, were dashed when it faded out. This was in spite of confident predictions of a brilliant display.

A comet, if near the earth, shows perceptible motion relative to the stars in just a few minutes. Few amateurs have the equipment necessary for accurate measurement of cometary positions, but interesting observations can sometimes be made if the comet passes in front of a star. Donati's comet of 1858 passed in front of the bright star Arcturus in the constellation Boötes, but the star's light was undimmed, proving the tenuous nature of even a great comet. If the comet is seen to be approaching a star, a rough estimate of its motion will indicate when the transit is due to occur. If it has a well-defined nucleus, and it passes directly over or very near the star, an accurate timing may be of great value in calculating its orbit—provided, of course, that the star in question can be identified afterward and its position obtained.

Any peculiarities should also be noted. Comet Arend-Roland, for instance, developed a sunward-pointing spike, or "beard," and sometimes the tail is curved instead of straight and shows considerable structure.

Comet-hunting

Comet-hunters have found that it takes, on average, about 300 hours of actual sweeping time to discover a comet. It is worth stating this at the outset for the benefit of those optimistic mortals who think that a casual glance at the morning or evening sky will reveal a long-tailed newcomer in a matter of weeks! There are, of course, exceptions to the rule—an amateur recently discovered a new comet while testing an eyepiece on the star Kappa Cephei—but such fortune is not to be taken as a general guide. Pons discovered comets at the rate of about one a year, while Brooks, using a more powerful instrument, achieved double the rate; at the Skalnaté Pleso Observatory in Czechoslovakia 19 were found in 11 years, with Antonin Mrkos apparently the most assiduous watcher. He found 11, thus achieving a one-a-year rate.

Alcock began his searches in 1953. When he made his most recent discovery, in 1965, he had spent 1,154 nights comet-sweeping, a total of 1,418 hours; but all his discoveries have been made with a pair of 4-inch binoculars that he did not bring into use until 1959, since when he had swept the sky with them for 735 hours to find four comets. It is interesting to note that the Czech observers actually averaged only 100 hours per discovery. This is partly due to their cooperative effort and partly to their excellent sky conditions; but they did suffer from a high western horizon, and so had to pay chief attention to the morning sky before dawn. Their success suggests that new comets are more likely to be discovered in that region than in the evening sky after sunset.

It is worth investigating this more fully; most books simply mention that comet-sweeping should be carried out in the region of the sun (where

Comet Seki-Lines. *Photographed at Gates Oasis in the Tucson mountains on April 10, 1962. Film used was Royal Pan. Focal length was 7 inches; exposure time was 40 seconds. (Donald J. Strittmatter, Tucson, Arizona.)*

they are most likely to be bright), and leave it at that. But if several years are to be spent sweeping for comets, it is sensible to study the economics of the situation. A few years ago, M. J. Hendrie, an amateur comet-hunter, raised the following interesting points in the B.A.A. *Journal*:*

Comet discoveries can be divided into two distinct classes: those made intentionally, by amateur or professional observers searching the region near the sun; and those achieved quite by accident, on photographic plates exposed for some other purpose. At the moment, three large observatories are leading the "accidental" discovery field: Palomar, Lick, and Lowell. All these take routine "patrol" plates, intended to spot any stars that may suddenly flare up, and it is not surprising that they have discovered the majority of new comets. Of the 61 comets discovered between 1948 and 1960, only 26 were found visually, most of these being sighted at Skalnaté Pleso.

* Vol. 72 (1962), 384–396.

204

If we then accept the fact that most comets brighten up into telescopic visibility somewhere between the orbits of Mars and the earth, it is obvious, from figure 41, that when we look toward the region of the sun, we are looking through a much greater volume of comet-holding space than when we look away from it. The interesting point is that the professional patrol cameras tend to scrutinize just this region away from the sun, as it is most favorably placed for stellar work, though least likely to hold comets. Far from being discouraged by the professionals' success, amateurs should take heart; the fact that relatively few are being sighted in the more favorable regions indicates that some are surely being missed, and that more observers are required to maintain a watch of the regions nearer the sun!

There is another, more suggestive, point. Considering the random appearance of comets, it might be expected that the number discovered to the east of the sun (i.e., in the evening sky) would about equal the number found to the west (in the morning sky). But this is not so, at least for the more conspicuous visitors. About three times as many discoveries of bright comets have been made in the morning sky, and this may be due to the more thorough evening searches, which reveal comets while still rather faint. The morning sky, for obvious reasons, is less well patrolled. Clearly, then, the best place and time to discover a bright comet is in the region of the eastern horizon, before dawn.

Comet-hunting is carried out in much the same way as sweeping for a known object, except that a much larger area of sky is covered. The instrument is moved slowly and regularly in azimuth, and stopped whenever a hazy gleam is spotted. It may be a comet, but it is far more likely to be a nebula. And this is where the tedious work begins.

When first seen, a comet usually appears to be a faint grayish stain on the sky. It is certainly unlikely to have developed a tail, the classical clue, and unfortunately the sky is full of dim objects that can easily be mistaken for the coma of a small comet. These are the *nebulae*, clouds of glowing gas that lie among the stars, and the *galaxies*, star systems similar to the Milky Way, which are so remote that they appear as mere blurs of light. Part III of this book deals with the observation of these objects; for the moment, we are concerned only with their nuisance value. For this purpose, they will be lumped together, very inaccurately, under the term "nebulae,"

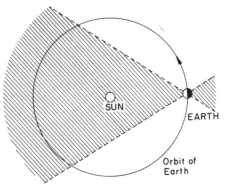

Figure 41. *The distribution of comets.*

since both types of object appear very similar when viewed through a small or moderate telescope.

So when a nebulous object comes into view, the first task is to note its position among the stars and to consult a star map. Like the stars, nebulae keep their positions from century to century, so it is a fairly straightforward matter to check up. *Norton's* marks the positions of more than a thousand of the brighter ones, and the chances are that the "comet" will be identified as a nebula that was catalogued many years ago, probably by Herschel himself.

If the object is not marked in the atlas, it does not necessarily indicate a comet discovery. There are several thousand nebulae in the sky that are within the range of an amateur's telescope, and *Norton's* lists only the brightest. Becvar's more comprehensive atlases—*Coeli, Borealis, Elipticalis,* and *Australis*—go considerably fainter than *Norton's* and aid identification. The final step is to consult the standard work on the subject, Dreyer's *New General Catalogue,* issued in 1888 and reprinted in 1953 by the Royal Astronomical Society, London. This lists over 7,000 nebulae and star clusters, giving brief notes on each and their exact positions in the sky. If the position of the suspicious object is noted, the N.G.C. will certainly provide the answer. If it is not listed as a nebula, it is a good idea to examine it with a more powerful eyepiece, since two or three faint stars lying close together can occasionally give the impression of something fuzzy and extended.

Two final checks must now be made. The first is to consult the year's ephemerides and to make sure that it is not the return of a known comet—although, if its recovery has not yet been announced, it must certainly be communicated right away. If this search is negative, the final vindication rests with the object itself. If it is a comet, it will be moving relative to the stars, and this motion should manifest itself in an hour or two at the most.

As soon as its cometary nature has been established, a telegram should be sent to Harvard Observatory, Oak Ridge, Massachusetts (if observing from the United States); or, in any other country, to the national observatory. All that is required is its position, measured as accurately as possible; the date, hour, and minute at which this position was taken; its rate and direction of motion; and its apparent size and brightness. It is also a good idea to mention the instrument used. This should give the professional observers all the information they need to turn their powerful telescopes onto the region and take over the task of following this new visitor to the sun.

This sequence of events is in the mind of every comet observer, but of course *Norton's* and the N.G.C. between them have a sad habit of dashing hopes. Nebula after nebula will be picked up, and most of the observer's time will be spent in consulting reference lists; but the situation improves as the same area is swept over night after night. Soon, out of initial disorder and frustration, comes a wonderfully intimate knowledge of the region. Every comet-hunter testifies to the compensations afforded by this type of work; these lonely vigils with the stars have an edifying effect on the mind, and the discovery of the wonders of the night sky will prove in the end to be as rewarding as any comets that may be picked up.

It is far better to work a small region thoroughly than a large area vaguely. At the same time, the work should be done as rapidly as is consistent with thoroughness, for the fertile region of dark sky near the sun is visible for only a short time; all too quickly during morning work, the east begins to lighten until it is ruinously bright. It is, however, worth glancing at the twilight region to make sure that no really prominent visitor has appeared out of the sun's rays.

Weather conditions and moonlight

To have much hope of success, a comet-hunter must live in an area favored with truly dark skies; this means rural or at least suburban conditions. This, combined with clear east or west horizons (preferably both), is a *sine qua non*.

Weather conditions can also affect matters, but here there is scope for initiative, and it is a matter of taking chances when they come. Few sites can rival Lick Observatory, which claims to enjoy 300 clear nights in the year, but it is amazing what can be done if a close watch is kept on the sky. Frequently, large breaks occur in the densest cloud; and if it has recently been raining heavily the atmosphere is likely to be of exceptional clarity, and hence extremely favorable for the detection of faint comets. Looking through the records, it is found that July and August have claimed more comet discoveries than any other months, with a noticeable preponderance of discoveries in the second half of the year. Denning, in his book *Telescopic Work*, analyzes the 289 cometary discoveries made between 1782 and 1890, noting that 38 comets were found in August, and that 123 were found in the first six months as against 166 in the remainder of the year. Hendrie's analysis of the discoveries between 1948 and 1960 shows the same tendency, with only 25 of the 61 being discovered in the first six months; there can be little doubt that weather conditions are responsible. Denning himself, who observed meteors as well as planets, managed to average about 36 hours of clear sky every month; and he not only observed from "cloud-laden" England, but also confined his meteor watches to periods when the moon was out of the sky. Sky conditions vary enormously in different regions of the United States, the West Coast being generally more favorable than the

East; but probably no place is less favorable than the British Isles, so that an enthusiastic observer should be able to log 200 or 300 hours in a year—especially if he has the necessary tendency toward insomnia.

Naturally enough, far fewer comets have been discovered around the time of full moon than when it is a crescent. Halley's Comet, at its 1910 return, reached its greatest brightness during the moonlit evenings, and so was seen at a disadvantage. But opportunities present themselves even at these unfavorable times. The moon, just before full, sets a couple of hours before dawn and so leaves a precious interval of dark sky; and after full the evening sky is available for some time before it rises. These moments should be profited by, since the majority of comet-hunters leave off work at this time, and the sky is less well patrolled, giving the persistent watcher an extra chance of success.

"False" comets

In 1781, Charles Messier issued a catalogue of 103 star clusters and nebulae that has remained a useful standard until the present day—even though thousands of fainter objects have since been recorded. The story goes that he was so frustrated by continually alighting on these objects and at first taking them for comets that he drew up the list as a warning of "objects to avoid." This is probably untrue; it is far more likely that he was interested in them for their own sake, but his catalogue is of value in listing some objects (prefixed by the initial M.) that do appear distinctly cometlike. For example, M.13 and M.92 in Hercules are globular star clusters (see page 236) that appear very much like the nucleus and coma of a bright telescopic comet when they are viewed with a low power. Among other bright false comets are M.2 (Aquarius), M.3 (Canes Venatici), M.15 (Pegasus), and M.49 (Virgo). The observer should begin by looking at these objects, and at the others in Messier's list, with his comet-sweeper.

Of more interest still are the dimmer and more treacherous objects—more treacherous because there are far more of them. Swift described a nebula in Draco as looking just like a small comet; this is N.G.C. 6654 (the letters refer to Dreyer's *New General Catalogue*). Its position is R.A. 18^h 26^m, Dec. +73° 6′, so that it lies near the north celestial pole. It is actually very near the bright star Chi Draconis, and if its position is marked on the chart it can be sighted. Nearby is a brighter nebula, N.G.C. 6643, which should be found without difficulty with a 4-inch refractor. This one is marked in *Norton's*. If these nebulae prove difficult or impossible to find, then the chances of finding a faint comet are low, although a bright one may still be obvious. Alcock has mentioned a nebula in Leo Minor, N.G.C. 3344, as looking very much like a comet. It lies between stars 40 and 41, and he comments: "What makes it look so much like a comet in a small, low-powered instrument is the fact that it has a star superimposed near the *p* rim, so that it appears to have a small sharp nucleus with a fainter following tail." The constellations Draco, Leo, Ursa Major, and Virgo are so full of nebulae that it requires great determination to sweep them and considerable courage to announce a discovery!

Some bright periodic comets

The regularly returning comets have periods ranging from $3\frac{1}{3}$ years (Encke's) to 76 years (Halley's), and some of the brighter members are mentioned below.

P/ENCKE. The second periodic comet to be "discovered" by analysis, this time by Johann Encke, later director of the Berlin Observatory. Before that, he had been a gifted mathematician, and it was this aptitude that induced him to compare the comets observed in 1786, 1795, and 1818, and to realize that they were the same body. The period of Encke's comet is much shorter than that of any other, and since its predicted appearance in 1822 it has been observed at every return. It was last seen in the autumn of 1967, when it approached the sun to within 30 million miles, and it is due back in 1970. Near perihelion, it is usually visible with binoculars.

P/TUTTLE-GIACOBINI-KRÉSÁK. The cumbersome name of this comet is due to its independent discovery in 1858 by three observers. It has a period of about $5\frac{1}{2}$ years, but due to computing errors it was not picked up again until 1907, after which it evaded discovery again until 1951. It was once more missed in 1956, but came within the range of moderate telescopes at its 1962 return. It seems to fluctuate greatly in brightness, and will be worth looking out for in the future.

P/GIACOBINI-ZINNER. This comet has a period of $6\frac{1}{2}$ years. It was bright enough to be well seen at its 1959 return, and it appeared again in 1966. The material of this comet was associated with prominent showers of meteors (the Giacobinids or Draconids) seen in 1933 and 1946; the relationship between comets and meteors is mentioned in the following chapter.

P/FINLAY. This is another short-period comet which is sometimes seen with small instruments. It last returned in 1960, and has a period of nearly 7 years.

P/SCHWASSMANN-WACHMANN I. This curious body moves in an orbit of very slight eccentricity, its distance from the sun ranging from that of

Jupiter to that of Saturn! Although normally extremely faint, it has occasionally exhibited bursts of activity, becoming as bright as the 10th magnitude.

P/PONS-BROOKS. With a period of more than 70 years, this comet has been observed at only three returns. At the last, in 1954, it was a naked-eye object.

P/OLBERS. At its 1956 return, this comet just reached the 6th magnitude, but was never striking. Period, 70 years.

P/HALLEY. The brightest of the short-period comets, but apparently not as striking now as it was two thousand years ago, due to the steady destruction of its material by successive returns to the sun.

The wear and tear explains why the short-period comets are always relatively small and faint. The really bright visitors are always unexpected, because their periods are so long that they have never before been recorded during the age of accurate observation. A great comet is long overdue. The previous century had three—in 1811, 1843, and 1882—as well as a number of lesser but still memorable ones; but the present century, since 1910, has been barren. By the law of averages, we may expect a spectacular visitor very soon; and there is no reason at all why it should not fall to a patient amateur to give first warning of its coming.

18

Meteors and Meteor Showers

On some clear and moonless nights, particularly in the fall, a casual sky-watcher will notice spasmodic streaks of light flying among the stars. Initially, they appear to be moving quite at random; but if a watch is maintained for an hour or two, it will become apparent that many of these streaks are radiating from certain regions of the sky. Evidently meteors, or "shooting stars," are not the haphazard bodies they seem to be.

Meteors have been known from the earliest times, but not until the early part of the nineteenth century did astronomers take them seriously enough to investigate their nature. They had previously been regarded as purely atmospheric phenomena, with no astronomical connection. But the night of November 12/13, 1833, precipitated a radical transformation, when, as the astronomical historian Agnes Clerke related in her *History of Astronomy in the Nineteenth Century*, "... a tempest of falling stars broke over the earth."

North America bore the brunt of the display [she wrote]. From the Gulf of Mexico to Halifax, until daylight with some difficulty put an end to the display, the sky was scored in every direction with shining tracks and illuminated with majestic fireballs. At Boston the frequency of meteors was estimated to be about half that of flakes of snow in an average snowstorm. Their numbers, while the first fury of their coming lasted, were quite beyond counting; but as it waned, a reckoning was attempted, from which it was computed, on the basis of that much diminished rate, that 240,000 must have been visible during the nine hours they continued to fall.

Numbers were what impressed the layman, and rightly too; but there was more to the matter than that. Perceptive observers noticed that the meteors did not appear to move in random directions, but seemed to radiate from a definite region—a point in the constellation Leo. Moreover, as the night wore on and the earth's turning took Leo high in the south and began to drop him on his nose in the west, the meteors still streamed from the same area. This proved conclusively that they were independent of the earth; in fact, they were interplanetary bodies. Thus, overnight, meteors were shifted from the meteorological to the astronomical sphere.

It was recalled that meteors had been seen in great numbers in November, 1799; and a further shower of these objects, now known as *Leonids* because of their place of origin in the sky, occurred in November, 1866. Europe had a better view this time, and, although the meteors' performance was inferior to the display of thirty-three years earlier, it was by far the densest falling-star shower in European memory. And by this time, astronomers had arrived at some conclusions. Observers such as Heis in Germany and the lunar astronomer Schmidt at Athens had discovered that many of the ordinary meteors which flash from night to night have similar regions of emanation, known as *radiants*. The explanation is that the meteors are really traveling in parallel paths; when they enter the earth's atmosphere and are consumed in a streak of fire (as in fig. 42), the

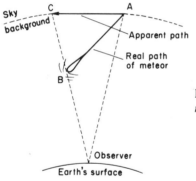

Figure 42. *Real and apparent paths of a meteor.*

observer sees their apparent motion as *AC*, whereas the real path is *AB*. This is because everything in the night sky, from nearby meteors to the remotest stars, appears to be at infinity, so that the observer is not aware that most meteors are much closer to him at the end of their path than at its beginning. A meteoric *shower* occurs when the earth passes through a *swarm* of particles, although "swarm" is perhaps a misnomer when we remember that actually the individual meteors may be hundreds of miles apart. Similarly, the term "shower" evokes visions of streaks in great abundance, whereas only on rare occasions are meteors to be seen at rates higher than about one a minute.

It now remained to find out where they went and from whence they came; and Schiaparelli, in the days before he turned his attention to Mercury and Mars, came up with results that at first amazed the scientific world, but were soon confirmed. First, he showed that meteors are true members of the solar system, revolving around the sun in closed orbits. Second, he pointed out that in some cases these orbits more or less coincide with those of known comets.

The meteor/comet relation noted by Schiaparelli was clinched by the 1866 Leonid display, which was well observed by astronomers. Schiaparelli now found that they moved in the same orbit as Tempel's comet, which had been seen early that same year and which had a period of 33 years, coinciding with the interval between the great showers. Any remaining doubts were dispelled six years later by Biela's comet, a short-period object which had been seen to divide into two parts at its 1845 return, and which reappeared in 1852 as two separate comets! Severe disintegration had obviously set in; this was confirmed when it escaped detection at the next two returns. The comet seemed to have gone to the grave; and then, in 1872, when it should have reappeared, there occurred a great meteor shower. This marked the remains of Biela's comet; its last solid fragments were being spread along its orbit, and it would never be seen again. Nowadays, the shower itself has become very feeble, only a few, slow meteors radiating from the constellation Andromeda every year during the month of November.

Yet it would be wrong to think that all meteor showers have established cometary relations. More than a thousand detectable showers are known, and of these only a few comets are officially recognized as "parents." Although there may be many associations, the comets themselves have either long since disintegrated, or have simply not been observed.

Some well-known showers

Under good conditions, between six and a dozen meteors will be seen every hour on most nights of the year. Some of these are *sporadic*, which means that they are unrelated to any particular swarm and move around the sun in independent orbits. Others belong to some of the many faint showers that may number only a single meteor in several hours of watching. These form the great majority of established radiants, and extensive watches are needed to form any firm deductions about these streams. But at certain times of the year Earth passes through much denser swarms, producing obvious displays. The principal ones are listed by name in Table VI.

TABLE VI. Most Prominent Night-time Meteor Showers[a]

NAME OF SHOWER	PERIOD OF DETECTABLE METEORS	DATE OF PEAK ACTIVITY	MAXIMUM VISUAL HOURLY RATES[b]	RADIANT COORDINATES (DEG.)[c] RIGHT ASCENSION	DECLI- NATION
Quadrantids[d]	Jan. 1–4	Jan. 3	50	231	+50
Corona Australids	Mar. 14–18	Mar. 16	(5)[e]	245	−48
Virginids	Mar. 5–Apr. 2	Mar. 20	(less than 5)	190	0
Lyrids	Apr. 19–24	Apr. 21	5	272	+32
Eta Aquarids[d]	Apr. 21–May 12	May 4	12	336	0
Ophiuchids	June 17–26	June 20	(20)	260	−20
Capricornids	July 10–Aug. 5	July 25	(20)	315	−15
Southern Delta Aquarids[d]	July 21–Aug. 15	July 30	20	339	−17
Northern Delta Aquarids[d]	July 15–Aug. 18	July 29	10	339	0
Pisces Australids	July 15–Aug. 20	July 30	(20)	340	−30
Alpha Capricornids	July 15–Aug. 20	Aug. 1	5	309	−10
Southern Iota Aquarids	July 15–Aug. 25	Aug. 5	(10)	338	−15
Northern Iota Aquarids	July 15–Aug. 25	Aug. 5	(10)	331	− 6
Perseids[d]	July 25–Aug. 17	Aug. 12	50	46	+58
Kappa Cygnids	Aug. 18–22	Aug. 20	(5)	290	+55
Orionids	Oct. 18–26	Oct. 21	20	95	+15
Southern Taurids	Sept. 15–Dec. 15	Nov. 19	(5)	52	+14
Northern Taurids	Oct. 15–Dec. 1	Nov. 19	(less than 5)	54	+21
Leonids	Nov. 14–20	Nov. 17	(5)	152	+22
Geminids[d]	Dec. 7–15	Dec. 13	50	113	+32
Ursids	Dec. 17–24	Dec. 22	15	217	+80

[a]Adapted from D. W. R. McKinley, *Meteor Science and Engineering* (New York: McGraw-Hill Book Company, Inc., 1961). [b] Number of meteors observable visually by a single observer at maximum shower activity. [c]+, North of the celestial equator, south of it, −. [d]Among the stronger and more consistent meteor showers. [e] Figures in parentheses less reliable than other figures for visual hourly rates and period of detectable meteors.

Reprinted from Joseph H. Jackson, *Pictorial Guide to the Planets*, New York: Thomas Y. Crowell, 1965.

It must be remembered that the dates given in Table VI are only approximate. Some meteors may be visible outside the limits, and the time of maximum may differ by a day or two from year to year, due to leap-year adjustments. The R.A. of meteor radiants is commonly given in degrees instead of hours and minutes, but the conversion is not difficult when one remembers that 1^h of R.A. is equivalent to 15°. The last column indicates the most conspicuous star near the radiant, to help in actually watching for the shower. The radiant point of the Taurids cannot be given with any accuracy, for this is a long-lived, diffuse shower with a number of radiants scattered around Taurus and Aries.

A meteor is a small body that may be anything from the size of a grain of sand to that of a pebble; anything smaller will give too fugitive a streak to be noticeable; a larger object will light up the whole sky and be termed a *fireball*, or *bolide*. Since all the various swarms seem to consist of particles of much the same size, it might be imagined that all showers will produce similar meteors. This is very far from the case, however, since it all depends on the angle at which they strike the earth.

Meteors, like comets, are traveling around the sun in large and eccentric orbits. This means that at the earth's distance from the sun, which is when contact occurs, they are traveling faster than the earth. This is not difficult to understand. If the earth suddenly slowed down from its speed of $18\frac{1}{2}$ miles per second, it would sweep in toward the sun; if it accelerated to about 25 miles per second, it would fly off at a tangent and move into a more or less cometic orbit. This is, in fact, the velocity at which meteors are traveling when they reach the earth's vicinity, although this speed varies slightly from shower to shower.

Because meteor swarms do not keep to the counterclockwise, uniform-plane restriction that binds the major planets, it is evident that they can meet the earth at various angles. The extreme cases are shown in figure 43, where swarm A is moving in a direction more or less opposite to the earth's orbital motion, while swarm B is traveling in the same general direction as the earth. It follows that a meteor in swarm A will pass through the earth's atmosphere at a velocity consisting of the sum of the orbital speeds— $25 + 18\frac{1}{2}$ miles per second. A B meteor, having to overtake the earth at its rear, will achieve a relative velocity of only $25 - 18\frac{1}{2}$ miles per second. It will therefore appear in the sky as a much slower object, perhaps leaving a faint luminous trail, or *train*, whereas an A meteor will be seen as a swiftly moving streak. Of the showers listed in Table V, the Lyrids, η Aquarids,

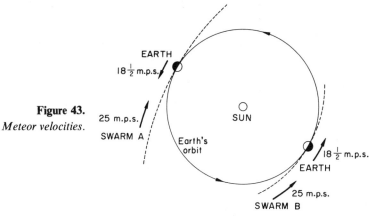

Figure 43.
Meteor velocities.

Perseids, Orionids, and Leonids are swift; the Quadrantids, δ Aquarids, Geminids, and Ursids are of medium speed, because they are hitting the earth more or less "beam on"; the Taurids are slow, lasting perhaps a second or two.

QUADRANTIDS.　This is a most awkward shower to observe. It is short, the radiant is rather near the sun, and it has a very brief maximum that occurs between 6^h U.T. on January 3 and the same time on January 4, the exact hour depending on the year. Sometimes, when this period occurs in daylight, only a few meteors can be seen during the hours of darkness. The most favorable conditions for observation occur every few years, when maximum activity takes place a couple of hours before dawn, and the radiant is reasonably high in the sky. The shower earns its name from the now-forgotten constellation of Quadrans Muralis, which lay in the Ursa Major–Boötes region.

This shower has been largely neglected by amateurs, partly, no doubt, because of the difficulties of observation. Nevertheless, even though conditions at the 1965 display were rather unfavorable, one amateur recorded 49 meteors in 33 minutes, while another wrote: "A bright Quadrantid is a characteristic electric blue color, with an expanding, mottled, silvery train." This elusive shower seems worthy of wider attention.

LYRIDS.　One of the few spring showers appearing April 19–24. The radiant can be well observed in the morning sky, reaching its highest altitude, or *culmination*, at around dawn, and the shower is well seen from northern temperate latitudes. At maximum activity, 6 or 8 swift meteors should be seen within an hour.

η AQUARIDS.　To be seen at their peak on May 4. These are two distinct showers with radiant points in Aquarius, so they are distinguished by citing the bright star nearest to the radiant. This is only 70° away from the sun and it rises not long before dawn; therefore, observation is difficult. It also lies on the celestial equator, so not many meteors are likely to be seen by observers in high northern latitudes. They are interesting, nevertheless, from the suggested association with Halley's comet.

δ AQUARIDS.　These meteors are of medium speed, and so are easily distinguished from the early Perseids that appear at about the same time in mid-July; because of their lower velocity, they appear yellowish rather than blue-white. The radiant lies south of the celestial equator, and so is poorly seen from latitudes higher than about 40°N; but observers in other regions may expect to see from 30 to 60 meteors an hour on the night

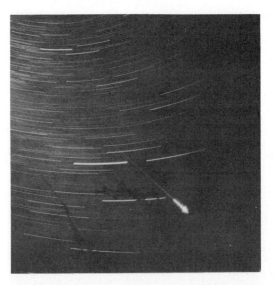

Perseid meteor. *T. Lloyd Evans used a stationary camera with an f/4 Ross Xpres lens of 5-inch focus for this photograph. Since the exposure time was 32 minutes, the stars trailed into arcs, and this brilliant exploding meteor was caught near one corner of the plate. The dark object is the outline of a weather vane.*

of maximum, while they show considerable strength on succeeding and preceding nights. This is the only major shower whose radiant lies well south of the equator; the meteors are of interest in passing very close to the sun at perihelion and in not being associated with any known comet. It is curious that the southern hemisphere should be so devoid of strong showers. A great deal of work has been carried out by both amateur and professional observers, and the deficiency is undoubtedly real.

PERSEIDS.   Probably the best known and most reliable of all the annual showers. The meteors usually reach their maximum on the night of August 11/12; up to 60 swift meteors an hour may be seen. Early Perseids are seen in mid-July, and persist for about a month, with the radiant shifting northeastward from night to night, beginning in Andromeda and finishing up in Camelopardus. This is an effect of parallax, caused by the earth's motion through the swarm. These "August meteors" have been recorded for at least a thousand years.

ORIONIDS.   A prominent display that reaches an intensity of 10 or 20 meteors per hour on October 20 depending on the altitude of the radiant; low-latitude observers have the best view, since Orion is on the celestial equator.

TAURIDS.   This is a complex, long-enduring system of slow meteors. The two most prominent radiants lie in R.A. 64°, Dec. +22°; and R.A. 55°, Dec. +13°; but they have about the same duration, and it is not easy to distinguish between them. However, the first group (the Northern Taurids) is somewhat faster than the other. Rates of about 10 meteors per hour occur at maximum, which comes in early November.

Two-point Leonid meteors. *This 3½-minute exposure was taken from Kitt Peak at about midnight U.T. November 17, 1966. A total of 61 Leonids radiate from the Sickle. A Voigtlander 105-mm f/3·5 lens was used with Tri-X 120 roll film, developed 12 minutes in D19 at 68°F. (Dennis Milon, Tucson, Arizona.)*

LEONIDS. These interesting meteors are the remnants of the famous showers seen in the past. The meteors, which reach their peak on November 16, are swift, with an unpredictable hourly rate; in recent times it has been low, but in 1961 there was a definite revival, increasing over the succeeding years and culminating in the magnificent 1966 display, during which observers in the United States recorded thousands of meteors per hour. The extraordinary concentration of these meteors is indicated when we find that observers in Europe, who had dark skies a mere nine hours before the Leonids' greatest intensity, recorded rates of only two or three a minute. It will be interesting to see what happens to the Leonids in future years.

GEMINIDS. A fine December shower, short-lived but prominent. The radiant reaches a considerable altitude for northern temperate observers; under good conditions the rate should match that of the Perseids.

URSIDS. A rather faint, short-lived shower of medium-speed meteors, to be seen the week before Christmas. The radiant lies near the polestar.

Meteor observation

The amateur's reign in detection and analysis of meteor showers lasted from about 1833 until 1945. But since World War II, as a result of the unprecedented development of electronic techniques, radar has to a very great extent supplanted the visual observer. When a meteor hurtles down through the atmosphere, the intense heat of its passage not only causes it to glow, but also chemically disrupts, or *ionizes*, some of the molecules in the surrounding air. The meteor itself is far too tiny to be picked up on a radar set, but this transient streak of ionization can be recorded, and its velocity and direction can be measured very accurately. In addition, clouds, moonlight, even daylight, have no disturbing effect; radar observations can therefore be carried out under all conditions.

On the other hand, since radar observation lies in the professional field it must be involved in definite schedules. This means that the watchful amateur may pick up some unexpected event, such as the intense Leonid display of 1961. It must also be remembered that what is a bright meteor to the visual observer may not be "bright" to a radar set. Since radar only detects the ionized trail, it reacts most strongly to swift meteors; this is because their greater velocity produces a higher temperature, and hence a greater degree of ionization. A bright but slow-moving meteor, on the other hand, being much cooler, may leave little or no detectable trail.

This discrepancy was well brought out on the night of December 5, 1956, when an unexpected meteor shower struck the earth. Amateur observers in New Zealand, Australia, and South Africa were amazed to find a great number of meteors radiating from the constellation Phoenix, a southern group; an hourly rate of up to 100 meteors was recorded. It so happened that the meteors were also picked up by radar workers, but the hourly rate was considerably less, a fact explained by their slow speed. Eyewitnesses recorded them as being exceptionally bright, rivaling Venus or, in a few cases, even the moon, and leaving conspicuous trains. Moreover, since amateurs were distributed throughout the area over which the shower was visible, it could be kept under observation for a long period as the earth spun on its axis, bringing fresh regions of the globe to face the shower. In this case, the amateur results were of definite value.

In the case of the well-known showers, the amateur's most useful duty is simply to count the number of meteors visible from hour to hour, noting any interesting features, such as brilliance, length of path, color, train, and other effects that may seem unusual. A note must also be kept of the number of sporadic meteors seen, as well as those radiating from the active area.

To determine the activity of a shower in definitive terms, it is not enough to record the *observed hourly rate* (OHR) and leave it at that, since the number of meteors visible to an observer, if we neglect meteorological and other factors, depends on the altitude of the radiant. If the radiant is low, some meteors will occur below the horizon while others will be lost in the haze. To produce uniformity, the results must be corrected to *zenithal hourly rate* (ZHR), which is the number of meteors that would be seen were the radiant directly overhead. Table VII gives the correction factors for different altitudes. If a watch of several hours' duration is maintained during the night (shorter spells are of little use), the number of meteors seen every hour or half-hour can be corrected to ZHR.

TABLE VII.　Altitude correction factors

ALTITUDE	FACTOR	ALTITUDE	FACTOR
0°		27·4°	
	0·1		0·6
2·6		34·5	
	0·2		0·7
8·6		42·5	
	0·3		0·8
14·5		52·2	
	0·4		0·9
20·7		65·8	
	0·5		1·0
27·4		90·0	

If the radiant altitude is equal to one of the tabulated values, the upper factor should be taken. For example, the factor for 27·4° is 0·5 and not 0·6.

When recording meteors in this way, one should note their magnitudes. Some showers consist predominantly of bright meteors, while others are more evenly graded. It is also necessary to make a note of sky conditions, recording the faintest star visible in the zenith to give a guide to the transparency.

Unexpected showers such as the Phoenicids, which lasted for only a few hours and have not been seen since 1956, are very rare indeed; but if unusual meteoric activity is noticed, attempts should certainly be made to find the radiant. This is done by plotting as many trails as possible on a star chart, afterward extending them back until they meet in what should be a small area of the sky—the radiant.

The moment a meteor is seen, and while its path across the stars is still fresh in the memory, a piece of string, or a straight rod known as a "wand," is held up at arm's length so as to coincide with the line of the track. Notes are then made of the positions (relative to the stars) of three points along this track, so that it can later be reproduced in the atlas; and the position of the beginning and end of the meteor's trail is also recorded. Other matters, such as its duration and color, are of relatively minor importance. The success of this method depends greatly on the experience of the observer, but in occasional emergencies even poor results are better than none at all. The same method should be adopted if a brilliant fireball is seen, since other observers may have made a similar observation, and the parallactic shift of the meteor against the stars as seen from different stations enables its true path through the atmosphere to be calculated.

Just occasionally, curious meteors are seen. If one happens to be traveling directly toward the observer it will show no lateral movement at all, simply shining out and fading away. Sometimes, too, a meteor describes a path that is twisted rather than straight, probably due to some irregularity on its surface.

Moonlight is the bane of the visual meteor watcher. A full moon will drown all but the brightest objects, and conditions vary from year to year, some showers being well seen while others are very unfavorable. It so happens that the Lyrids, Perseids, Orionids, Leonids, and Geminids are all separated by rough multiples of the lunar month, so that moonlight conditions are rather similar for all of them. This is all very well if it happens to be near new at the critical time, but in some years very little work can be done on the major showers.

The well-known scientist J. B. S. Haldane once remarked that "the observer of meteors requires a clear sky, a thick coat, a notebook, a knowledge of the constellations, infinite patience, and a tendency to insomnia." This list is fundamental but not inclusive. To it can be added: a deck chair, allowing the observer to recline at a comfortable angle; a lightweight lapboard to hold the observation log; and a dim red light worked by a convenient switch so that notes can be made immediately a meteor is seen.

Telescopic meteors

Any observer who habitually uses a low magnification and a large field of view, as in comet-hunting and variable-star observation, will occasionally have his attention distracted by a *telescopic meteor*. Sometimes a fast-moving, naked-eye meteor flashes across the field, but the truly telescopic variety are faint, and many seem to move relatively slowly, so that their paths can be followed without difficulty. There is as yet no satisfactory explanation of this anomalous velocity. One might be inclined to attribute it to their great height, if calculations did not show that their altitudes would be above the farthest reaches of the atmosphere, where there is no resisting medium to cause a glow. Another explanation is that they always move in a path directed more or less toward the observer, so that they do not seem to cover a large arc of sky. Whatever the explanation, the effect is undoubtedly real. Some telescopic meteors move so slowly that they can be seen distinctly as starlike points of light, fading out after paths covering a degree or less of the sky.

Since the introduction of radar into the naked-eye meteor field, some amateurs have turned to a study of these objects. As yet, however, the field is hardly touched, and most telescopic meteor reports come from comet-hunters. For example, Denning noted 95 telescopic meteors between May and November, 1890, while sweeping for comets with his 10-inch reflector. Altogether, he observed 635 during 727 hours' sweeping. Much more recently, Alcock recorded 201 between April 1 and October 11, 1964, using 25 × 105 and 11 × 80 binoculars, which brought his total since the beginning of 1953 to 1,698. Moreover, amateur observers have lately enjoyed a boost in the supply of faint moving objects—the various items of hardware moving in orbits well above the earth's atmosphere. These now exist in such profusion that it is impossible to keep track of them all. Their low velocity and long paths distinguish them from meteors, but they sometimes appear in impressive numbers; during a week's work, an amateur recently counted 48 telescopic meteors and 27 satellites!

Very little has as yet been published on the subject of telescopic meteors. The following notes are based on researches carried out by a British amateur, K. B. Hindley, who specializes in the observation of these objects.

FREQUENCY.   Naked-eye meteors show an annual activity curve like that in fig. 44. There are two minima, one in February, the other at the beginning of June, while the extended Perseid shower provides a marked peak at the beginning of August. In the autumn the general rate is considerably higher than during the rest of the year; added to this, we find a considerable diurnal variation. During the early morning, the observer will see two or three times as many sporadic meteors as in the evening, because, as the night wears on, the earth's rotation has carried him into the region facing the planet's direction of motion. Consequently, the morning meteors are faster (and therefore brighter) than those seen in the evening, and there

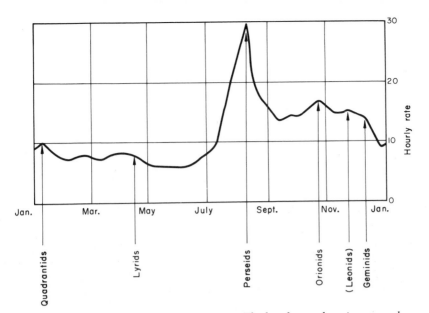

Figure 44. *Meteor activity throughout the year. The hourly rate here is averaged over a fortnight, so that only showers of considerable duration have an effect on the curve.*

are more of them, since, as explained earlier, the evening meteors have a much harder job to do in overtaking the earth at its rear.

Telescopic meteor activity shows the same general change. After the June minimum, activity increases until the second half of July, when the rates have a broad maximum until the first half of November. A smaller increase then occurs, coinciding with the appearance of the Geminid meteor stream; subsequently, the curve falls to the February minimum. Using a 5-inch short-focus refractor, with a magnification of × 18 and a field of view slightly exceeding 3°, rates of between 5 and 9 meteors per hour are the average on good nights.

NAKED-EYE SHOWERS. It might be supposed that telescopic meteor activity shows an increase on the nights of the major naked-eye showers, but this is not usually so. In the case of the Perseid and Leonid showers, for instance, the majority of meteors are bright; the same is true of the δ Aquarids and the Taurids. All these showers are deficient in faint meteors. The Geminids and Quadrantids, on the other hand, show considerable telescopic activity right down to the 10th and 11th magnitudes. Indeed, the Geminids are active telescopically before they become noticeable with the naked eye.

TELESCOPIC SHOWERS. Of even more interest, perhaps, are the exclusively telescopic showers. Both the end of August and the end of

223

September are active telescopically, with a number of faint streams, many of which have probably not yet been identified. One of the most interesting showers of all has its radiant near the star 11 Canis Majoris, and is active on December 11. It seems that these meteors move in a very elongated orbit that carries them within 3,500,000 miles of the sun at perihelion—ten times closer than sweltering Mercury.

However, telescopic showers are not easy to identify. This is because the sporadic rate is relatively high—there may well be more sporadic meteors than shower meteors, so that prolonged watches may be necessary before any preferential direction of flight becomes obvious.

OBSERVATION. The study of telescopic meteor rates is straightforward enough, but if attempts are being made to find a radiant, considerable preparation is necessary. The field of view must be drawn, preferably tracing it from a large-scale atlas, such as *Atlas Borealis* or *Eclipticalis*, or possibly from the *Bonner Durchmusterung*. The paths of meteors seen are then drawn directly onto the chart, and their magnitudes can be estimated from those of the stars in the field. After a suitable interval of time, the telescope can be shifted to another, nearby field, and the process repeated. By this procedure, any divergence of the trails from a common radiant will become obvious. For the same reason, meteors from a known radiant can best be analyzed by choosing two fields 10° or 15° from the radiant, but forming an angle of 90° with it.

Half-hour watches are best. The strain of viewing an unchanging field is considerable, and the observer tends to find himself hypnotized by one of the stars, so that frequent rests are necessary. The observer must stop when he finds his powers of concentration failing, for the subsequent inaccuracies will prejudice the good work performed while he was fresh. Comfort and alertness are major contributors to the accuracy of the final results; and, provided they do not involve other adverse factors, no measures designed to increase the observer's sense of well-being are to be scorned.

THE STARS AND NEBULAE

19

The Stars

Apart from observing the long-period variable stars, those curious, remote suns that brighten and fade in an inexplicable and unpredictable manner, there is little original work open to the amateur beyond the confines of our own solar system. The stars constitute the professionals' realm. They pose problems that require great telescopes for their investigation, while the mathematics involved is so advanced that no person without specialized, university-level training has the slightest hope of making useful contributions. Times have changed drastically since William Herschel and the other great pioneers swept unexplored skies. In this age of modern astronomy, there is an essential difference between the two branches of the science: Amateur astronomy is mainly *qualitative*, or descriptive, whereas professional astronomical research, involved with explanations of behavior and in deriving theories in terms of mathematics applied to physical laws, is entirely *quantitative*. It depends on the measurement of actual amounts rather than on generalities. On the whole, the amateur simply does not have either the apparatus or the knowledge required for such measurements.

Since a 3-inch refractor can reveal something like a million stars over the whole sky, it would be presumptuous to say they are of no interest. Yet, sadly, this is what many amateurs do. Intent on following lines of useful work, they have no inclination to stand and stare at something that, however beautiful, is of no immediate concern to them. Such people are missing half the inexhaustible delight and fascination of astronomy. Indeed, scientific research has become so hallowed that it takes considerable courage to admit that one derives pleasure from making technically useless observations! The study of the heavens from a purely esthetic point of view is scorned in this technological age.

Except, then, for a discussion of certain variable stars (Chap. 20), this section might be considered a plea for "useless" observations; an invitation to every telescope owner to spend an occasional evening away from Jupiter's cloud belts and the moon's inhospitable crags, to wander instead through the almost limitless tracts of the heavens. Here there are wonders in plenty—double stars, multiple stars, stars of strange colors; here and there one detects gleams of nebulae, and just occasionally a superb, encrusted star cluster masses its members against the black sky. The observer has left the solar system far behind him; he is wandering where in our time no man will ever wander, with only his thoughts and speculations for company.

Stars and the Galaxy

To give a full description of the nature of these objects would require much more space than would be appropriate in a work devoted to practical observation. In any case, I have dealt with them at length in *Stars and Planets*, so that only a brief outline of the main facts will be given here.

The sun is a star, unremarkable on the grand scale but of tremendous importance to us, since it is the controller and benefactor of our solar system. However, it is only one among perhaps 50,000 million stars that together form our particular *galaxy*. Even the nearest and brightest of these stars are, however, so far away that they shine very faintly in the sky, and we cannot see them with the naked eye until nightfall. Even then, only about 6,000 stars are detectable over the whole sky. The rest—millions of them—are so far away that a telescope is necessary to show them. The larger the telescope, and the more light it collects, the fainter the stars that it will reveal; but even the greatest telescopes in the world are unable to show all the galactic stars, so that the value of 50,000 million members is a statistical estimate only.

Some of the stars are far more luminous than the sun; others are much fainter. This depends partly on size, partly on temperature; the size of a star can be measured only indirectly, but it is not difficult to classify a star in terms of temperature by noting its color. Some are white, with a tinge of blue or green; these are the hottest, with surface temperatures of about 25,000°C. Pure white stars are considerably cooler (about 11,000°C), whereas a tinge of yellow suggests a temperature of about 7,500°C. The so-called yellow stars, of which the sun is one, are about 6,000°C and therefore temperate by stellar standards. "Orange" and "red" stars are still cooler, with temperatures down to about 2,600°C. These colors are subtle; there are few glaring stellar tints. To call a star "red" is to exaggerate its hue considerably, but after some practice the regular observer can distinguish different shades or colors quite easily. As an extreme example, there is a clear difference between the blue-white star Vega (overhead in temperate northern latitudes during late summer) and the red Antares (low in the south at the same time); clearly, Antares is the cooler of the two.

Most of the stars in the Galaxy are immensely far apart by interplanetary standards. If we construct a scale model of the solar system, with the sun about 4 inches across, the earth will be about 25 feet away, the size of a grain of sand, and Pluto will be about 300 yards away. But the nearest star to the sun, represented by another 4-inch globe, would have to be placed almost 1,500 miles away! It is obvious, then, that the whole Galaxy is of enormous extent, and that the mile is an absurdly inadequate unit of distance. Instead, astronomers make use of the *light-year*. A ray of light travels at 186,000 miles per second, so that it takes 8 minutes 20 seconds to reach us from the sun; and a light-year, the distance traveled by light in one terrestrial year, is just under six million million miles. The nearest star to the sun is $4\frac{1}{3}$ light-years away, which means that the light reaching our eyes left that star $4\frac{1}{3}$ years before—and this is just the *nearest* star!

The stars in the Galaxy are grouped together, forming a regular system. At the center is a roughly spherical nucleus with a diameter of about 11,000 light-years, and extending from this nucleus are two immense trains of stars that have been wrapped into a spiral by the system's slow rotation. The sun does not lie near the nucleus, as we might like to think; instead, it occupies a not very impressive position out on one of the arms, about halfway from the center to the perimeter. The Galaxy itself measures about 60,000 light-years across, and since it is very flattened, we naturally see more stars per square degree of sky when we look through the plane of the arms than at right angles to them. This explains the *Milky Way* effect, the Milky Way being our "inside" view of the galactic arms. Even a small telescope resolves it into depthless swarms of stars.

We cannot see the nucleus of the Galaxy. It is hidden from our eyes by clouds of interstellar dust, so much of our knowledge is hypothetical. These dark, obscuring clouds, known as *dark nebulae*, occur in many parts of the Milky Way. In the constellation Cygnus, for example, the naked eye perceives apparent irregularities and gaps in the nebulous course of the Milky Way, and these are simply our view of dark nebulae projected against the bright background.

Some, but not all, of the stars are lone wanderers, like the sun. Since, without exception, they are so remote that they do not show real disks in the greatest telescopes, they are not particularly interesting unless they happen to be of some unusual color, or vary in brightness. But other stars form fascinating telescopic objects. For instance, they may be "double," consisting of two or more individual stars lying so close together in the sky that a telescope is required to resolve them; or they may form a spectacular *star cluster*. These two classes of objects, together with the nebulae, form the main diet of the stellar observer.

The constellations and stellar nomenclature

From earliest times, the star patterns have been divided into rough groups, or *constellations*. There is nothing very scientific about a constellation; it is simply an arbitrary region of the sky and until recently, in fact, the boundaries between adjacent constellations were not well-defined. In 1930, however, definite demarcations were established by the International Astronomical Union, and the limits are now properly fixed.

The ancient astronomers were content simply to recognize the brightest stars in each constellation, and they associated their pattern with the outline of some suitable figure: the Dipper, or Great Bear (Ursa Major); the Hunter (Orion); the Scorpion (Scorpio); and so on. This was all very well in the early, rough-and-ready days, but as soon as people took a more critical interest in the stars it became necessary to list them individually. The first "modern" catalogue, issued in 1603 by the German astronomer Johann Bayer, allotted to each bright star in every constellation a Greek letter, followed by the genitive form of the constellation's Latin name. In general, too, he classified them in order of brightness, so that the brightest star in Boötes (the Herdsman) is known as Alpha (α) Boötis. This system worked so well that it is still in use. The more prominent stars are also endowed with proper names, usually derived from ancient Greek or Arabic apellations: Alpha (α) Boötis is known as Arcturus (the Bear Watcher); Alpha (α) Scorpionis, as Antares (Mars-like); Alpha (α) Lyrae, as Vega (the Falling Vulture); and so on.

Since the Greek alphabet has only twenty-four letters, and most constellations have more than twenty-four naked-eye stars, some other system was required to make the cataloguing really comprehensive. This was achieved in Flamsteed's catalogue of 1725. John Flamsteed, first British Astronomer Royal (1675), observed all the naked-eye stars visible from the latitude of Greenwich ($51\frac{1}{2}°N$), from the very brightest down to those of the 6th magnitude. In his catalogue he classified the stars in each constellation in order of right ascension, starting at the western boundary with 1 and running up to whatever number the constellation contained. In so doing, he reclassified all Bayer's stars, so that by his reckoning Arcturus, for example, is 16 Boötis. In these cases, however, Bayer's Greek letter is usually retained.

Catalogues of telescopic stars (i.e., those below the 6th magnitude) are numerous, but these are of less concern to the average amateur; the only telescopic stars likely to interest him are doubles and variables, and these have their own special classification. Mention must nevertheless be made of Friedrich W. A. Argelander's monumental general catalogue of all stars down to a declination of −2°, subsequently extended by others to cover the southern sky as well. First issued in 1862, and listing some 458,000 stars, Argelander's catalogue is still widely used. It ignores the constellations; instead, it covers the sky in bands of declination just 1° wide. Any star of between the 6th and 9th magnitude is usually referred to by Argelander's reckoning.

Stellar magnitudes

The magnitude of a star, as we have already seen, refers not to its size but to its brightness. Although early astronomers were content to call the brightest stars "1st magnitude" and the faintest "6th magnitude," the system has now been refined to two or three decimal places. The three brightest stars in the sky, Sirius, Canopus, and Arcturus, are actually assigned negative values, and the magnitude ratio has been adjusted so that a ratio of 5 magnitudes is equivalent to a brightness difference of exactly 100 times. A gap of one magnitude corresponds to a brightness ratio of about $2\frac{1}{2}$ (more accurately, 2·512). In this connection, Table VIII may be of interest.

TABLE VIII. Stellar Magnitude and Brightness

MAGNITUDE DIFFERENCE	BRIGHTNESS DIFFERENCE	MAGNITUDE DIFFERENCE	BRIGHTNESS DIFFERENCE
1·0	2·51	7·0	631·0
1·5	4·0	7·5	1,000·0
2·0	6·3	8·0	1,585
2·5	10·0	8·5	2,512
3·0	15·9	9·0	3,981
3·5	25·1	9·5	6,310
4·0	39·8	10·0	10,000
4·5	63·1	11·0	25,120
5·0	100·0	12·0	63,096
5·5	158·5	13·0	158,490
6·0	251·2	14·0	398,110
6·5	398·1	15·0	1,000,000

From this guide it follows that the brightest star in the sky, Sirius, with a magnitude of −1·44, is almost a thousand times as bright as a star of the

6th magnitude. Yet the faint stars—so faint that they can be seen only with a telescope—are so much in the majority that they send us far more *total* light than do the naked-eye stars. In this connection, it is interesting to examine the total number of stars of each magnitude that are to be found in the sky. An examination of Argelander's catalogue, which covers just over half the sky, gives the numbers of stars for each broad magnitude division as shown in Table IX.

TABLE IX. Magnitude Distribution of Stars
(numbers of stars in a one-magnitude interval)

1ST	2ND	3RD	4TH	5TH	6TH	7TH	8TH	9TH
20	65	190	425	1100	3200	13,000	40,000	142,000

The proportion of faint stars becomes still greater when we delve into the dimmer regions. Over the whole sky there are probably five million stars between magnitudes 11·0 and 12·0. They add considerable illumination to the background of the night sky—especially along the course of the Milky Way, in which we see probably 90 per cent of all the stars in the Galaxy.

Double stars

On a clear night, a glance at Zeta (ζ) Ursae Majoris (known as Mizar), second star from the end of the Dipper's "handle," will show that it is not alone. Mizar is a 2nd-magnitude star, and very close to it there is a fainter, 5th-magnitude star. If a telescope is turned onto this pair, which together constitute a naked-eye double star, Mizar will be seen to consist of two stars of magnitudes 2·1 and 4·2. These are so close together—the angular separation (known as *distance*) being only 14″·5—that a telescope is required to reveal the two separate stars. When viewed through the telescope, the 5th-magnitude naked-eye companion is of course seen very clearly.

Something like one-fourth of all the stars in the sky are double. Some, like Mizar, are easy; they can be resolved with a small telescope. Many others tax the powers of great instruments. But there are literally thousands within the range of a 3-inch refractor. Some consist of stars of about equal magnitude; in other cases, one star is so much brighter than its companion, or *comes* (pronounced kō-mez), that the second star is difficult to see. Some doubles have components of finely contrasted tints. And since most of these pairs are genuine stellar systems, with the two members slowly revolving around each other under the tie of gravity, we have cases where their appearance gradually changes as the years go by, the components apparently either moving closer together or else opening up. Few sights are more impressive than the steady progress of one of these so-called *binary* systems over the years, the only evidence the amateur has of actual movement in the stellar heavens. Even if the pair is of the *optical* kind, where the stars are not physically related at all, but simply happen to lie in almost the same line of sight, it may still have its interest. The amateur with a 3-inch refractor will find here an inexhaustible fund of interest and pleasure.

A double star such as Mizar is defined by three quantities: first, by the magnitudes of the components, commonly given to an accuracy of 1/10 (e.g., 2·1 and 4·2); second, by the distance, in seconds of arc (e.g., 14"·5); and, third, by the *position angle* (P.A.), which is the orientation of the fainter component relative to the brighter.

Position angle is measured in degrees, counterclockwise, starting from north, through east, south, west, and back to north again. Thus, N = 0°, or 360°; E = 90°; S = 180°; W = 270°. It is important to remember that *directions are reversed* in the field of an astronomical telescope, so that to an observer in the northern hemisphere, north is at the bottom, with east to the right (fig. 45). On the other hand, this is correct only when an object is on the meridian. When newly risen, the P.A. orientation is tilted over to the left; when near setting it is inclined to the right. It is important to bear this in mind when making an estimate of position angle. The P.A. of Mizar is 150°, which means that the comes (companion) is to the southeast. The complete details are written: 2·1, 4·2; 14"·5; 150°. Where a double star consists of three or more components, they are labeled *A*, *B*, *C*, etc., in order of decreasing brightness.

The terms "preceding" and "following" are also very useful in double-star work. They refer to the apparent drift of the object through the field of view, which is always from east to west. Combined with the north and south points, they enable rough positions to be assigned: *north-following* (*nf*) indicates the 45° quadrant; *south-preceding* (*sp*) that at 225°; and so on. By the use of these terms, plus an estimate of distance in either seconds or

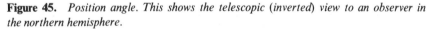

Figure 45. *Position angle. This shows the telescopic (inverted) view to an observer in the northern hemisphere.*

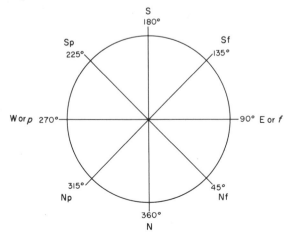

minutes of arc, the position of any star in the field can be assigned quite accurately; although for precise measures a special micrometer is necessary.

We have already seen how the resolving power of a telescope depends on its aperture. Knowing the aperture, it is possible to decide which double stars are likely to be resolved. The resolving limit of a 3-inch is about 1″·5; therefore it is no use trying to split a double whose components are 1″·0 apart, although the image may be elongated if conditions are favorable. Other factors are involved, however. The resolving limit applies to stars of the same brightness and of about the 6th magnitude. The brighter the star, the larger its diffraction disk, so that it may prove impossible to resolve a pair of 2nd-magnitude stars, even though they are slightly wider than the "theoretical" limit. On the other hand, if the stars are too faint, they are difficult to glimpse. Even more serious is the effect of one star being much brighter than the other. A case in point is the brilliant Sirius—Alpha (a) Canis Majoris—which has a 7th-magnitude companion with which it forms a binary system, the distance varying from about 2″ to 11″·5 in a period of fifty years. When at its elongation the comes is hard to see even with a moderate instrument, and when closest (a position known as *periastron*), the intense glare of the bright star makes it invisible in the greatest telescopes.

The double stars listed in Chapter 21 have been chosen for their visibility in small telescopes. The brighter ones were listed in Bayer's and Flamsteed's catalogues, and have been nominated accordingly. The fainter ones, and the southern objects, are listed according to the catalogues of the various observers who have specialized in this kind of work. Herschel himself discovered more than 800, all being identified by the letter H; but this designation is rarely used, for his stars were remeasured and re-catalogued by the great Russian astronomer F. G. W. Struve. Struve's work was begun in 1819, three years before William Herschel's death, and in 1824 Fraunhöfer's splendid 9½-inch refractor, then the biggest in the world, was installed at the Dorpat Observatory, where Struve worked. With this instrument he discovered about 2,200 new double stars between 1825 and 1827, and during the following decade he made accurate micro-metrical measures of all the known pairs. This monumental research was embodied in his *Mensurae Micrometricae*, published at St. Petersburg (now Leningrad) in 1837. It runs to 3,112 stars, all designated by the Greek capital sigma (Σ), and includes most of the doubles that are visible with a small telescope. Further pairs were listed by his son Otto (OΣ).

So far, the northern celestial hemisphere had been the center of attention. But in 1833, after spending eight years reexamining his father's stellar objects, Sir John Herschel left England for the Cape of Good Hope to lead the assault on the southern skies. Four years later, he returned with

2,102 new doubles, identified by the letter h. In this way, the Herschels, father and son, and the Struves, father and son, exhausted the entire sky of its more obvious pairs. Even so, an unsuspected number remained, the components so close together and difficult of separation that they had so far been overlooked. Of the stars detected by subsequent observers, the catalogue of most interest to the amateur is that of S. W. Burnham, a Chicago lawyer who later became a professional double-star observer at the Lick Observatory. In 1900, he published a catalogue of 1,290 new doubles, more than one thousand of which he had discovered from his back garden during whatever leisure time was afforded by his legal profession. The Greek letter beta (β) designates these stars, not many of which are within the range of a 3-inch. Burnham himself as an amateur used only a 6-inch refractor, which testifies to his remarkable keenness of vision, since most of his pairs are extremely close and difficult.

The following abbreviations are the ones most likely to be used for doubles visible with a small telescope:

β = S. W. Burnham (1906)
H = W. Herschel (1782–1822)
h = J. Herschel (1847—southern)
Hh = J. Herschel's catalogue of W. Herschel's doubles (1833)
Ho = G. W. Hough
Hu = W. J. Hussey
I = R. T. A. Innes (1927—southern)
L = N. L. de Lacaille (1847—southern)
Σ = F. G. W. Struve (1837)
OΣ & O$\Sigma\Sigma$ = Otto Struve (1850)

Mention should also be made of a standard work, R. G. Aitken's *New General Catalogue of Double Stars* (1932), listing 17,180 pairs (Carnegie Institution, Washington). The most recent and exhaustive work is the Lick Observatory's *Index Catalogue* (1964).

Star clusters

The Galaxy contains two main types of star clusters. In some parts of the sky, particularly along the track of the Milky Way, we find glorious assemblages of stars sprinkled across the sky like glittering crushed glass. Some of these so-called *open* clusters are such superb spectacles that the observer instinctively returns to them again and again. The impression wrought by these crowded suns is overwhelming. In some open clusters the stars are bright, perhaps set in festoons like a diamond brooch; in others, a vast aggregation of faint specks powders the night sky. Presented with these sights, above all others, the observer suffers a feeling of awe that can be matched by nothing else in the sky. Here, immensity and delicacy are fused into a quite unearthly concept of grandeur.

The *globular* clusters, on the other hand, are somewhat disappointing objects in anything less than an 8- or 10-inch telescope. These are colossal balls of stars, massed together in numbers estimated by the hundred thousand, and are impressive objects in photographs; yet the individual stars are packed so closely together that a small telescope shows only a spherical blur, with perhaps a hint of individual stars around the margin. Not many globulars are known—a small telescope will reveal perhaps thirty over the whole sky—but they are interesting enough, even if nowhere near as spectacular as the open clusters.

Nebulae

One of the most notorious points of confusion in the field of astronomy is the difference between *nebulae* and *galaxies*. For there *is* a difference, not withstanding the fact that in the older catalogues they have all been listed as "nebulae"! Let us examine what is now known about these two classes of objects.

True nebulae *belong to the Galaxy*. They are clouds of gas and dust, very thin but of immense extent, in most cases being thousands of times larger than our solar system. The dark nebulae, already mentioned, are visible only because of the stars they hide from view; but of more interest are the *bright nebulae*, which appear as glowing wisps of matter. Their individual appearance varies enormously. The Great Nebula in the constellation Orion is easily seen with the naked eye, but only because it is exceptionally near the solar system. Most of these nebulae are rather faint and frankly unspectacular, but here and there the telescope will pick up well-known examples. The *planetary nebulae*, or *planetaries*, form an interesting subgroup, for they show small but definite disks, rather like ghostly planets. However, not more than a dozen planetaries are accessible with a small telescope.

As well as these galactic nebulae, there are many other dim gleams of light in the sky. A 3-inch refractor will show quite a few in Leo, Virgo, and Coma Berenices, and there are accumulations elsewhere in the sky. These objects, unlike the nebulae, *do not belong to our galaxy*. They are independent galaxies in their own right, each containing perhaps as many stars as there are in our own system. Millions of light-years away, they appear to us as mere stains against the sky. The universe is known to contain millions of galaxies, of which our own star system is an unremarkable member. Most of the *external galaxies* are very remote, but it is not surprising that the nearest ones should be bright enough to be conspicuous in even a small telescope; indeed, one of these can be seen with the naked eye in the constellation Andromeda. Lying more than two million light-years away, it appears to our vision as an elongated blur of light; yet this is a star city like our own galaxy, comprising thousands of millions of stars!

We have no direct means of telling how far away these other galaxies are, because every celestial object, from the moon to a remote star system, appears to be at infinity. To establish deep-space distances involves indirect investigations, and it was not until the present century that the external galaxies were finally identified as such. Before then, since the individual stars could not be seen with the available telescopes, they had simply appeared to be gaseous nebulae; accordingly, they are so listed in the classic catalogues. Modern catalogues, of course, differentiate between the two types of object; but the old lists, of which the N.G.C. is the most comprehensive, are still in general use. To the eye, indeed, there is no perceptible difference; they all look nebulous, and the designation has remained. Hence, an object classed as a "nebula" may, in fact, be a mass of glowing gas inside our own galaxy—but it is more probably an external galaxy.* As a general visual guide, the external galaxies have a regular appearance, whether spherical, elliptical, or extremely elongated, whereas the galactic nebulae are more irregular and the planetaries are quite sharply defined. In the constellation notes in Chapter 21, the distinction will be made wherever possible.

In general, nebulae and clusters have been listed together in the same catalogues. William Herschel, in his pioneer work on the northern sky, divided them into eight different classes:

   I. Bright nebulae
  II. Faint nebulae
 III. Very faint nebulae
 IV. Planetary nebulae
  V. Very large nebulae
 VI. Very compressed clusters
VII. Compressed clusters of bright and faint stars
VIII. Coarse clusters

This is a most convenient system, for it offers a preliminary guide to the observer. Thus, a bright planetary nebula in the constellation Draco is listed as H.IV.37—or, more simply, 37^4—while two beautiful open clusters in Perseus are listed as 33^6 and 34^6.

Sir John Herschel's subsequent visit to the Cape produced a fine

* Because of their visual similarity—they all look nebulous—they are sometimes referred to as "extragalactic nebulae"; but this term is misleading.

southern-sky sequel to his father's list of 2,500 nebulae and clusters. His total came to 1,708, and subsequent additions brought the number of combined observations up to 5,079. These were published in a great catalogue in 1864, which was afterward extended by Dreyer to more than 7,000 objects and published in 1888 as the *New General Catalogue*, which remains the standard list. Perhaps a thousand of the objects listed are discernible with a small telescope (though most of these are simply gleams of light), so the *N.G.C.* is of value to all observers. Unfortunately, it lacks the elder Herschel's system of classification, so that without the descriptive catalogue it is impossible to tell whether a certain object is a cluster or a nebula. Because of this, most of Herschel's original designations have been retained, while Messier's list of 103 nebulae and clusters, subsequently extended to 107, is also a useful guide to the bright objects.

Magnification and resolution

So far as magnification is concerned, each double star imposes its own conditions. A wide pair, such as Mizar, can be easily divided with × 50; a higher power, which separates the stars even more, loses some of the effect. The same is true of the beautiful double Beta (β) Cygni, where the stars are yellow and blue (partly a contrast effect), at a distance of 35″. Here, a power of × 30 is adequate; it shows Beta's splendid tints and also includes many other stars in the field of view. On the other hand, there are pairs such as Epsilon (ε) Boötis (3·0, 6·3; 3″·0; 340°), whose stars are so close that a high magnification is required to give a clear separation. The regular observer will become accustomed to these idiosyncrasies.

The nebulae, being dim and ill-defined, require a low power to concentrate the light and show them to the best advantage. Many are quite imperceptible with a powerful eyepiece, because of the loss of contrast; and some very large ones are so faint and extended that they are more conspicuous in the finder than with the main telescope. Similarly, open clusters are generally best seen with low powers and wide fields, whereas planetary nebulae and globular clusters require considerable magnification.

The resolution of a double star depends to a great extent on the seeing. Take for example the bright red star Antares (Alpha Scorpionis), which, with respect to color, has been aptly termed "the rival of Mars." This is a 1st-magnitude star with a 7th-magnitude companion at a distance of 3″. On an unsteady night, the image of the bright star flares and expands far beyond its nominal size, sometimes extending beyond the first and second diffraction rings. Under these conditions, it is clearly hopeless to look for the comes. Only when the great star subsides into something like its proper diameter can the faint attendant be seen alongside its rays. Obviously, the telescope cannot be blamed for failing to find it on bad nights. Antares is a notoriously difficult object to resolve from the latitude of the British Isles or extreme northern United States, where it is always low in the sky; but from stations farther south it is much easier, since it appears higher above the horizon, where the seeing conditions are superior.

The above example proves that the statement (encountered in so many books) that double stars are a test of telescopic performance is gravely inaccurate. They are far more truly a test of atmospheric steadiness. By far the best test of a mirror or object glass is the intrafocal and extrafocal test, which can be performed under almost any atmospheric conditions. Stellar resolution may be a by-product of optical excellence, but there is no reason to make it a criterion.

Magnitude limits

The concept of "limiting magnitude" is another widely-fostered misconception. It has been claimed that a 3-inch telescope should show stars down to magnitude 11·4; a 6-inch, down to 12·9; a 12-inch, to 14·4, and so on. However, there are so many influential factors at work that the unwary beginner may be unjustifiably disappointed when his performance fails to match with the tables. On some nights, it may be difficult or impossible to see the 9th-magnitude companion to the polestar—Alpha (a) Ursae Minoris—with a 3-inch. On other nights, it may be obvious, and stars as faint as the 11th magnitude may be glimpsed. By indulging in deep breathing before making the observation, then holding his breath and using averted vision, a friend of mine claims to have glimpsed stars of the 13th magnitude, using a 3-inch refractor. Continued practice and refinement of technique will naturally lead to superior results.

Whatever its capabilities on a particular night, a telescope cannot be expected to approach its limiting magnitude in the case of a star very near a more brilliant one. This is partly due to the effect of glare; there may also be some temporary desensitizing of the retina in the region of the bright image. The satellites of Saturn indicate this anomaly very well. For instance, Rhea can be seen with a 3-inch when near elongation, but in so small a telescope disappears from view when it approaches the planet's limb. Ariel, innermost of the four bright Uranian satellites, is the most difficult to see, though of the four it is the brightest; this paradoxical effect misled many early observers and is responsible for errors even today.*
The companion to Sirius, a famous teaser, used to be rated 9th magnitude

---

* The usually authoritative B.A.A. *Handbook* lists Ariel as being fainter than both Titania and Oberon.

because of the difficulty of observation, but is now generally accepted to be as bright as the 7th. It is advisable to use the highest possible power for observations of this sort, since this increases the apparent separation. A high magnification also has the effect of darkening the sky background, thus augmenting faint points of light.

Atmospheric steadiness is essential for delicate observations of this sort. To the naked eye, the sky may appear black and crowded with faint stars; but these conditions are of no help to the telescope if the seeing is bad, for the atmospheric ripples will blur the pinpoint images of the tiniest stars and efface them as effectively as haze. The nebulae, being extended objects, do not suffer materially from the effects of bad seeing, but faint companions to double stars demand both transparency and steadiness, a combination that occurs only on rare nights.

When preparing to observe faint objects, the eye must be given a chance to become thoroughly dark-adapted. Here again we can take a hint from William Herschel, who knew that the only chance of detecting dim stars and nebulae was to give his eye the greatest possible sensitivity before commencing observations. As Agnes Mary Clerke, the astronomical historian, wrote, in *The Herschels and Modern Astronomy*:

> His [*William Herschel's*] *sense of sight was exceedingly refined, and he took care to keep it so. In order to secure complete* "*tranquillity of the retina,*" *he used to remain twenty minutes in the dark before attempting to observe faint objects; and his eye became so sensitive after some hours spent in* "*sweeping,*" *that the approach of a 3rd-magnitude star obliged him to withdraw it from the telescope. A black hood thrown over his head while observing served to heighten this delicacy of vision. Details are* "*of consequence,*" *he wrote,* "*when we come to refinements, and want to screw an instrument up to the utmost pitch.*"

It is worth pointing out that even Herschel's "bright nebulae" are mostly dim objects in a 3-inch refractor, and that class II and III objects are mostly imperceptible without a moderate aperture. The remarkable fact that he *discovered* many of these with a 6-inch reflector testifies to his "delicacy of vision."

For bright double stars, where transparency is of little account, adequate observations can be made from towns. But the observation of faint stars and nebulae is severely handicapped by urban conditions, and it must be admitted that the night sky of most towns does little to gladden the stargazer's heart. The atmospheric haze, its effect heightened by nocturnal illuminations, utterly blots out a nebula, while the swarms of faint stars in an open cluster will also be lost to view. Just occasionally, conditions improve—I have on a few occasions glimpsed the brightest regions of the

Milky Way from near the center of London—and formerly invisible objects may be detected; but such revelations act more as a frustration than anything else. Facts must be faced: The town-dweller's opportunity for useful work lies with the moon and planets, whose brilliant disks are dimmed and steadied by the haze; in this field, therefore, he may well have an advantage over those observers who enjoy a black sky and a brilliant Milky Way.

The celestial sphere

It may be wise at this point to deal more fully with the concept of right ascension and declination, since the pinpointing of an object on the celestial sphere is of great importance in stellar work.

The stars and nebulae retain the same relative position from night to night and, to all intents and purposes, from century to century. Their only obvious movement is their diurnal passage across the sky, and this comes as a result of the earth's rotation. Since the earth spins from west to east, the stars appear to revolve in the opposite sense, from east to west.

Since all celestial objects appear to be equally far away, the night sky assumes the appearance of a colossal sphere, with the stars attached to its inner surface, revolving around the earth once in a sidereal day. Figure 46 shows an external view of this imaginary sphere; certain fundamental points on the earth's surface are mirrored on the sphere. Projecting the axis makes it touch the sphere at just those two points that appear to be stationary in the sky: These are the north and south celestial poles, around which the rest of the stars seem to revolve. Since the angle of the earth's axis

Figure 46.   *The celestial sphere.*

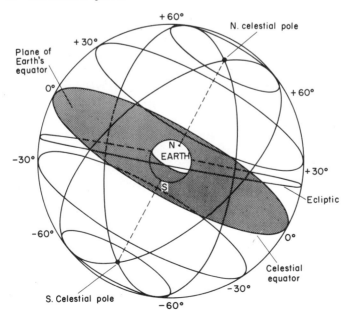

is virtually constant, the celestial poles remain in the same place. The north pole is marked approximately by the polestar, of the 2nd magnitude, which happens to lie nearby; but the south pole occurs in a rather barren patch of sky and does not have a conspicuous marker. An observer on the earth's equator would, theoretically at least, see both poles at his north and south horizons; as one travels northwards, the north celestial pole rises higher and higher in the sky. If one ventured as far as the earth's north pole, the polestar, would be directly overhead.

In a similar way, the celestial equator can be inscribed on this imaginary sphere by extending the plane of the earth's equator. An equatorial observer sees the celestial equator as an imaginary line running from the east to the west horizon, and passing overhead. To an observer moving progressively north or south away from the equator, it is inclined lower and lower in the sky; by the time he reaches the north or south pole, it is level with the horizon. A polar observer will always see just one hemisphere of stars, the other half of the sky being permanently hidden from view by the body of the earth.

Now that the sphere has been inscribed with poles and equator, lines of declination can be added. These are analogous to terrestrial latitude, the equator being 0° and the poles 90°. With respect to longitude, or *right ascension* (R.A.), it is more convenient to divide the sphere into 24 hours than into 360°, since this provides a direct conversion to its rate of rotation.

The zero position for right ascension (the celestial equivalent of the Greenwich meridian), is derived from the apparent motion of the sun. As we have seen, the earth's annual circuit of the sun makes the sun itself appear to revolve around the celestial sphere. One way of demonstrating this is to stand a chair in the middle of a room and walk slowly round it; the chair will be seen projected against successive parts of the room, until it seems to have completed a full circle.

Since the earth's axis is tilted with respect to its orbit at an angle of $23\frac{1}{2}°$, the sun's apparent path around the celestial sphere is inclined to the equator at this critical angle, crossing it at two points. The first, traversed on about March 21 when the sun is traveling northward, is called the *vernal equinox*, and this point marks the 0^h line of right ascension. The other, reached on about September 23 when the sun is sinking into the south celestial hemisphere, is called the *autumnal equinox*. This, of course, is on the opposite point of the equator, and marks the 12^h meridian. It follows from this that the part of the ecliptic lying between 0^h and 12^h is in north declination; the remainder, from R.A. 12^h to 24^h, is south.

This is the way in which the celestial sphere is marked out with its fundamental reference lines. The stars keep virtually the same positions from century to century, but the sun, moon, and planets are constantly shifting, always keeping to the region of the ecliptic, so that they cannot be marked on a star map.

Precession

There is, however, a very slight drifting of the stars. This occurs through a slight wobble, or *precession*, of the earth's axis; it is turning, very slowly, through a small circle, rather like a dying top, and the drifting effectively pulls the grid of right ascension and declination with it. The result is that the stars, relative to this grid, are changing their positions.

Precession is a very leisurely process. It will take about 26,000 years for the celestial poles to make their revolution; nevertheless, the change from century to century is appreciable. Since many useful catalogues are now out of date by this amount, it is necessary to apply a slight correction if an object's position is to be plotted accurately on a modern atlas. The *Bonner Durchmusterung*, for example, is correct for the epoch of 1855; there is therefore a considerable discrepancy between the positions given in this and those given in *Norton's*, which is based on the 1950 epoch. The tables in Appendix VI will enable the observer to allow for precession when working with old atlases.

20

Variable Star Observation

The observation of variable stars deserves a separate chapter, because it is one branch of stellar astronomy in which the amateur can do really useful work. These are stars which change in brightness over periods ranging from a few hours to a year or more, while some fluctuate quite erratically. Generally speaking, it is only the erratic variables that are of interest to the amateur, for the predictable ones have been closely studied at professional observatories.

Variable stars can be divided into two broad classes. There are the *eclipsing* types, which are simply binary systems seen more or less edge-on to the orbit, so that the stars periodically occult each other; and the *intrinsic* type, where the star actually changes in luminosity due to physical instability in its gaseous shell, which in many cases produces fluctuations of pressure which, in turn, affect its temperature and brightness. The light fluctuations of the eclipsing type are, of course, perfectly regular. When one star is occulted by the other, the total brightness is reduced; and since these systems are so close that the individual components cannot be distinguished even with the greatest telescopes, the effect is of a single star appearing first to dim, then to brighten again.

Eclipsing variables

The most famous eclipsing variable in the sky lies in Perseus. It is known as Algol—Beta (β) Persei—and it can be found very easily, for it lies south of the line joining Alpha (a) Persei and Gamma (γ) Andromedae. For most of the time, Algol shines at a steady magnitude of 2·3, which in brightness is midway between Alpha (a) and Zeta (ζ) Persei; but every $2\frac{1}{2}$

244

days it fades quite rapidly, dimming to 3·5 (fainter than Gamma) in five hours. In another five hours it regains its original magnitude, and the cycle begins again.

Algol belongs to the subclass of *dark-eclipsing* variables, since one of its components is much larger and dimmer than the other. The main drop in brightness therefore occurs when the dark component occults the bright one. When the reverse happens, the total brightness drops only very slightly. Actually, there is a "secondary minimum" in the middle of the 2½-day spell during which this occurs, but the fall is only about $\frac{1}{20}$ of a magnitude—imperceptible without accurate measuring instruments.

If, however, the two components are about equally luminous, the secondary minimum will be much more noticeable, and there will be two distinct fadings during the stars' revolution around each other. The prototype of this *bright-eclipsing* variety is Beta (β) Lyrae, near the brilliant Vega. The period is 12 days, during which time it drops from its maximum value of 3·4 to 4·3 (main minimum) and to 3·8 (secondary minimum). Both these stars can be represented by the light curves shown in figure 47.

Intrinsic variables

Eclipsing variables are remarkable enough, but they are not as interesting as the *intrinsic* type. These can be grouped into four classes: *regular*,

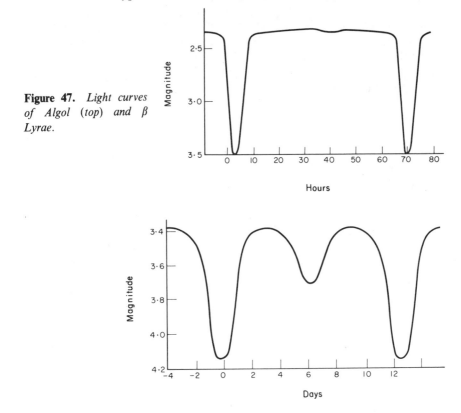

Figure 47. *Light curves of Algol* (*top*) *and* β *Lyrae.*

semiregular, *irregular*, and *novae*. Here again, the regular types are of interest only to the professional. Two well-known varieties are the *Cepheids* and the *RR Lyrae* stars, which apparently produce their light variations by expanding and contracting in a regular rhythm. The prototype of the Cepheids, Delta (δ) Cephei, varies from magnitude 3·8 to 4·6 in a period of 5⅓ days, and a characteristic of most of these stars is their sharp rise to maximum (Delta Cephei takes just over a day) and their rather slower fall to minimum. Cepheids are much larger and more luminous than the sun, but since they are very far away we cannot see many with the naked eye. The polestar is actually a Cepheid variable, though its range of magnitude is very small.

The other intrinsic variables are of much greater interest to the amateur, since it is with these that really useful work can be done. Many backyard astronomers are engaged in following these "unpredictable" stars, but there will always be room for more, since the sky contains far more erratic variables than a hundred observers can hope to cover adequately. Teamwork is important; during a star's critical period, a great deal can happen in a few nights, and an obstructive period of cloud can completely frustrate the issue. The more widespread the coverage, the greater the chance that someone will register an observation during the vital time.

Semiregular variables

If we can speak of a prototype of nonconformity, the type-star of the semiregular or long-period variables is Omicron (*o*) Ceti (Mira). It can be sighted in the rather barren northeast corner of Cetus; it lies slightly south of the celestial equator. Mira is a "giant" star, much bigger than the sun, but it has a lower density and is cooler, which means that its color is redder. In fact, most of the semiregular variables have a definite red hue, which helps in identification.

Mira's caprices were first noticed as far back as 1596, when the Dutch observer David Fabricius discovered that Cetus contained a new 2nd-magnitude star. He first noticed it on August 13, and followed it for some weeks until it had sunk below naked-eye visibility. Some years later, in 1609, he reobserved this curious object, apparently unaware that Johann Bayer, while collecting material for his famous star map "Uranometria," had seen it in 1603, not recognizing it as a variable star, and had recorded it as Omicron Ceti. It was sighted twice again, in 1631 and 1638, but not until 1639 were these sightings established as being of one and the same object, and another thirty years went by before a definite periodicity of about 11 months came to light.

But Mira, while admitting to a general law of fluctuation, has characteristics of its own. Its period can vary from about 300 to 360 days; and while it usually falls to about the 9th magnitude at minimum, detectable with a 2-inch refractor, its maximum brightness is unpredictable. In November, 1868, for instance, it reached only the 5th magnitude and was visible with the naked eye for only a few weeks; in 1799, on the other hand, Herschel recorded it as being almost as bright as Alpha (*a*) Tauri (Aldebaran), which is of the 1st magnitude. At a very bright maximum it has been seen with the naked eye for as long as six months at a time. It is hardly surprising that Omicron was called Mira, the Latin word for "wonderful." Usually it reaches the 3rd or 4th magnitude, rising from minimum somewhat faster than the subsequent fading; but it is dangerous to trust to average form, and Mira is well worth watching for fluctuations in behavior. As an aid to its identification, figure 48 shows a chart of the region.

There are many Mira-type stars in the sky, and, because their periods are mostly between about 150 and 500 days, they are usually referred to as *long-period variables*. Some other LPV's, such as Chi (*χ*) Cygni, are visible with the naked eye at maximum, but none has become as prominent as Mira, and most are entirely telescopic objects. Notes on the more

Figure 48. *Field of o Ceti (Mira). Based on a chart issued by the Variable Star Section of the British Astronomical Association, this shows a field of 9° around the variable, and will allow magnitude estimates to be made with binoculars. Numbers against some of the stars refer to Flamsteed's catalogue of 1726. Not all stars are given a magnitude, since some are unsuitable for estimates.*

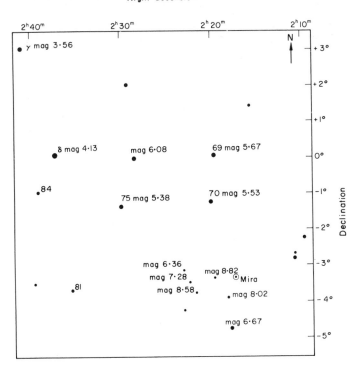

interesting stars of this type are included with the constellation descriptions in Chapter 21.

While many of the bright variables had been catalogued as fixed stars (albeit unwittingly) by Bayer and Flamsteed before their vagaries were noticed, the telescopic variety have received their own system of nomenclature. One, devised by Argelander, who discovered several variables during his work, identifies the stars in each constellation by the letters R, S, T, and so on, up to Z. This provides for only nine stars, so after that they are designated RR, RS, RT, and so on, followed by SS to SZ, TT to TZ—and so on, to ZZ. This allows for 54 variables in each constellation; if more are present, we return to the beginning of the alphabet with AA to AZ, BB to BZ, and so on, down to the letter Q (but omitting the letter J). This extremely cumbersome system, which allows for a total of 334 variable stars in each constellation, has been established for a century and is still used in standard lists. If the constellation contains more stars than can be accommodated by Argelander's nomenclature, subsequent variables are designated as 335V, 336V, etc. Argelander began his system with the letter R to avoid any possible confusion with the A–Q lettering used, instead of Greek letters, to identify the naked-eye stars in some southern constellations.

A more convenient system of identification, often used in conjunction with the above symbols, was introduced by Harvard Observatory. It consists of six numbers, the first four referring to the right ascension and the last two to the declination of the variable. For example, SW Geminorum, at R.A. 6^h 53^m, Dec. $+ 26°$, is referred to as 065326. If the declination is southern, the last two numbers are underlined.

Aside from the LPV's, there are other classes of semiregular variables which are of great interest to amateurs. Indeed, they are observed more consistently than any of the others. There are four broad types, in each of which the members show roughly the same behavior, and they are called after the first star of the class to be discovered:

RV TAURI STARS. These have irregular periods, usually of several months. The minimum magnitude is usually fairly constant, but the maxima are alternately bright and faint. The range is usually two or three magnitudes, and the period quoted is for the whole cycle of bright and faint maxima. R Scuti is a bright RV Tauri type, sometimes reaching the 5th magnitude.

U GEMINORUM STARS. This is a most interesting class. Here, the star remains at minimum brightness for perhaps months on end, suddenly surging up for a brief maximum, or *rise*, lasting for a few days at most.

In general, the longer the period (which cannot be predicted), the greater the maximum. The range of these stars can be five magnitudes, or even more. None is ever visible with the naked eye.

Z CAMELOPARDALIS STARS. A subclass of the U Geminorum type. Here, the star often suffers a "standstill" during its decline. These may last for any period from a few weeks to a year or more, and are quite unpredictable.

R CORONAE BOREALIS STARS. These perform in reverse, spending most of their time at maximum and suddenly dropping by up to 6 or 7 magnitudes to a minimum that can last for weeks or months. At maximum, the prototype is just visible with the naked eye; at minimum, it may be invisible with a 12-inch telescope.

All these stars need constant watching. A period of cloudy weather may mean that a brief rise of the U Geminorum type is completely missed. Obviously, co-operation among observers is essential. The American Association of Variable Star Observers (A.A.V.S.O.), Harvard College Observatory, Cambridge, Mass., exists to help these observers and to analyze results; in the United Kingdom, the same work is done by the Variable Star Section of the British Astronomical Association. These bodies have kept faithful records of certain selected stars for more than half a century, and our knowledge of these semi-regular variables is due almost entirely to the work of amateurs.

Irregular variables

One of the most interesting stars in the sky is Alpha (a) Orionis (Betelgeuse), which to an observer's view marks the Hunter's left shoulder. Alpha glows in the sky with a magnificent orange tinge, and month-to-month observations show that it undergoes definite variations in brightness. Its fluctuations are slow, but since the range is from about 0·1 to 1·4 they become obvious enough after a time. It lies near the bright orange star Aldebaran, in Taurus, whose magnitude of 0·78 makes it a useful comparison star. Beta (β) Geminorum (Pollux) is also nearby; it has a magnitude of 1·16.

Irregular variables have no definite periods, and there are a number of these interesting stars visible with the naked eye. Alpha (a) and Gamma (γ) Cassiopeiae are both of this type. Alpha has been seen alternately brighter and fainter than Beta (2·4), though the variations are very slow. The other star, Gamma, is more energetic; it rose quite quickly, from the same brightness as Beta to magnitude 1·7, in 1937, so that it was much brighter than any other star in the region. It also faded quickly, and still suffers variations, sometimes appearing as faint as the 3rd magnitude. Since it may brighten up again at any moment, this is a star which should be glanced at from week to week.

Another bright irregular is Mu (μ) Cephei, Herschel's "Garnet Star," which shines with a beautiful velvety color. Mu Cephei's reddish tint is rivalled by Hind's "Crimson Star," R Leporis. R Andromedae is another star with a most conspicuous tint, which has been likened to the color of a glowing cigarette.*

Mu Cephei varies from magnitude 3½ to 5; Alpha (a) Herculis, another bright example, fluctuates between 3 and 4, and there are many other variables of this type. The more interesting ones are included in the constellation chapter.

One of the most erratic stars in the sky is the variable T Coronae Borealis, aptly nicknamed "the Blaze Star." Normally of the 9th magnitude, in May, 1866, it shot up more or less overnight to the 2nd magnitude. After a week of naked-eye visibility, it vanished from view once more, returning to its original brightness until February, 1946, when it surged up to the 3rd magnitude. Once more it faded rapidly, and it is now visible as a magnitude 9·5 object about a degree south of Epsilon (ε). No doubt it will one day flare up again, although it may not be for years; but whenever it does, the first warning will probably come from an amateur who has noticed "something wrong" with the familiar group of Corona Borealis (the Northern Crown).

The most famous "blaze star" of all lies in the southern hemisphere, but for some time now it has been quiescent. This star, Eta (η) Carinae, was first catalogued by Edmund Halley, who noted it as a 4th-magnitude object while observing from the island of St. Helena in 1677. Since the Greek astronomer Ptolemy, who drew up a star catalogue in the second century A.D., had not noted a star in its place, it seems certain that at that epoch it was beyond naked-eye visibility. Drastic changes soon followed. In 1687, and again in 1751, it was seen as a 2nd-magnitude object, fading down between times to its more usual luster; while in 1827, it shot up to the 1st magnitude, declined slightly, and finally summoned a burst of energy that brought it up almost to the level of Sirius, the brightest star in the sky! After holding this position for several years, this extraordinary star began to fade until, in 1868, it was lost from naked-eye view. By 1886,

---

*Two nineteenth-century observers, J. Birmingham and T. E. Espin, produced extensive catalogues of red stars; the final list, drawn up by Espin in 1888 and incorporating the work of both observers, is often referred to. If a star is marked "E–B," it is certain to have a reddish tint.

it had reached a minimum magnitude of 7·6, at which it has remained to the present time. Whether it will ever repeat this splendid course, only time will tell.

Novae and Supernovae

The most remarkable "variables" of all are those stars which seem literally to explode. Once every three years or so, on an average, one of these inconspicuous 10th- or 11th-magnitude stars suddenly suffers some internal instability, forcing the surface layers outwards in a colossal eruption that blasts it up into naked-eye visibility. It takes just a few hours to increase its light output by perhaps 50,000 times, remaining for a day or two perhaps the most luminous star in the Galaxy. So far as astronomers can tell, there is nothing exceptional about a star that decides to turn itself into a *nova*, and there is no way of forecasting where and when the next one is likely to appear. The only statistical probability of use to nova-hunters is the 90 per cent chance of one occurring within the Milky Way, since this is where we see the majority of stars.

A recent bright nova was found on February 6, 1963, by a Swedish amateur astronomer, Elis Dahlgren and, independently, by the American comet-hunter L. C. Peltier, of Delphos, Ohio. On that date it appeared of magnitude 3·9, lying on the border of the constellations Lyra and Hercules, and only 6° from Vega. The find was not reported in the newspapers until February 13 (and then very inaccurately), but I managed to sight it early on the following morning, when its magnitude was about 4·5. Like all novae, it faded much more slowly than it rose. By the beginning of March, it had declined to 4·8, but it did not drop below the 6th magnitude until early April; a year later, it was of magnitude 7·5 and therefore easily visible with binoculars. At the time of writing, two and a half years after the initial outburst, it has sunk to between the 12th and 13th magnitudes and so needs a moderate telescope for its detection. Since the star was found to lie just within the confines of Hercules, it is now referred to in the standard form: *Nova Herculis, 1963*.

Still more recently, on July 8, 1967, the British comet- and nova-hunter George Alcock was rewarded with the discovery of a bright new star in the small constellation of Delphinus. When discovered, after only twenty minutes' sweeping with his 11 × 80 binoculars, its magnitude was 5·6. He immediately notified the Royal Greenwich Observatory, and on the following night the discovery was confirmed by professional astronomers. Nova Delphini has proved to be a most unusual star; instead of sinking down quite rapidly after its outburst, it fluctuated between magnitudes 3·5 and 5·5 for several months, attracting the fascinated attention of amateurs all over the world. Less than three months later, on October 27, 1967, the variable star RS Ophiuchi, which had suffered nova-like outbursts in 1898 and 1933, was discovered by amateurs in Europe and the United States to have flared up again.

These suicidal stars, which afterwards dim down as if exhausted and return to their quiescent state, have proved a rich harvest for the casual sky-watcher. Every amateur who spends regular evenings with the stars, whether hunting up doubles or nebulae or watching for meteors in the quiet reaches of the night, soon develops an intimate knowledge of the star groups. The first step in becoming an amateur is to learn the main constellations: the Great Bear, or Dipper; Orion; Cygnus; Cassiopeia; and other distinctive star patterns that can never again be mistaken. For these groups, a very simple star map of the kind published regularly in many newspapers is the best, since it shows only the brightest stars and does not invite the confusion of a more detailed chart. But once these "guide groups" have been found, the smaller constellations fit themselves into place. Vulpecula, Sagitta, and Delphinus emerge in the region south of Cygnus; even the stragglers, like Draco and Pisces, which contain few bright stars in proportion to their great length, suddenly appear quite distinctive in a region of sky that formerly seemed barren and undistinguished.

By this time, the amateur will certainly be more familiar with the sky than are many professionals, who rarely need to look at the stars at all; it is not surprising that many of the naked-eye novae have stuck out like sore thumbs to regular sky-watchers. The lunar observer Julius Schmidt, who just missed discovering the remarkable rise of T Coronae Borealis in 1866 (it rose three hours after he had observed the region, and was found by the red-star observer John Birmingham), was the first to observe Nova Cygni, in 1876—a 3rd-magnitude object near Rho (ρ) Cygni. In 1891 and 1901, the Scottish amateur meteor observer Dr. T. D. Anderson discovered two novae; the second, Nova Persei, was a splendid zero-magnitude star that he noticed shining near Algol. Espin found Nova Lacertae in 1910; several observers saw Nova Aquilae in 1918; and W. F. Denning picked up another nova in Cygnus in 1920. In 1934, a nova appeared in Hercules, not far from the site of the 1963 nova; it was discovered by J. P. M. Prentice, then director of the Meteor Section of the British Astronomical Association. The year 1936 produced no fewer than three naked-eye novae, of which two were picked up by an amateur experimenting in astrophotography. This is certainly an impressive tally, and since nova-hunting essentially requires nothing more than a clear sky, and a good knowledge of the constellations, it is remarkable that more amateurs do not make a five-minute survey of the Milky Way a regular part of their observing program. As with comet-hunting, success will eventually reward the persistent.

Even more drastic than the novae are *supernovae*, stars that explode so violently that they emit as much light as the other galactic stars put together! These are excessively rare; only two have been recorded in our Galaxy in the last five hundred years, in 1572 and 1604. At their peak, these stars seemed as bright as the planet Venus and were visible with the naked eye in broad daylight, so there is little chance of an eruption of this type being overlooked.

Comparison stars

Observing a variable star consists of making estimates of its magnitude. These estimates are made by using certain standard *comparison stars*, afterwards working out the variable's magnitude from the accurate values available for the comparison stars. Societies dealing with the observation of the semiregular variables issue standard guide charts for each star, showing the nearby stars and giving magnitude values. In the case of naked-eye estimates of the bright irregulars, it is up to the observer to choose his own comparisons; the same is true if a nova happens to put in an appearance. Of course, it is necessary to make sure that none of the comparison stars is itself a variable—this has happened more often than one might imagine!

Like all programs in amateur astronomy, variable-star estimates require practice and experience before they can be made of the highest accuracy. Experienced observers can sometimes reckon to $\frac{1}{10}$ of a magnitude, when conditions are favorable; but consistent accuracy to $\frac{1}{3}$ is good enough for most practical work. Indeed, *consistency* is the watchword. It does not matter too much whether one's estimates are slightly bright or slightly faint, provided they all err by the same amount. The *form* of the light curve is the important thing, so that one can follow the rises, falls, and standstills as they occur. To achieve consistency, it is necessary to use the same set, or "sequence," of comparison stars for all estimates, and to make sure that these standard magnitudes all come from the same catalogue. There are sometimes inconsistencies even in the charts and sequences provided by observing societies, and it must not be assumed that just because a value is given to $\frac{1}{100}$ of a magnitude, which is quite usual in professional catalogues, it is necessarily accurate to anything better than $\frac{1}{10}$. A gross error will be introduced if the magnitudes for different stars are taken from different catalogues, since these sometimes differ by as much as half a magnitude.

It is worth examining the reason for these inconsistencies, for it sheds light on one of the problems of the variable-star observer. Inconsistencies arise because stars are of different tints. Most are white, with a hint of blue at one extreme end and of yellow at the other; as we descend the temperature scale, the color deepens into yellow and red. The human eye is most sensitive to yellow-green light; it is also fairly sensitive to blue, but it is rather insensitive to red. Moreover, eyes themselves vary. Some people have a much more delicate appreciation of subtle color differences than others, and it is well known that some eyes can detect rays that are quite beyond the grasp of normal vision. With some observers, too, each eye responds slightly differently. This is bad enough, but, to make matters worse, most standard star catalogues have been prepared photographically, and the usual photographic plate is especially sensitive to the blue and ultraviolet regions of the spectrum. Thus, if a star is very blue, it will appear brighter photographically than it does visually; if it is red, the reverse happens. This gives us the basis for a star's *color index*, which may be loosely defined as the difference between its photographic magnitude (using a blue-sensitive plate) and its visual magnitude. If a star is appreciably red, it might appear of magnitude 5·0 to the eye but only 5·3 on a photograph; the difference (5·3 — 5·0) gives + 0·3 for the color index. If the index is negative, the star must be blue. For the most reliable magnitudes, comparison stars should be as white as possible, with a very small color index. Many charts, to avoid this error, use accurate magnitudes derived by visual means, but this is not always possible.

A permanent difficulty is added to the situation when the variable itself has a definite tint. This is usually the case, for most LPV's have a conspicuous reddish hue, a problem we shall turn to presently.

Since all the interesting variables are marked in *Norton's*, finding them may sound an easy task—until one remembers that the star in question may be of the 11th or 12th magnitude! It is therefore necessary to have a large-scale guide chart showing the more prominent stars in the region. This region is first identified by using the finder, or a low-power eyepiece. The stars are then used as pointers to the variable itself. The first attempt may take some time, especially if it lies in a crowded Milky Way region; but once the star has been picked up on a few different occasions, the field will be engraved in the memory and can be located in a matter of seconds. Astronomical societies such as the A.A.V.S.O. or B.A.A. usually provide at least two charts, one showing the general vicinity of the variable, the other giving a "close-up" view, showing perhaps a square degree of sky. All the stars lying within the variable's probable range of fluctuation are marked, and the ones with standard magnitudes, to be used for comparison in making estimates, are identified by letters or numbers.

Just occasionally, emergencies occur. A variable not on the observer's list may start behaving oddly and require estimates, or a nova may appear. In such a case, the only thing to do is to construct one's own guide chart, plotting all the stars in the field as accurately as possible and identifying them by symbols. It does not matter much if the actual magnitudes are unknown, since they can be looked up later on; the vital thing is to get estimates made while they are of value. If the nova is very bright, it can of course be estimated against other naked-eye stars in the same region; and this goes for the conspicuous variables like γ Cassiopeiae and Betelgeuse.

Fractional and step methods

To estimate a variable, examine its brightness in relation to the comparison stars, and select the ones that lie slightly on either side of the variable's magnitude. The next step is to decide just where it lies in the sequence, and it is here that the two main methods differ slightly.

The *fractional* method, which is somewhat the simpler of the two, is more suitable for the beginner to attempt. Here, the variable's magnitude is determined as a ratio between the brightness of two comparison stars A and B. If it lies midway between them, it is recorded thus in the standard shorthand: A 1 V 1 B, which means that the differences on both sides are equal. (A, the brighter star, is always written first.) It may, however, be judged $\frac{2}{3}$ fainter than A and $\frac{1}{3}$ brighter than B; in this case, the record will be A 2 V 1 B. If it is still closer to B in magnitude, the ratio might be judged in quarters instead of thirds; the entry will then be A 3 V 1 B.

The number of divisions that can be determined accurately depends on the difference between the magnitudes of the comparison stars. Even an experienced observer cannot judge values reliably to less than $\frac{1}{10}$; thus if A and B differ by only $\frac{1}{5}$ of a magnitude it is impossible to work in terms of more than two steps. Usually, however, the difference between adjacent comparison stars will be greater than this. If the variable is judged to be exactly equal to a comparison star, the magnitude can be derived directly.

At least two sets of estimates must be made, using different comparison stars, since these give a cross-check on accuracy. If the two reductions agree to $\frac{1}{5}$ of a magnitude, this is satisfactorily enough for most purposes; if there is a larger discrepancy, the observation must be checked with further estimates. So far as is humanly possible, all previous estimates must be ignored; so must one's natural expectancies of how the star will behave.

The *step* method is more sophisticated, and requires considerable training of the eye. In this case, the observer chooses several comparison stars and estimates the variable against each one separately. The magnitude difference is estimated in terms of "steps," which may be defined as the smallest difference of magnitude to which the observer's eye is sensitive. In most cases, it is about $\frac{1}{10}$ of a magnitude, and the precise value can be found by trial and error. If the variable is estimated to be 2 steps fainter than A and 1 step brighter than B, the entry would be A $-$ 2, B $+$ 1. Further stars should also be used if they are available.

There may at first seem to be little practical difference between the two procedural methods, but each has its advantage. If the difference between the variable and the comparison stars is about half a magnitude or more, the step method becomes unreliable. On the other hand, if the variable is brighter or fainter than any visible comparison star, then there is no "sequence" in which the fractional method can operate. The advantage of the step method is that reasonable estimates can be made against just one comparison star. Once proficiency has been gained, however, the observer will decide almost subconsciously which method to use under different circumstances.

When beginning variable-star work, a very useful exercise is to "estimate" stars whose magnitudes are known, both with the naked eye and with the telescope. In this way, one gets a good idea of what a magnitude "looks like," and by choosing stars that are closer in brightness, the detectable difference can be reduced to the smallest possible value. Experience and efficiency go hand in hand; the first results may be quite wild, but they will soon improve. When recording observations, it is necessary to give an estimate of the probable accuracy, and it is far better to be pessimistic than over-optimistic.

Some sources of error

The observation of variable stars is a field in which the amateur is attempting quantitative rather than qualitative standards. This means that exceptional care must be taken to allow for all the factors that can cause error and affect the result. Some of the more important ones are discussed below.

ATMOSPHERIC ABSORPTION. If naked-eye stars are being estimated, allowance must be made for dimming at low altitudes. A star near the horizon appears fainter than it would if near the zenith, so that the variable and its comparison stars should all lie at roughly the same altitude. If they are higher than 45°, dimming can be neglected; Table X provides the allowances necessary for lower altitudes:

TABLE X. Atmospheric Dimming
(relative to zenith brightness)

ALTITUDE	43°	32°	26°	21°	19°	17°	15°	13°	11°	10°	6°	4°	2°	1°
DIMMING (MAG.)	0·1	0·2	0·3	0·4	0·5	0·6	0·7	0·8	0·9	1·0	1·5	2·0	2·5	3·0

This table ignores the presence of haze, which may dim very low stars by more than a magnitude and is bound to add extra uncertainty to the results. Telescopic variables are unaffected by this relative absorption, since all the stars in the field will lie at more or less the same altitude. Even so, it is wise to make estimates when the star is as high in the sky as possible.

MOONLIGHT, TWILIGHT, AND HAZE. Both moonlight ·and twilight spread a bluish cast in the sky. Naturally, this effaces the faintest stars, but of more consequence is the effect of the cast on stars of different colors. If a red and a blue star appear equal under dark conditions, the red one will appear superior in a bright sky, since the blue loses contrast with the background. A similar effect will be noticed if the observer happens to be surrounded by nocturnal illumination of any pronounced color. Haze and thin cloud, on the other hand, absorb red light more efficiently than other colors; so, under these conditions, a red star will be dimmed. These differences can amount to half a magnitude, or even more.

EYEPIECE AND RETINAL ERRORS. Neither eyepieces nor eyes are perfect over the whole of their surfaces. In an eyepiece, marginal stars appear somewhat blurred compared with central ones, and this blurring reduces their apparent magnitude. To minimize this defect, it is standard procedure with most observers to bring the variable and comparison stars alternately to the center of the field, holding them there just long enough to memorize their brightness. If the stars are close together, this precaution may not be necessary.

There is considerable controversy over the relative virtues of direct and averted vision. Some observers consider direct vision more reliable because the same part of the retina—the *fovea centralis*—is used for all observations. In using averted vision, different areas of the retina may be used for different stars, and these areas may have a wide range of sensitivity. On the other hand, averted vision is considerably more acute than foveal vision, increasing the telescope's grasp by perhaps two magnitudes; indeed, it may be that a variable at minimum is perceptible only by averted vision. Whichever choice is made, it is essential to keep to the same method for all observations of a given star. A switch from foveal to averted vision halfway through the series will certainly introduce errors.

THE PURKINJE EFFECT. This mysterious anomaly has often been noticed when estimates are made with different telescopes. It arises from the fact that the eyes of most observers are more sensitive to increases of red light than to increases of white or blue light. For instance, if a red and a white star appear of precisely the same magnitude when observed with a 3-inch refractor, the red will appear markedly superior when observed with a 12-inch telescope, for the image is considerably brighter. It also means that a red variable at maximum will appear somewhat brighter than it should.

Little practical action can be taken to combat the Purkinje effect. Using a red filter makes all the stars appear the same color as the variable—assuming that it is red—but it means that the magnitudes of the comparisons will have to be redetermined. The most obvious precaution is to use the same telescope for all comparisons.

POSITION ANGLE EFFECT. If two equally bright stars of the same color are situated horizontally in the field of view, they appear equally bright; if they are situated vertically, the lower star usually appears the brighter of the two, sometimes by as much as a magnitude. This error can be minimized if each star is examined in turn at the center of the field of view.

BRIGHTNESS EFFECT. If two stars are very bright or very faint, it is hard to detect small differences between them. Generally speaking, the most accurate results are obtained in the region from 2 to 4 magnitudes above the limit of the telescope.

Clearly, variable-star observing has become a greatly refined art. On the other hand, it contains no difficulties that cannot be overcome with patience and enthusiasm. The actual stars to be selected for observation depend greatly on the available aperture. Some, the ones not sinking to below the 11th magnitude, can be followed with a 3-inch, but most of the interesting semiregulars need a 12-inch if they are to be caught at minimum. However, there is no reason why the unpredictable rises should not be caught with a much smaller instrument, so there is always plenty to do. An example of amateur work is shown in figure 49.

Nova-hunting

Estimates of a nova's decline and fall can be made by following the standard variable-star procedure. Figure 50 shows the combined work of two British observers, B. A. Carter and R. S. Lomas, on the fall of Nova Herculis, 1963. It is clear that the fading has not been regular; but other novae, such as Nova Persei, 1901, have been much more erratic. Some, such as Nova Herculis, 1934, have gone through perceptible color changes during their descent from glory. As with all the other objects in the night sky, we can never take anything for granted, and in many cases it falls to the patient amateur to investigate these deviations from the usual, and to hand over his findings to the more intensive scrutiny of the great observatories.

Nova-hunting, like comet-hunting, is a task that, though it might appear hopeless, offers tremendous compensations. It is fair to say that most novae

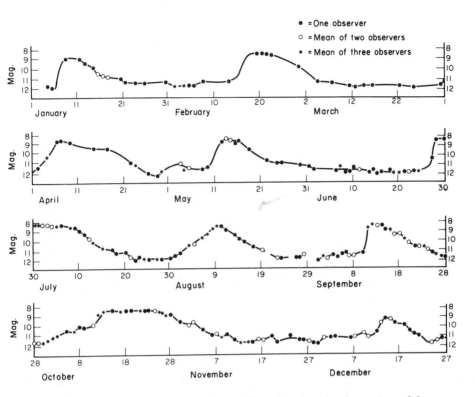

Figure 49. *Light curve of SS Cygni in 1964. This is based on the observations of three British amateurs: B. A. Carter (95 observations), J. B. Glasby (185 observations), and R. S. Lomas (103 observations).*

Figure 50. *Light curve of Nova Herculis, 1963. This is based on the work of two British amateurs: B. A. Carter (188 observations) and R. S. Lomas (176 observations).*

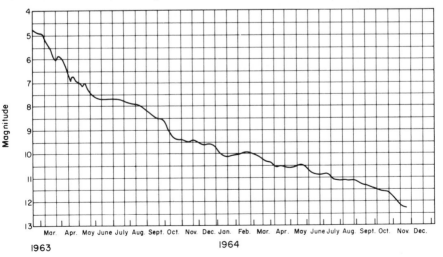

have been discovered by chance, but just how often has chance been implemented by one's own initiative? If he is an earnest observer, the most "casual" glance at the sky or at a planet should be a moment at which the amateur is acutely attentive. Do any of the constellations look odd? Is there a delicate new belt on Jupiter? Did those meteors come from a known source? It is well worth spending five minutes checking up on something that may at first sight seem to lead nowhere, for it is just this that may discourage other observers from investigating further—and even if the trail is a false one, something new will have been learned. Often, too, a sixth sense comes into play, as is revealed by W. F. Denning's account, in *Telescopic Work*, of his discovery of one of his five comets:

> *On July 11, 1881, just before daylight, I stood contemplating Auriga, and the idea occurred to me to sweep the region with my comet eyepiece, but I hesitated, thinking the prospect not sufficiently inviting. Three nights later Schaeberle at Ann Arbor, U.S.A., discovered a bright telescopic comet in Auriga! Before sunrise on October 4 of the same year I had been observing Jupiter, and again hesitated as to the utility of comet-seeking, but, remembering the little episode in my past experience, I instantly set to work, and at almost the first sweep alighted upon a suspicious object which afterwards proved itself a comet of short period.*

He goes on:

> *These facts teach one to value his opportunities. They cannot be lightly neglected, coming as they do all too rarely. The observer should never hesitate. He must endeavour to at least effect a little whenever an occasion offers; for it is just that little which may yield a marked success—greater, perhaps, than months of arduous labour may achieve at another time.*

So when the amateur, having concluded his observing program for the night, spends a few minutes scanning the Milky Way and its environment, he should consider just what opportunities are presented for the detection of a new star. The moon is the principal scene-changer, circling the ecliptic once a month and spending between two and three days in each zodiacal constellation. If a region of the Milky Way (e.g., in Orion or Sagittarius) has recently emerged from the moon's glare, it could conceivably harbor a nova which has not yet been detected; and around the time of full moon, the sky is less well scanned than when conditions are favorable, so that it is well worth putting up with the difficulties of observation in bright moonlight. Very faint naked-eye stars will be missed, of course, but of the 19 novae seen with the naked eye in the present century, 11 were brighter than magnitude 4·5 at discovery, so the chances of picking one up will still be fairly good.

Norton's Star Atlas is indispensable for this work; it shows stars down to about magnitude 6·5 and some fainter ones, so that any bright intruder can be clearly distinguished from any of the regular stars. Of course, there is always the possibility of its being a variable star near maximum (several variables can brighten up to the 4th or 5th magnitude), but the principal ones are represented in the atlas by small circles. One rule of thumb, though never to be used as more than a general guide, is that most novae are white or blue-white, while most LPV's are red. (Remember, though, that several "novae" have turned out to be *planets*; it is hoped that no reader of this book falls into that trap!)

To summarize: If a bright object is seen where neither star nor variable is marked in the star atlas, and if the positions of all likely planets can be accounted for, then the intruder is probably a nova. It should be reported at once giving its magnitude, position, exact time of observation, as described for a comet discovery (Chap. 17).

One sight that has given many amateurs, including myself, several shocks is a brilliant white object which on closer examination proves to be moving slowly across the sky. This is one of the bright balloon satellites, Echos I and II and Pageos A, which are more remote than most of the artificial satellites that now enliven the night sky. They move so slowly that at first glance they really do appear to be a new fixed star.

Nova discoveries have fallen off in recent years. Only four naked-eye ones have been observed over the whole sky since 1939, whereas eight were seen between 1910 and 1927. This may be due to some random fluctuation, in which case we can expect a crop in the next few years; but it may also be because observers do not study the sky as thoroughly as they used to. Generally speaking, interest in the hobby of sweeping the constellations for doubles and nebulae has declined; there are also fewer meteor observers than there used to be. All this means that fewer observers are on sufficiently intimate terms with the stars to notice a 3rd- or 4th-magnitude visitor. G. E. D. Alcock, who looks not only for comets but also for faint novae with 11 × 80 binoculars, has commented: "I am most puzzled by the fact that so few novae have turned up in recent years. I am sure that many are still missed, especially those well away from the Milky Way; the type like Nova Herculis (1934 and 1963); T Coronae Borealis (1866); Nova Serpentis (1948); and Nova Pictoris (1925)—which is quite a list."

While few observers are likely to have the dedication to spend hundreds of hours every year in scanning the stars for a telescopic visitor, it does seem likely that a little more naked-eye effort by amateurs would have a beneficial effect on the rate of discovery of bright novae. It is futile to expect quick results—indeed, one may never make a discovery—but those rewarding acquaintances, the constellations, will more than compensate for that.

21

The Constellations

A separate book would be required to carry a full description of the spectacular objects to be found scattered across the night sky. The list given here is intended as merely a preliminary guide. Each item is marked in *Norton's Star Atlas*, and with a little care (and the assistance of a good finder) they can be swept up quite easily.

The stargazer's standard handbook, Webb's *Celestial Objects for Common Telescopes*, is once more easily available, having been reprinted in 1962 by Dover Books; unfortunately, it has not been brought up to date. Another useful compilation is Olcott and Putnam's *Field Book of the Skies*. *Norton's* itself includes useful lists of the brighter objects, and marks many others without giving details.

As a guide to the time of year at which any particular constellation is most suitably placed for observation, the period at which it is due south at midnight is given. An asterisk indicates that the group is so far south as to be wholly or mostly invisible from a latitude of 45°N; the standard three-letter I.A.U.† abbreviation is also included. An unlettered number for a nebula or cluster refers to the N.G.C.‡ The various objects are listed in order of increasing right ascension.

Andromeda (And; mid-October)

An important northern constellation, distinguished to the naked eye by the three bright stars running from the N.E. corner of the Great Square

---

†International Astronomical Union.
‡Dreyer's New General Catalogue, 1888.

of Pegasus toward Perseus. The Milky Way travels through its northern border.

Σ 3042   (7·0, 7·0; 5"·5; 85°); both white
Σ 3050   (6·0, 6·0; 1"·7; 262°); yellowish; binary system, stars closing
Σ 24   (7·2, 8·0; 5"·2; 284°)
          (4·1, 8·0; 46"; 173°); white and blue
Σ 79   (6·0, 7·0; 7"·6; 193°); white and bluish
M.31   Easily found *np* Nu (*v*), and visible with the naked eye
          In a small telescope it reveals a small bright nucleus, surrounded by an extensive elliptical haze. This is the nearest galaxy to our own, being a mere 2,200 million light-years away. Two small "satellite" galaxies (M.32 to the south and H.V.18 *np* at a greater distance) can also be made out.
H.VII.32 Open cluster of faint stars
R (var.) 5·0–15, 409ᵈ; remarkably deep red tint
W (var.) 6·7–14·5, 397ᵈ

Andromedid meteors are active during the period Nov. 17 to 30. Maximum about Nov. 27; slow-moving; radiant near Gamma (*γ*).

*Antlia, the Air Pump (Ant; late February)

An inconspicuous group near the southern rift in the Milky Way. It contains no star brighter than the 4th magnitude.

ζ¹ (5·9, 6·7; 8"·2; 211°)

*Apus, the Bird of Paradise (Aps; mid-May)

Distinguished by a small triangle of 4th-mag. stars near the southern celestial pole.

I 236   (5·7, 8·5; 1"·9; 110°)
θ (var.) 6·4–8·6, 119ᵈ

Aquarius, the Water Bearer (Aqr; late August)

A zodiacal constellation. An extensive but inconspicuous group lying between Pegasus and the bright southern star Fomalhaut. Contains prominent groups of small stars in the S.E. corner.

12   (6·0, 8·1; 2"·8; 192°); yellow and blue
41   (5·6, 7·6; 4"·9; 116°); deep yellow and blue; fine object

Aquarius (continued)

ζ   (4·4, 4·6; 1″·8; 249°); binary, closing; at the limit of a 3-inch
53   (6·0, 6·5; 5″·0; 320°); both white
107   (5·3, 6·5; 6″·5; 135°); white and bluish
M.72   A small globular cluster. The individual stars are so faint that a
           small instrument shows it simply as a circular nebulosity.
H.IV.1   Bright, elliptical planetary nebula. Found most easily with a
           moderate power, to distinguish it from a star; bluish; rather ill-
           defined
M.2   Large and bright globular cluster, visible in a good finder. A 4-inch
           resolves the outer regions into stars.
R(var.)   6·2–11, 387ᵈ

η Aquarids are visible during the first week in May; maximum about
May 6. Meteors swift; not an intense shower.

δ Aquarids occur from mid-July to mid-August; maximum about July 29.
Medium speed; rich shower in low latitudes.

Aquila, the Eagle (Aql; mid-July)

Distinguished by its 1st-magnitude star Altair, and lying in a rich region
of the Milky Way, Aquila contains fine star fields and is well worth sweeping
with a low-power. Altair forms the southern corner of the distinctive
"summer triangle" (the other stars being Vega and Deneb) that character-
izes the late summer sky.

5   (5·6, 7·4; 13″; 121°); white and bluish
Σ 2404   (5·8, 7·0; 3″·4; 182°); fine contrast of yellow and blue
23   (5·5, 9·5; 3″·4; 8°); difficult with 3-inch
π   (6·0, 6·8; 1″·4; 113°); stars yellowish
57   (5·2, 6·2; 36″; 171°); wide, colors curious
6709   Scattered group of 9th- to 11th-magnitude stars
R (var.)   6·2–12, 300ᵈ, period shortening

*Ara, the Altar (Ara, mid-June)

A small constellation lying south of Scorpio. It is in the Milky Way,
and contains a number of fine clusters.

h4949   (6·5, 7·5; 3″·2; 267°)
6204   Small cluster of faint stars
6208   Scattered cluster of bright and faint stars
6250   Cluster containing 8th-magnitude and fainter stars

Aries, the Ram (Ari; late October)

A zodiacal constellation. The stars Alpha (a), Beta (β), and Gamma (γ) form a conspicuous triplet to the south of Andromeda's line. There is poor sweeping in this region, but it contains some fine double stars.

1	(6·2, 7·4; 2″·8; 166°); fine contrast of yellow and blue
γ	(4·2, 4·4; 8″·4; 360°); one of the finest pairs in the sky; both yellow; easy with low power
λ	(4·7, 6·7; 38″; 46°); white and yellowish
10	(6·1, 7·1; 39″; 274°); whitish and yellowish; wide
ε	(6·0, 6·4; 1″·5; 205°); both white; at the limit of resolution of a 3-inch
U (var.)	7–13, 370^d

ε Arietids are visible from October 12 to 23. Meteors are very slow; maximum about October 15.

Auriga, the Charioteer (Aur; mid-December)

A splendid constellation, distinguished by its yellow leader Capella (mag. 0·2), a star of interest in being very similar to the sun. This is one of the distinctive winter groups. The Milky Way passes through Auriga, in which lie three magnificent open clusters. There are many doubles; fine sweeping.

ω	(5·0, 8·0; 5″·8; 360°); white and bluish; pretty
14	(5·0, 7·2; 14″; 225°); cream and dull-blue
Σ 698	(6·2, 7·7; 31″; 346°); yellow and bluish
Σ 718	(7·2, 7·2; 7″·8; 74°); both white
θ	(2·7, 7·2; 2″·8; 332°); difficult with less than 4-inch
41	(5·2, 6·4; 7″·8; 355°); a pretty pair, both white
Σ 872	(6·0, 7·0; 11″; 217°); white and bluish
H.VII.33	Wide grouping of stars in a splendid region
M.38	Extensive cluster of bright stars ranged against star dust, with a cruciform outline. Closely south is a smaller cluster, H.VII.39.
M.36	Superb group of bright and faint stars
M.37	Magnificent cluster of faint stars, the individual members being glimpsed as powdery points against the sky
ε (var.)	Eclipsing type; range from magnitude 3·3 to 4·2; period 27 years—longest known for this kind of star
R (var.)	6·7–13·7, 458^d
UU (var.)	5·1–6·8, ±300^d

a Aurigids. There are two faint showers from this radiant: February 5–10 (slow); August 12–October 2 (very swift).

Boötes, the Herdsman (Boo; April-May)

The major star in this group, Arcturus (mag. −0·1), is the third bright-est in the sky, and is easily found by continuing the curve marked out by four of the bright stars in Ursa Major. The constellation lies well away from the Milky Way and contains no distinctive clusters; but there are many doubles.

Σ 1785	(7·2, 7·5; 3″·1; 148°); yellowish and bluish; neat binary pair
Σ 1816	(7·0, 7·1; 1″·9; 80°); yellowish pair
κ	(5·1, 7·2; 13″; 237°); white and lilac; attractive contrast
ι	(4·9, 7·5; 38″; 33°); white and gray pair in attractive field
Σ 1835	(5·5, 6·8; 6″·4; 195°); neat white pair
π	(4·9, 6·0; 5″·8; 110°); white pair
ζ	(4·4, 4·8; 1″·2; 308°); white, too close for 3-inch
ε	(3·0, 6·3; 2″·8; 340°); fine contrast of yellow and green; needs high power
39	(5·8, 6·5; 3″·3; 45°); white and bluish
ξ	(4·8, 6·9; 7″·0; 344°); yellow and bluish; binary system
R (var.)	6·0–13·0, 222ᵈ
34 (var.)	5·2–6·1, irregular

*Caelum, the Chisel (Cae; late November)

A small, inconspicuous asterism, west of Columba, containing little of interest. It used to be considered a part of the constellation Sculptor.

γ   (4·7, 8·5; 2″·9; 310°)

Camelopardus (or Camelopardalis), the Giraffe (Cam; late December)

A large but very obscure constellation near the north celestial pole, between Ursa Major and Cassiopeia. It contains no star brighter than the 4th magnitude.

Σ 485	(6·1, 6·2; 18″; 304°); white and bluish
1	(5·1, 6·2; 10″; 307°); white and bluish
2	(5·1, 7·4; 1″·6; 280°); yellow and bluish
Σ 1127	(6·2, 8·0, 9·2; 5″·5, 11″; 340°, 174°); triple; brighter stars white and gray
Σ 1625	(6·5, 7·0; 14″; 219°); both white
Σ 1694	(4·9, 5·4; 21″; 326°); yellowish and bluish
Z (var.)	10·2–14·5, irregular; subject to long standstills

Cancer, the Crab (Cnc; early February)

A small zodiacal constellation between Leo and Gemini; marked out by five 4th-magnitude stars, but containing its share of fine objects.

Σ 1177	(6·5, 7·4; 3″·5; 355°); white and bluish
ζ	(5·6, 5·9, 6·1; 1″·1, 5″·6; 348°, 82°); three stars, all yellow. A splendid sight, the close stars forming a binary system
ψ²	(6·3, 6·3; 5″·0; 216°); white and grayish
ι	(4·4, 6·5; 31″; 307°); beautiful contrast of yellow and blue
σ²	(5·9, 6·4; 320°; 1″·5); both yellow; elongated with 3-inch
M.44	Known as Praesepe (the Beehive), and visible with the naked eye. A coarse cluster of bright stars, best seen in the finder since it is too extensive for ordinary telescopic fields, lying between Gamma (γ) and Delta (δ).
M.67	A splendid scattered cluster of bright and faint stars
R (var.)	6·0–11·3, 362ᵈ
X (var.)	5·9–7·3, 165ᵈ(?)

Canes Venatici, the Hunting Dogs (CVn; early April)

Lying below the curve of the "handle" of the Big Dipper (Ursa Major), this group is marked by only three conspicuous naked-eye stars. It lies in an extensive region of galaxies that extends from Ursa Major southward to Virgo, but few are bright enough to be seen well in small instruments.

2	(5·7, 8·0; 11″; 260°); deep yellow and blue; attractive pair
α	(3·2, 5·7; 20″; 228°); known as Cor Caroli; yellowish; a bright pair
25	(5·1, 7·1; 1″·7; 105°); white and blue; binary pair
M.94	A small cometlike nebulosity
M.63	An elliptical nebulosity with a brighter center. This is a distant spiral galaxy seen at an acute angle.
M.51	The famous Whirlpool Galaxy. In a small telescope, it is seen as two nebulae, one much larger than the other, almost in contact. Long-exposure photographs show it to be a spiral galaxy, with the smaller nucleus connected to the main system by an outflung arm.
M.3	A fine, bright globular cluster. The stars are too closely packed to be seen individually with a 3-inch, but they reveal themselves in larger instruments.
R (var.)	6·1–12·7, 333ᵈ
Y (var.)	5·2–6·6, 158ᵈ; a fine red star

Canis Major, the Greater Dog (CMa; early January)

A small but brilliant constellation lying southeast of Orion, near a rich part of the Milky Way. It cannot possibly be overlooked, for its leader, Sirius, is the brightest star in the sky, and it contains four 2nd-magnitude stars. It is rather low for observation in north temperate latitudes.

v^1 (6·0, 8·0; 17″; 263°); yellow, bluish

α (−1·4, 7·0; 10″; 85°). At its widest (11″·5 in 1975), it should be visible with an 8-inch reflector or a 6-inch refractor. This is a binary system, with a period of 50 years. The comes is a white dwarf star; it is about the size of Uranus, but almost as massive as the sun. It is only 1/2500 as luminous as Sirius A.

μ (4·7, 8·0; 3″·0; 339°); yellow and blue

M.41   An open cluster, lying 4° south of Sirius and visible with the naked eye. The brighter stars, some of which are orange, are arranged in distinctive curves. A splendid low-power sight.

H.VII.12   A beautiful powdery cluster of faint stars

Canis Minor, the Lesser Dog (CMi; mid-January)

Marked to the naked eye by its yellow leader, Procyon, east of Orion. Contains few objects of interest.

Σ 1103   (7·0, 8·5; 4″·3; 245°); white and grayish

Capricornus, the Goat (Cap; early August)

A zodiacal group lying south of Aquarius. A dull-looking constellation, but interesting for its leader, which is a naked-eye double.

α (3·2, 4·2; 376″; 291°); both yellow

π (5·1, 8·7; 3″·4; 145°); yellowish and bluish

o^2 (6·3, 6·8; 22″; 238°); white and bluish

M.30   A globular cluster appearing in a small instrument as a bright spherical nebulosity, centrally condensed

*Carina, the Keel (Car; late January)

The ancient, unwieldy constellation Argo Navis has been divided into Carina, Puppis (the Poop), and Vela (the Sails). Of these, Carina is the southernmost; it contains the second brightest star in the sky, Canopus (mag, −0·9). The original Greek-letter designations are retained; hence, we find Alpha (*a*) and Beta (*β*) in Carina, Gamma (*γ*) and Delta (*δ*) in Vela, and so on. The Milky Way passes through the region, which lies southeast of Orion and Canis Major.

C	(5·3, 8·0; 3″·8; 64°)
h4213	(6·0, 9·4; 8″·8; 327°)
υ	(3·2, 6·0; 5″·0; 128°)
2808	A rich globular cluster, appearing as a nebulous blur in a small telescope
3114	A loose cluster of bright and faint stars
R (var.)	5·6–11·0, 309ᵈ
S (var.)	4·5–10·0, 149ᵈ

Cassiopeia (Cas; mid-October)

One of the most distinctive northern constellations; its characteristic M or W—depending on whether it appears above or below the polestar —can always be recognized. It lies in a rich part of the Milky Way, and the sweeping is superb.

σ	(5·4, 7·5; 3″·1; 327°); white and bluish; in a superb region
Σ 3053	(6·0, 7·3; 15″; 71°); yellow and blue
η	(3·7, 7·4; 11″; 298°); yellowish and purple; an attractive binary pair
ψ	(4·4, 8·9; 20″; 120°); yellow and blue; companion a close double
Σ 163	(6·2, 8·2; 35″; 36°); rich gold and blue; fine contrast
Σ 191	(6·2, 8·5; 5″·6; 191°); white and blue
ι	(4·2, 7·1, 8·1; 2″·4, 7″·4; 251°, 113°); a splendid triple star; yellow, blue, blue
M.52	A most beautiful cluster, somewhat triangular. A 3-inch shows it granular with faint stars.
H.VIII.78	A curious group of 9th-magnitude stars, shaped rather like a mushroom
H.VI.30	A large, faint, compressed cluster
	There are many other clusters in this constellation.
R (var.)	4·8–13·6, 431ᵈ
S (var.)	6·2–15·3, 610ᵈ
ρ (var.)	4·1–6·2, irregular
γ (var.)	2·0–3·3, irregular

*Centaurus, the Centaur (Cen; late March)

An extensive southern constellation lying partly in the Milky Way and containing some fine objects. The leader is a splendid binary star; a third, fainter member of the same system is the nearest star to the sun.

I 178	(6·3, 6·3; 1″·0; 94°)
D	(5·3, 6·5; 2″·9; 245°); both yellow; a fine object
γ	(3·1, 3·2; 1″·6; 2°); a fine binary pair
Q	(5·4, 6·8; 5″·2; 164°)
k	(4·5, 5·9; 7″·6; 110°)
y	(5·6, 5·8; 1″·2; 102°)
α	(0·3, 1·7; 14″; 200°); both yellow; perhaps the finest binary in the sky. A nearby 11th-magnitude companion, belonging to the same system and known as Proxima Centauri, is the sun's nearest neighbor.
T (var.)	5·2–10·0; 91^d
3766	Rich, condensed cluster of bright and faint stars
ω	Appears as a hazy "star" to the naked eye; a magnificent globular cluster ablaze with faint stars—probably the largest and finest in the sky
5460	A loose cluster of bright stars

Cepheus (Cep; late September)

This group extends almost to the north celestial pole. It contains few bright stars, but there is some good sweeping in the southern region. An arm of the Milky Way intrudes from Cygnus.

κ	(4·0, 8·0; 7″·4; 122°); white and blue
Σ 2751	(6·0, 7·0; 1″·9; 344°); both white
β	(3·3, 8·0; 14″; 250°); greenish white and blue
Σ 2816	(6·3, 7·9, 8·0; 12″, 20″; 120°, 340°); yellowish, with bluish companions at either side
Σ 2840	(6·0, 7·0; 20″; 194°); white and blue; an attractive pair
ξ	(4·7, 6·5; 8″·0; 280°); yellowish and bluish
Σ 2893	(5·5, 7·6; 29″; 348°); yellowish and bluish
δ	(var., 5·3; 41″; 192°); yellow and blue; fine contrast The bright star is the prototype Cepheid variable, ranging from magnitude 3·8 to 4·6 in a period of 5⅓ days.
Σ 2950	(6·0, 7·2; 2″·3; 290°); yellow and grayish
o	(5·2, 7·8; 3″·0; 210°); yellow and greenish
T (var.)	5·1–10·5, 387^d

μ (var.)   3·7–4·7, irregular. Herschel's "Garnet Star", shining like a drop of blood. There is a rough period of between 5 and 6 years.

Cetus, the Whale (Cet; mid-October)

A dull, extensive constellation, extending from the west of Aquarius northward toward Taurus. Since the ecliptic passes very close to its northern boundary, the planets can sometimes lie in this constellation.

42	(6·2, 7·2; 1″·4; 30°); both white
Σ 147	(6·0, 7·3; 2″·9; 89°); white and yellowish
66	(6·0, 7·8; 16″; 232°); yellow and blue
γ	(3·7, 6·2; 3″·0; 295°); yellowish and grayish; curious colors
M.77	Spiral galaxy, appearing as a rather dim nebulous patch
T (var.)	6·6–7·7, 160^d
o (var.)	Mira; extreme range 1·7–9·6, period 330^d

*Chamaeleon, the Chameleon (Cha; late February)

A small group lying near the south celestial pole, containing five 4th-magnitude stars.

ε	(5·4, 6·2; 1″·1; 310°)
3195	A small planetary nebula

*Circinus, the Compasses (Cir; April-May)

This small group is situated in the Milky Way, near Centaurus, and so contains some good sweeping.

γ	(5·5, 6·0; 1″·3; 108°)
a	(3·4, 8·8; 16″; 232°); yellow and reddish
5715	A loose cluster of faint stars

*Columba, the Dove (Col; mid-December)

An inconspicuous constellation south of Lepus, marked to the naked eye by the small triangle of Alpha, Beta, and Epsilon (a, β, ε). It contains no objects of interest for a small telescope.

Coma Berenices, Berenice's Hair (Com; March-April)

Virtually an extensive naked-eye cluster of faint stars, north of Virgo. Like its neighbors (Virgo, Leo, and Canes Venatici), it contains a great

Coma Berenices (continued)

number of dim galaxies. Only a few, however, are bright enough to be at all noticeable in a small telescope.

2	(6·0, 7·5; 3″·9; 235°); white and blue
24	(4·7, 6·2; 20″; 271°); yellow and blue
M.98	Faint galaxy, elongated in an E–W direction; very close to star 6
M.99	A large, pale galaxy on the other side of 6 from M.98
M.100	Circular nebulosity with little central condensation
M.85	Small nebulosity with a bright, almost stellar, central condensation. There is a 9th-magnitude star f.
M.88.	Elongated nebulosity, centrally condensed
M.64.	Rather faint elliptical nebulosity
M.53.	Small cluster of faint stars, much compressed
40 (var.)	5·5–5·9, 37ᵈ

*Corona Australis, the Southern Crown (CrA; late June)

Marked by a curve of faint stars south of Sagittarius.

h5014	(5·8, 5·8; 1″·6; 221°); binary pair
κ	(6·0, 6·6; 22″; 359°)
γ	(5·0, 5·0; 2″·7; 33°); a fine pair

Corona Borealis, the Northern Crown (CrB; mid-May)

A distinctive semicircular group of stars east of ε Boötis.

ζ	(4·0, 4·9; 6″·3; 306°); white and turquoise; beautiful
σ	(5·7, 6·7; 6″·3; 231°); yellowish and grayish; a beautiful pair
R (var.)	5·8–14·8, irregular; long maxima with sudden falls
S (var.)	5·8–13·9, 361ᵈ
T (var.)	2–9·5, irregular; the "Blaze Star"

Corvus, the Crow (Crv; late March)

A small constellation south of Virgo, easily identified by its distinctive trapezoid appearance. In this, it resembles Crater, its western neighbor.

δ	(3·0, 8·5; 24″; 212°); yellowish and bluish
Σ 1669	(6·1, 6·2; 5″·4; 308°); both yellowish
R (var.)	5·9–14·4, 317ᵈ

Crater, the Cup (Crt; mid-March)

Marked by a trapezium of 4th-magnitude stars. There are few objects of interest for a small telescope.

Σ 1509 (7·2, 9·0; 33″; 15°); brighter star yellow

*Crux, the Cross (Cru; late March)

A splendid, compact constellation lying in that part of the Milky Way nearest the south celestial pole, and containing the famous black aperture known as "the Coalsack," which is simply a nearby dark nebula blotting out the stars beyond it. Crux is the smallest group in the sky, but with its clearly cruciform shape it is unmistakable.

α   (1·4, 1·9; 4″·7; 119°); a noble pair
ι   (4·7, 7·8; 26″; 25°)
μ   (4·5, 5·5; 35″; 17°)
4755 A magnificent open cluster of more than a hundred bright stars surrounding Kappa (κ). They range from the 7th magnitude downwards, and in a telescope of sufficient power a number of red and blue shades are visible. Sir John Herschel described it as resembling "a superb piece of fancy jewelry."

Cygnus, the Swan; also, the Northern Cross (Cyg; July-August)

A fine constellation which might aptly be called the Northern Cross, Cygnus lies in a superb region of the Milky Way and its low-power fields are encrusted with stars. There seems to be no end to its pairs, triplets, and clusters. Fresh combinations continually delight the eye, and the background to these patterns is powdery with half-glimpsed points of light. There are distinctive dark nebulae near Alpha (α) and Gamma (γ); and south of Gamma the Milky Way divides into separate streams.

Σ 2486   (6·0, 6·5; 8″·9; 210°); yellow pair in a rich field
β   (3·0, 5·3; 35″; 55°); mid-yellow, intense blue. One of the showpieces of the sky, being an easy pair that can be divided in any telescope
16   (5·1, 5·3; 38″; 134°); yellow pair, superb field
δ   (3·0, 6·5; 2″·1; 240°); difficult because of the brilliant primary; easiest in a twilight sky
ε 2578   (6·6, 7·4; 15″; 127°); white and pale blue; a pretty pair
OΣΣ 191 (6·0, 8·0; 38″; 28°); gold and blue
ψ   (5·0, 7·5; 2″·9; 170°); white and pinkish

Cygnus (continued)

Σ 2671   (6·0, 7·4; 3″·4; 336°); white and ashen

61   (5·3, 5·9; 28″; 140°); both yellow; first stars to have their distance measured (in 1838)

Σ 2762   (6·0, 8·0; 3″·5; 316°); white and bluish

H.VII.59   A small aggregate of faint stars

Two views of Cygnus. *Taken with a Polaroid camera and ASA 3000 film. Left: Cygnus star trails, photographed on July 21, 1963. Below: Star clouds in Cygnus. This photograph was taken with a hand-driven equatorial mounting. (Thane P. Bopp, Kirkwood, Missouri.)*

M.29	A small group of 8th-magnitude stars with fainter associates
H.V.14	Part of the Filamentary Nebula, well seen only in long-exposure photographs. A small telescope shows about 120° of a large nebulous circle that fits inside the margin of a low-power eyepiece. There are other faint nebulosities in the region.
H.I.192	Small nebulosity surrounding a 9th-magnitude star
ζ	There is very extensive, extremely faint nebulosity surrounding this star. It is best seen in the finder, or with binoculars.
7039	A small cluster of 9th-magnitude and fainter stars, lying between two stars of the 7th-magnitude
M.39	A coarse, triangular cluster of bright stars, with a double star at the center. Best seen in the finder
χ (var.)	2·3–14·3, 406^d
R (var.)	5·9–14·6, 426^d
RT (var.)	6·2–13·0, 190^d
T (var.)	5·5–6·0, irregular
U (var.)	6·1–12·2, 462^d
W (var.)	5·0–7·6, 131^d + 125^d (double period)

κ Cygnids. A short shower of slow meteors occurs on January 17; a second shower, medium speed, radiates from August 10 to 20.

α Cygnids. A prolonged shower of swift, trained meteors occurs during July and August.

Delphinus, the Dolphin (Del; July-August)

A compact and unmistakable constellation lying on the southern border of the Milky Way, near Aquila; the arrangement of its five main stars is somewhat fishlike. There are some rich fields here.

γ	(4·0, 5·0; 10″; 268°); yellow and turquoise; a charming pair
U (var.)	5·6–7·5, irregular

*Dorado, the Swordfish (Dor; mid-December)

An otherwise obscure far-southern group, made noteworthy by containing the Nubecula Major, or Greater Magellanic Cloud.

NUBECULA MAJOR. Appearing to the naked eye as a detached fragment of the Milky Way, this is the more prominent of two "satellite" star systems revolving around the Galaxy. It is about 200,000 light-years away (one-tenth of the distance of the Andromeda Galaxy), and since it is the

Dorado (continued)

nearest external system it is of great importance to professional astronomers. It contains many telescopic objects, the most prominent being the Great Looped Nebula, bright enough to be seen with the naked eye.

R (var.)   5·7–6·8,   360ᵈ

Draco, the Dragon (Dra; mid-May)

An extensive constellation winding for almost 180° around the north celestial pole. The p region, that part north of Ursa Major, contains some dim nebulae. The easiest way of beginning identification is to find the two pairs of bright stars—Beta (β) and Gamma (γ); Eta (η) and Zeta (ζ)—which lie between Vega and β Ursae Minoris. After that, the rest of the Dragon's body can be traced.

Σ 1984	(6·2, 8·5; 6″·6; 274°); white and bluish
17	(5·0, 6·0; 3″·7; 116°); cream and bluish
v	(4·6, 4·6; 62″; 313°); both yellowish; well seen in the finder
ψ	(4·0, 5·2; 31″; 15°); yellow and lilac
40	(5·4, 6·1; 20″; 234°); yellow and pale yellow; the companion is known as 41
39	(4·7, 7·7; 3″·1; 6°); white and reddish; 7·1-magnitude star nearby
Σ 2348	(5·9, 8·1; 26″; 273°); fine contrast of yellow and blue
ε	(4·0, 7·6; 3″·5; 7°); cream and blue
R (var.)	6·3–13·9, 245ᵈ
RY (var.)	5·6–8·0, irregular
H.IV.37	A bright planetary nebula looking exactly like a 5th-magnitude star slightly out of focus. Best picked up with a medium power, which exaggerates the disk. There is an 8th-magnitude star np.

Quandrantids. Known after the forgotten constellation Quadrans Muralis. An intense shower of bright, swift meteors occurring between December 30 and January 4, maximum on January 3.

ι Draconids. Short-lived shower of slow meteors, June 27–30, maximum June 28.

γ Draconids. Extensive shower lasting from June until August. Meteors slow; maximum June 25.

ζ Draconids. These occur between August 21 and 30; medium speed. Fainter meteors radiate from near Omicron (o) around August 22.

Equuleus, the Little Horse (Equ; mid-August)

A tiny asterism on the eastern border of Delphinus.

ε   (5·7, 7·1; 11″; 72°); yellowish and dull white. The brighter is a very close binary.

*Eridanus, the River (Eri; mid-November)

From the region west of Orion, this figure straggles southward toward its leader, Achernar (mag. 0·6), whose declination is −57°.

θ	(3·4, 4·4; 8″·2; 88°); a fine pair
f	(4·9, 5·4; 7″·8; 211°)
32	(4·0, 6·0; 7″·0; 347°); brilliant yellow and blue-green; a superb object
39	(6·0, 8·8; 6″·5; 146°); yellow and blue
55	(6·2, 6·7; 9″·3; 317°); both yellowish
H.IV.26	A small planetary nebula with a nucleus that is not perfectly central, but nearer the *sp* border

*Fornax, the Furnace (For; late October)

A large but unremarkable constellation lying in the dull region south of Cetus and the delta of Eridanus.

ω	(5·5, 8·0; 10″; 244°)
h3532	(6·5, 8·0; 5″·5; 145°)
H.V.48	Conspicuous nebulosity extended in the *sf* direction

Gemini, the Twins (Gem; early January)

The two principal stars, Castor and Pollux (mags. 1·6 and 1·2, respectively), can be found without difficulty some 40° northeast of Orion; the other bright stars take the form of an elongated parallelogram. There are many interesting objects in this group.

20	(6·0, 6·9; 20″; 211°); yellow and blue; fine field
38	(5·4, 7·7; 7″·0; 150°); yellowish, bluish
δ	(3·2, 8·2; 6″·2; 220°); pale yellow, reddish; delicate object with 3-inch
α	(2·0, 2·9; 1″·9; 151°), Castor; both stars yellowish. This is the brightest binary pair in the northern hemisphere; the stars have just passed periastron and are beginning to open up again. The widest separation, 6″·5, will be reached in about 80 years' time.

Gemini (continued)

κ   (4·0, 8·5; 6″·8; 236°); deep yellow, pale blue; beautiful
M.35   A striking, extensive cluster of bright stars, somewhat too large
           for normal fields, seen against a rich background. Visible with
           the naked eye
H.IV.45   A bright planetary nebula surrounding an 8th-magnitude star
η (var.)   3·2–4·2, 231^d
R (var.)   5·9–13·8, 370^d

Geminids. A prominent shower of swift meteors lasting throughout the
first half of December, reaching maximum on the 10th.

*Grus, the Crane (Gru; early September)

This group is not difficult to identify, for it lies immediately south of
Fomalhaut, the leader of Piscis Austrinus. There are other celestial "birds"
nearby: the Phoenix, the Toucan, and the Peacock.

θ   (4·5, 7·0; 1″·4; 50°)
D246   (6·1, 6·8; 8″·4; 257°)
S (var.)   6·0–15·0, 400^d

Hercules (Her; mid-June)

This extensive and important constellation is not too easy to make
out, since it contains no star brighter than the 3rd magnitude; the best
signpost is the trapezium formed by Pi (π), Eta (β), Zeta (ζ), and Epsilon
(ε), which lies between Vega and Corona Borealis. Once identified, Hercules
provides an almost inexhaustible store of fine doubles, of which only a
few can be listed here.

κ   (5·0, 6·0; 29″; 14°); yellow and bronze; fine field
Σ 2063   (5·7, 8·2; 16″; 194°); white and bluish
Σ 2104   (6·2, 8·0; 5″·9; 20°); yellowish, clear blue; a very pretty pair
α   (var., 6·1; 4″·4; 110°); golden-yellow and greenish; a fine pair.
           The primary varies from 3rd to 4th magnitude.
ρ   (4·0, 5·1; 3″·8; 317°); white and grayish
Σ 2194   (6·2, 8·5; 16″; 9°); gold and blue
Σ 2245   (6·8, 7·0; 2″·6; 295°); a neat pair, both white
95   (4·9, 4·9; 6″·2; 259°); yellowish and white; beautiful
100   (5·9, 5·9; 14″; 183°); both white, a superb equal pair
M.13   The largest and brightest globular cluster in the northern sky,

just visible with the naked eye. A small telescope shows it as an extensive spherical nebulosity, brighter at the center; a high magnification allows some of the marginal stars to be detected by averted vision. A superb sight in a large telescope.

Σ 5N   A small planetary nebula, like a bright star out of focus; one of the few distinctive objects overlooked by Sir William Herschel, and later discovered by F. G. W. Struve. A high magnification is needed to make the bluish disk obvious.

M.92   A smaller version of M.13. The stars are more compressed, and there is only a suspicion of marginal resolution if a small telescope is used.

30 (var.)   4·7–6·0, irregular
S (var.)   5·9–12·5, 300^d
U (var.)   6·2–13·3, 406^d
a (var.)   3·1–3·9, irregular

*Horologium, the Clock (Hor; mid-November)

A barren far-southern group nearly devoid of interesting telescopic objects.

R (var.)   6·3–15·0, 401^d

Hydra, the Water Monster (Hya; mid-March)

The longest and largest constellation in the sky, with an area of 1,303 square degrees; it is also one of the most obscure. Named after Hydra, the nine-headed serpent, or monster, of Lake Lerna, slain by Hercules. Its "head" lies north of the equator, between Leo and Canis Minor; but it extends eastward almost to Scorpio. Considering its size, it is poorly stocked with objects.

Σ 1245   (6·0, 7·0; 10″; 26°); pale yellow and reddish
ε   (3·8, 7·8; 3″·6; 270°); yellow and blue
Hh376   (5·8, 5·9; 9″·1; 212°); white and bluish; the companion may be variable
β   (4·4, 4·8; 1″·2; 360°); a fine close pair
54   (6·0, 7·5; 9″·0; 129°); yellow and bluish
H.IV.27 A bluish planetary nebula of the same apparent size as Jupiter, with a bright nucleus. Lies 2° south of Mu (μ).
R (var.)   4·0–10·0, 386^d
U (var.)   4·5–6·0, irregular
V (var.)   6·0–12·5, 532^d

*Hydrus, the Water Snake (Hyi; late October)

A much smaller serpent than Hydra, the monster, Hydrus lies near the south celestial pole; its name is distinguished in the genitive form by the masculine ending i (Hydri), as against Hydra's feminine form, Hydrae.

h3475   (6·5, 6·5; 3"·3; 38°); an attractive pair
h3568   (5·7, 7·7; 15"; 224°)

*Indus, the Indian (Ind; mid-August)

A straggling southern constellation in a dull region.

θ (4·7, 7·1; 6"·0; 275°)

Lacerta, the Lizard (Lac; late August)

An obscure group lying between Cygnus and Andromeda, containing some fine Milky Way fields.

Σ 2894   (6·0, 8·2; 16"; 194°); white and bluish
8   (6·0, 6·5; 22"; 186°); yellowish; two faint stars *sf*
H.VIII.75 A bright cluster set in a rich region

Lacertids. These rather faint meteors radiate during August and September; no definite maximum.

Leo, the Lion (Leo; February-March)

A splendid zodiacal constellation, in form very reminiscent of a crouching lion. The ecliptic passes just south of its leader, Regulus (mag. 1·3), which suffers periodical occultation by the moon. Leo contains a number of faint galaxies.

γ (2·4, 3·8; 4"·3; 122°); both golden-yellow; a magnificent binary pair
49   (6·0, 8·7; 2"·4; 158°); white and bluish
54   (5·0, 7·0; 6"·3; 110°); white and blue
83   (6·3, 7·3; 29"; 150°); yellow and reddish
88   (6·4, 8·2; 15"; 330°); pale yellow and bluish
90   (6·0, 7·3; 3"·4; 209°); white and bluish
R (var.)   5·4–10·5, 312^d
M.95   Circular nebulosity
M.96   Circular nebulosity, less well defined than M.95; two faint nebulae *nf*

M.65 &   Two elongated nebulosities lying in the same low-power field
M.66

Leonids. An unpredictable display, usually faint, but prominent in
1961 and 1965 and magnificent in 1966. Meteors, swift-moving, occur
between November 9 and 17 with a maximum about November 16.

Leo Minor, the Lesser Lion (LMi; late February)

A small group to the north of Leo. It contains a few galaxies, but none
bright enough to be of general interest.

Lepus, the Hare (Lep; mid-December)

Easily found, since it lies directly south of Orion and contains a conspicuous trapezium of bright stars. Here is found the famous "Crimson
Star" R.

ι	(4·2, 10·5; 13″; 335°); white primary; companion difficult with 3-inch
κ	(5·0, 7·5; 2″·6; 360°); yellowish and bluish
a	(4·0, 9·5; 35″; 156°); a group of four faint stars f
M.79	A globular cluster, appearing in a small telescope as a bright, central condensed patch
R (var.)	6·0–10·4, 430^d. The celebrated star which its discoverer, John Russell Hind, described in 1845 as "resembling a blood-drop on the background of the sky; as regards depth of color, no other star visible in these latitudes could be compared with it." In a small telescope, its striking tint can be well seen only near maximum.

Libra, the Balance (Lib; mid-May)

A dull group but easily found, since it lies between Virgo and Scorpio.
Its brightest star, Beta (β), has a somewhat greenish tinge, which is not,
however, obvious to the casual glance.

μ	(5·4, 6·3; 2″·0; 350°)
Σ 1962	(6·3, 6·4; 12″; 187°); both white, a fine pair
H.VI.19	A globular cluster, large and dim
ι (var.)	4·3–5·0, irregular

*Lupus, the Wolf (Lup; mid-May)

Marked by a conspicuous group of 3rd- and 4th-magnitude stars along the western border of the Milky Way, south of Scorpio.

h4715 (6·1, 6·6; 3"·0; 278°)
π (4·7, 4·8; 1"·5; 75°); fine sight in a 4-inch
κ (5·2, 6·5; 27"; 144°)
μ (4·8, 5·2; 1"·6; 145°)
ε (4·0, 9·0; 26"; 175°)
ζ (5·5, 6·0; 11"; 49°); a fine pair
η (4·0, 8·0; 15"; 22°); the primary may be variable
5822 A small cluster of 8th-magnitude and fainter stars
5986 Bright globular cluster, but unresolved in a small telescope; visible in the finder

Lynx (Lyn; mid-January)

One of the dullest northern constellations, filling the gap between Auriga and Ursa Major. There are many fine doubles, but most of them are faint.

12   (5·2, 6·1; 1"·7; 100°); both white; a third star at 8"·6, 310° makes it triple
Σ 958 (6·0, 6·0; 5"·1; 257°); both yellowish; beautiful
19   (5·3, 6·6; 15"; 315°); white and bluish
38   (4·0, 6·7; 2"·9; 230°); both yellowish

Lyra, the Lyre (Lyr; early July)

Small in size but rich in objects, Lyra lies in the Milky Way and contains a great many pairs, triplets, and beautiful fields. Its leader, Vega (mag. 0·0), is the brightest star in the northern hemisphere, and during late summer in north temperate latitudes passes almost directly overhead.

α (0·0, 9·0; 60"; 175°); the companion is hard to see against the blaze of the primary. A 3-inch shows many other stars in a low-power field.
Σ 2380 (6·7, 8·2; 26"; 10°); cream and blue; a pretty pair
ε 4·0, 4·5; 208"; 173°); a naked-eye pair, though very difficult to resolve. This is the famous double-double, i.e., each star is itself a binary pair: ε^1 (4·6, 6·3; 2"·9; 355°); and ε^2 (4·9, 5·2; 2"·3; 100°). All four stars are white except the 6·3, which is bluish.
ζ (4·2, 5·5; 44"; 150°); white and cream; fine low-power object

Lyra. *The constellation photographed on July 30, 1962. (Stephen A. Walther, Stevens Point, Wisconsin.)*

Σ 2470	(6·7, 8·2; 14″; 267°); white and bluish
Σ 2474	(6·7, 8·0; 17″; 259°); cream and pale blue; in the same field as Σ 2470 forming a second double-double
M.57	A remarkable object: an annular planetary nebula, bright, bluish, and slightly elliptical, looking like a smoke ring—hence the name Ring Nebula
M.56	A globular cluster, unresolved in a small telescope but bright, with a curious V of 7th-magnitude stars *nf*
R (var.)	4·0–4·7, 46ᵈ

Lyrids. One of the few spring showers, swift meteors occurring between April 16 and 22 (maximum, April 20); occasional Lyrids are also seen in May. Records of "April meteors" go back for some 2,500 years, so they are clearly distinctive.

*Mensa, the Table (Men; mid-December)

An obscure group very near the south celestial pole, and containing part of the Nubecula Major. It was originally christened Mons Mensae

Mensa (continued)

(for Table Mountain, south of Cape Town), presumably to immortalize Sir John Herschel's expedition to the Cape of Good Hope; but his arduous researches in the southern skies deserve greater recognition than this barren offering.

2058   A conspicuous nebula, with a central condensation, lying in the Nubecula Major

*Microscopium, the Microscope (Mic; early August)

An almost imperceptible group south of Capricornus; contains only one star brighter than the 5th magnitude.

α   (5·0, 8·5; 22″; 164°)

Monoceros, the Unicorn (Mon; early January)

Contains few conspicuous stars, but lies in a splendid region of the Milky Way to the east of Orion and is replete with memorable telescopic objects.

8	(4·0, 6·7; 13″; 27°); rich yellow and bluish; magnificent field
11	(5·0, 5·5, 6·0; 7″·2, 2″·5; 132°, 105°); all white; a glorious triple; one of the showpieces of the skies
Σ 921	(6·0, 8·2; 16″; 4°); yellowish and bluish
15	(6·0, 8·8; 4″·0; 100°); dull-white and blue; fainter pairs nearby
Σ 1183	(5·5, 7·8; 31″; 326°); yellowish and white
H.VII.2	A splendid open cluster of bright and faint stars, including 12 Mon (yellow)
H.VI.27	A fine, bright open cluster
M.50	Attractive cluster of faint stars, in a glorious region
H.VI.37	A great heap of powdery stars
U (var.)	5·9–8·0, 92ᵈ
V (var.)	6·0–14·0, 334ᵈ

*Musca, the Fly (Mus; March-April)

A small group in the vicinity of Crux, containing some attractive Milky Way fields.

h4432	(5·7, 6·5; 2″·5; 302°)
h4498	(6·2, 7·9; 8″·7; 61°)
β	(3·9, 4·2; 1″·3; 6°)

θ (5·8, 8·0; 5″·7; 186°)
4833   A globular cluster, too condensed for resolution

*Norma, the Square (and Rule) (Nor; mid-May)

Lies in a rich region of the Milky Way, to the south of Scorpio, and offers much telescopic work. A low-power will reveal many clusters and attractive combinations of stars.

ι^1 (5·5, 8·5; 10″; 252°)
ε (4·8, 6·5; 24″; 335°)
6067   A fine open cluster
6087   A scattered cluster of bright stars
6115   A concentration of stars in a region of unbounded splendor
T (var.)   6·2–13·4, 243^d

*Octans, the Octant (Oct; August)

The south-polar constellation, but containing no conspicuous marker as does the north; can be almost equally well observed at any season of the year, though lacking in interesting objects. The 5th-magnitude star Sigma (σ) is only 1° away from the celestial pole.

λ (5·5, 7·7; 3″·1; 67°)

Ophiuchus, the Serpent Bearer (Oph; mid-June)

An extensive constellation north of Scorpio. The boundary is well marked out with stars, the interior obscure; but it contains many fine objects, especially the southern part, which intrudes into a magnificent region of the Milky Way.

ρ	(5·7, 6·4; 3″·4; 350°); yellowish and reddish
36	(5·6, 5·7; 4″·3; 180°); both rich yellow; a splendid pair
39	(5·5, 6·0; 11″; 355°); deep yellow and blue
Σ 2166	(5·6, 7·4; 28″; 283°); white and deep blue
61	(5·5, 5·8; 21″; 94°); both white, very neat
τ	(5·3, 6·0; 1″·9; 273°); both cream, just divided with 3-inch
70	(4·3, 6·0; 3″·4; 78°); both golden-yellow; a superb pair
ε 2276	(6·0, 6·3; 6″·8; 258°); both white
M.12	A fine, bright, condensed cluster, partly resolved in a small telescope
M.10	Globular cluster; appears as a bright nebulosity with a blazing center
M.19	Globular cluster, resolved with large instruments

Ophiuchus (continued)

H.I.45 & H.I.147	Two faint nebulae seen in almost the same low-power field
M.9	A globular cluster seen as a bright nebulosity; a faint star to the south
M.14	An extensive globular cluster, resolvable with large instruments. There is a wide double *p* and a coarse triple *f*.
H.VIII.72	A fine open cluster, just visible with the naked eye, consisting of 8th-magnitude and fainter stars; it has two distinct nuclei. The very ground of the Milky Way is seen glittering with minute points.
R (var.)	6·2–14·4, 302ᵈ
RS (var.)	4·3–12·3, irregular; subject to occasional outbursts
X (var.)	5·9–9·2, 335ᵈ

Orion, the Hunter (Ori; mid-December)

The grandest constellation in the sky, most happily placed on the celestial equator so that it can be appreciated by observers all over the world. Famous for the Great Nebula, visible with the naked eye, it also contains many fine doubles, and lies on the western border of a magnificent part of the Milky Way. Oddly enough, it contains no distinctive clusters. The star Delta (δ) lies only 20′ south of the celestial equator.

Orion. *Photographed on February 22, 1963, with a hand-driven Polaroid 110A camera, exposure time 20 minutes, using an f/47 lens, 5-inch focal length. (Thane P. Bopp, Kirkwood, Missouri.)*

Σ 627	(6·3, 6·5; 20″; 256°); a neat pair, curious colors
ρ	(4·7, 9·0; 7″·1; 63°); yellow and bluish; companion not easy with 3-inch
β	(0·1, 6·7; 9″·4; 203°); Rigel; a good atmospheric test; primary blue-white
33	(6·0, 7·3; 2″·0; 26°); both white
λ	(4·0, 6·0; 4″·2; 43°); yellowish and grayish
Σ 747	(5·6, 6·5; 36″; 223°); white and bluish; split in the finder; in a superb region
Σ 750	(6·0, 8·0; 4″·3; 59°); primary white; beautiful field
σ	In a fine group of two pairs: (4·0, 10·0; 11″; 236°); (7·0, 7·5; 13″; 56°); the faint star rather difficult with 3-inch
ζ	(2·0, 5·0; 2″·8; 159°); white and grayish; pretty
52	(6·2, 6·2; 1″·3; 209°); reddish
W (var.)	5·9–7·7, 200ᵈ
M.42	The Great Nebula in Orion, visible with the naked eye as a greenish haze around Theta (θ). A small telescope converts this into a convoluted veil, with bright condensations, streamers, and an especially distinct black intrusion into the center from the north. At the tip of this intrusion is the multiple star Theta (mags. 6·0, 6·5, 7·0, and 8·0), which is easily seen. This nebula is about a thousand light-years away from the sun. Ramifications extend over many degrees, but these are invisible except by photography, although local concentrations can be made out, especially around the star Iota (ι). The star Theta, also known as the Trapezium, contains some fainter objects, as shown in figure 51; these form interesting test-objects for users of moderate telescopes.
H.V.28	A faint, extensive nebula closely f ζ; also a part of the Great Nebula

Figure 51. *The Trapezium. Stars A, B, C, and D can be seen in a very small telescope. Stars E and F have been glimpsed with a 3-inch, but rarely. G and H are very elusive.*

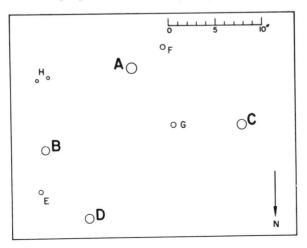

Orion (continued)

M.78   Another faint concentration with a definite "combed" structure
α (var.)   0·0–1·4, irregular; a very rough period of about 5 years
U (var.)   5·3–12·6, 374ᵈ

Orionids. A prominent shower of swift meteors active between October 9 and 29, with maximum about October 20.

*Pavo, the Peacock (Pav; mid-July)

A far-southern asterism containing some distinctive naked-eye stars.

ζ   (4·3, 8·1; 3″·5; 154°)
L8550   (5·8, 5·8; 2″·7; 91°)
L8625   (5·8, 6·1; 8″·1; 136°)
6752   A small globular cluster, resolvable with large instruments only
Y (var.)   5·7–8·5, 233ᵈ

Pegasus (Peg; August-September)

A constellation marked to the naked eye by the Great Square of Pegasus formed by α, β, and γ Peg and γ And. The Square lies west of Andromeda, but the constellation actually extends much farther westward. Considering its size, it is poorly stocked with objects of general interest, most of the doubles being wide or faint.

1   (4·5, 8·6; 36″; 311°); deep yellow and bluish
3   (6·0, 7·4; 39″; 349°); white and pale blue; fine field
Σ2978   (6·8, 8·0; 8″·4; 146°); white and bluish
M.15   A noble globular cluster, visible in the finder; seen nebulous with
           a low-power, blazing in the center. With a high-power, a small
           instrument achieves traces of resolution around the margin.
ε (var.)   Average magnitude 2·5, but suspected of variation
β (var.)   2·4–2·9; irregular, with a rough period of 35 days

Pegasids. A brief shower of swift meteors, radiating from near η about May 30.

Perseus (Per; early November)

So far as north temperate observers are concerned, this constellation, occupying a magnificent region of the Milky Way before it sweeps southward through Auriga toward Orion, offers some of the richest fields to be found anywhere in the sky. Its leader Mirfak can be found by extending eastward the line of Andromeda; here we find the dark-eclipsing variable Algol, and clusters and doubles are ranged against the sky in dazzling profusion.

Σ 268	(6·9, 8·2; 2″·7; 129°); white and tawny
η	(4·0, 8·5; 28″; 301°); intense yellow and deep blue; fine contrast
Σ 331	(5·3, 6·7; 12″; 85°); bluish and yellowish
Σ 336	(6·5, 8·0; 8″·2; 9°); yellow and blue
40	(4·2, 9·5; 20″; 237°); primary white
ζ	(2·7, 9·3; 12″; 208°); primary white; two faint companions
ε	(3·1, 8·3; 9″·0; 10°); white and bluish
Σ 533	(6·0, 7·5; 20″; 60°); reddish and bluish; grand field
Σ 552	(6·3, 6·5; 9″·0; 114°); splendid pair, both white
M.76	A small nebulosity with two distinct nuclei
H.VI.33 & H.VI.34	The famous Double Cluster, visible with the naked eye as a concentration in the Milky Way. A low-power reveals two brilliant open clusters, each larger than the moon, set side by side against a background granular with faint stars. This is a superb object, one to which the observer returns again and again; one never tires of surveying this dazzling array of suns, and the only pity is that few telescopes can include both clusters fully in the same field of view.
M.34	A loose cluster of bright stars, visible with the naked eye
H.VI.25	A beautiful cloud of faint stars; requires careful observation
H.VII.61	A coarse cluster of bright stars
ρ (var.)	3·3–4·1, irregular

Perseids. The most famous and reliable of all meteor showers. Swift meteors are noticed by the casual observer during the second half of July and much of August; a well-defined maximum occurs on August 10–11, when the radiant lies near Eta (η). A shower radiates from the region of Beta (β) between July 25 and August 4, but since these too are swift they can be confused with the main Perseids unless observed carefully.

ε Perseids. A shower of swift meteors occurring between September 7 and 15.

*Phoenix (Phe; early October)

There is little of note in this constellation, which lies between Achernar and Fomalhaut.

| β | (4·1, 4·2; 1″·3; 357°); a binary pair |
| ζ | (4·1, 8·4; 6″·8; 245°) |

Phoenix (continued)

θ (6·3, 6·9; 4″·2; 272°)

625   A faint nebula with central condensation

*Pictor, the Painter (Pic; mid-December)

An undistinguished constellation marked by the brilliant star Canopus, which lies nearby.

ι (5·0, 6·0; 12″; 58°)

I5   (6·4, 8·5; 2″·9; 269°)

Pisces, the Fishes (Psc; late September)

A zodiacal constellation. The head is marked by a small group of stars south of the Great Square of Pegasus, but the northeastern reaches of this extensive constellation are obscure. The sun lies in Pisces at the vernal equinox, when it moves into the northern hemisphere.

35	(6·2, 7·8; 12″; 149°); white and bluish
51	(5·0, 9·0; 27″; 82°); primary white
55	(5·5, 8·2; 6″·6; 193°); deep yellow and clear blue
65	(6·0, 6·0; 4″·5; 297°); both yellowish; a fine pair
ψ^1	(4·9, 5·0; 30″; 160°); both white; splendid low-power field
ζ	(4·2, 5·3; 24″; 63°); white and grayish
α	(4·3, 5·2; 1″·9; 291°); curious tints, somewhat greenish; a binary pair, closing beyond the range of a 3-inch
M.74	A spiral galaxy, visible in a small telescope as a dim nebulosity

*Piscis Austrinus, the Southern Fish (PsA; late August)

Very low in temperate latitudes, but easily distinguished by its bright leader, Fomalhaut (mag. 1·1).

β (4·4, 7·8; 30″; 172°)

γ (4·5, 8·5; 4″·3; 264°)

*Puppis, the Poop (Pup; early January)

One of the fragments of Argo Navis, a splendid constellation, lying beyond Monoceros in the Milky Way and forming the south and east borders of Canis Major. It has been ill-treated by celestial cartographers, and objects quoted in old catalogues as belonging to Puppis may now be found in any of the neighboring groups. Considerable revision is necessary, and it is worth taking trouble in identification, for the views will more than reward the effort involved.

D31	(5·0, 6·5; 13″; 317°); yellow and blue
D32	(5·7, 7·0; 8″·4; 276°)
h3966	(6·5, 6·5; 7″·0; 141°)
D49	(5·7, 6·5; 9″·4; 52°)
n (Hh269)	(6·0, 6·0; 9″·0; 108°); both yellowish
k	(4·5, 4·6; 9″·9; 318°); fine pair; both yellowish
2	(6·2, 7·0; 17″; 340°); white and pale blue
5	(5·3, 7·4; 3″·4; 6°); yellowish and tawny
r	(5·4, 6·2; 4″·0; 190°)
H.VIII.38	A brilliant, extensive, naked-eye group, somewhat diamond-shaped, containing the small pair Σ 1121
M.46	A large mass of faint stars, sprinkling the field of view with tiny points of light
H.IV.64	A small planetary nebula resembling a slightly hazy 8th-magnitude star; found most easily with a moderate-power
M.93	A small cluster of bright and faint stars
H.VII.11	An extensive group of faint stars easily found np 19 Pup
L₂ (var.)	3·4–6·2, 140^d

(Many other clusters and groups can be found by sweeping this wonderful region.)

*Pyxis, the Compass (Pyx; early February)

Some authorities consider this small constellation to have been a part of Argo; it is certainly in the right position, to the east of the Poop. It was introduced by the French astronomer Nicolas de Lacaille during his pioneer work on the southern skies in the mid-nineteenth century, after which the German observer and mathematician Johann Bode added a Log and Line to the Ship's outfit. This constellation (Lochium Funis), together with some others of Bode's invention, was forgotten almost as soon as it was introduced. Later, he actually installed a "typewriter" a few degrees east of Sirius!

H.VII.63	A small cluster of faint stars
2818	A small planetary nebula lying in a coarse group of stars

*Reticulum, the Net (Ret; mid-November)

A small far-southern group, lying between Achernar and Canopus.

θ (6·2, 8·0; 4"·5; 4°)
h3670   (5·9, 8·4; 32"; 99°); yellow and blue

Sagitta, the Arrow (Sge; mid-July)

A tiny asterism north of Aquila, obscure to the naked eye, yet lying in a superb region of the Milky Way. It is worth more attention than it is usually accorded.

Hh630   (6·5, 8·6; 28"; 301°); reddish and blue
ζ (5·7, 8·8; 8"·5; 313°); white and blue; a fine pair
θ (6·0, 8·3; 11"; 327°); yellowish and grayish; a nearby 7th-magnitude
          star completes a fine triple
M.71   A large cluster of very faint stars, appearing nebulous in a small
          telescope

*Sagittarius, the Archer (Sgr; early July)

This splendid zodiacal constellation, with its neighbors Ophiuchus and Scorpio, marks out the richest region in the sky for the observer of clusters. Sagittarius contains no fewer than fifteen of the objects catalogued by Messier; and the star clouds of the Milky Way are brilliant, even finer than those in Cygnus. It is therefore unfortunate that this part of the sky lies too far south for satisfactory observation from north temperate latitudes. Observation is handicapped, too, by the region's appearance during the short nights of midsummer.

h5003   (6·0, 7·0; 4"·8; 180°); bronze and blue; lies in a starry region
κ^2 (6·0, 7·3; 1"·1; 230°); elongated with 3-inch
M.23   A fine open cluster of 9th-magnitude stars arranged in festoons;
          partly resolved in the finder
M.8   A coarse, rather spherical cluster of bright stars wrapped in
          luminous haze, with an open cluster f; known as the Lagoon
          Nebula
M.24   A globular cluster, visible as a nebulous patch, lying on the
          edge of a region of indescribable richness. There is a brilliant
          naked-eye cloud of stars between this object and Mu (μ).
M.18   A small cluster of faint stars

M.17	A wide, bright, nebulous streak with the *p* end overlaid by dark matter; contains two 9th-magnitude stars; known as the Omega Nebula
M.28	A small, bright, globular cluster with a blazing center
M.22	A superb globular cluster, partly resolved with a small telescope; visible in the finder and lies between two 9th-magnitude stars
M.54	An unusual globular cluster; center so condensed that it looks like an 8th-magnitude star with a hazy surround
6723	An extensive and bright nebulosity
M.55	A large, bright globular cluster, with little central condensation
M.75	A rather faint globular cluster resembling M.54
RR (var.)	6·0–14·0, irregular
RU (var.)	5·5–14·0, 354^d
RY (var.)	6·3–14·0, 241^d

Scorpio, the Scorpion (Sco; early June)

A magnificent zodiacal constellation that cannot possibly be mistaken, for it not only lies in the Milky Way, but also contains the brilliant orange star Antares (mag. 0·9) whose name means "Mars-like." The tail of the "scorpion" hangs low in the sky, and many of its objects cannot be well seen from latitudes higher than 40°N due to inevitable horizon haze.

ζ	(4·4, 7·2; 7″·4; 62°); cream and bluish; the primary is a close binary
β	(2·9, 5·2; 14″; 23°); white and grayish
L6706	(6·5, 8·0; 15″; 86°); white and bluish; a pretty pair
ν	(4·2, 6·5; 41″; 336°); yellowish and grayish; the companion is a close double
σ	(3·1, 7·8; 20″; 272°); yellowish primary
h4850	(6·5, 7·0; 6″·9; 352°); both golden; a pretty pair
α	(0·9, 6·8; 3″·0; 275°); reddish and greenish. Notoriously difficult when Antares is low in the sky, but easily seen with a 3-inch when high. It is easier in strong twilight or moonlight than against a dark sky, when the primary's glare is accentuated.
M.80	A brilliant globular cluster with a blazing center
M.4	An extensive globular cluster immediately *p* Antares; visible in the finder; partly resolved
6231	A coarse cluster of bright stars, with fainter members, lying in a glorious region (especially to the north)

Scorpio (continued)

6242	An irregular cluster of bright and faint stars
M.62	A globular cluster with a blazing center
6281	A curious trapezoidal cluster in a fine field
6388	A globular cluster with a blazing center
M.6	An open cluster, visible with the naked eye. In a small telescope, the stars are seen to radiate from the center, suggesting the appearance of an open flower; brighter stars are ranged around the perimeter. This is certainly one of the finest objects in the sky.
H.VI.13	A small, condensed cluster of faint stars, lying in a superb region
M.7	A brilliant, scattered mass of bright stars, visible with the naked eye. They fill a low-power field of view and include one of yellow tint.
RR (var.)	5·6–11·3, 279ᵈ
RS (var.)	6·0–12·7, 320ᵈ

Scorpiids. Very slow-moving meteors which radiate from near Antares between June 2 and 17.

*Sculptor (Scl; late September)

A drab constellation south of Cetus and Aquarius, containing only four 4th-magnitude stars.

D253	(6·0, 7·0; 6″·8; 267°)
ζ	(5·5, 6·5; 6″·1; 165°)
ε	(5·0, 8·5; 4″·5; 47°); white primary
H.V.1	Conspicuous extended nebula
H.VI.20	Compressed cluster of faint stars
H.I.281	Bright nebula
R (var.)	6·2–8·8, 376ᵈ
S (var.)	6·3–13·4, 365ᵈ

Scutum, the Shield (Sct; June-July)

A small but rich constellation occupying the part of the Milky Way between Aquila and Sagittarius. It used to be more extensive than it is today—the constellation realignment of 1930 robbed it of Messier's objects 16, 17, 18, and 24—but enough remains to afford magnificent sweeping. Many of the "clusters" here are mere concentrations in the endless strata of stars.

6682   This marks the position of two sprinklings of faint stars. A rich region lies to the southwest.

M.26   A small cluster, consisting of a few bright stars seen against a haze of fainter ones

M.11   The Wild Duck cluster. A superb fan-shaped cluster, granular with stars, with a 9th-magnitude star at the apex and a small double to the north. The surrounding region glitters with faint stars.

H.I.47 A small but distinct nebulosity

R (var.) 6·3–8·6, 144^d

Serpens, the Serpent (Ser; May-June)

This constellation consists of two separate groups: the head (Caput) to the west of Ophiuchus, the body (Cauda) to the east. The stars are listed as for a single constellation.

Σ 1919   (6·1, 7·0; 24″; 10°); yellowish and bluish
Σ 1931   (6·2, 7·6; 13″; 167°); yellowish and bluish
δ   (3·0, 4·0; 4″·0; 176°); white and grayish; fine pair
59   (5·5, 7·8; 3″·9; 317°); yellow and bluish
Σ 2375   (6·2, 6·6; 2″·4; 116°)
θ   (4·0, 4·2; 22″; 103°); both white; a superb pair in a fine field
M.5   A splendid globular cluster, partly resolved
M.16   Hexagonal cluster of bright stars and star dust
R (var.) 5·5–13·4, 357^d

Sextans, the Sextant (Sex; late February)

A barren group south of Leo.

35   (6·1, 7·2; 6″·4; 235°); yellow and grayish
H.I.163   Bright, centrally condensed nebula

Taurus, the Bull (Tau; November-December)

A fine winter zodiacal constellation. Its leader, Aldebaran (mag. 0·8), glows red to the northwest of Orion, and the Pleiades and Hyades clusters are readily distinguishable with the naked eye.

Σ 401 (6·5, 7·0; 11″; 270°); both white; a fine pair

Taurus (continued)

χ (5·7, 7·8; 20″; 25°); white and lilac
62   (6·2, 8·0; 29″; 290°); white primary
Σ 548   (6·0, 8·0; 14″; 36°); yellowish and bluish
a (0·8, 11·2; 121″; 34°). The comes has been seen easily with a 3-inch, but with such an aperture it is certainly a good test of vision and steadiness.
118   (5·8, 6·6; 4″·8; 205°); white and bluish
Σ 730   (5·8, 6·7; 9″·8; 142°); yellowish and bluish

PLEIADES.   A well-known naked-eye group. Six stars are easily visible to normal sight, and some observers have recorded a dozen or more, but the cluster is too widespread to be a satisfactory telescopic object. It is best seen in the finder, or with binoculars. A chart of the brighter members is shown in figure 52. There are faint nebulae associated with the group, very conspicuous photographically but obscure to visual observers. Like the nebula around Xi (ξ) Cygni, they tend to be more easily visible with small apertures and very low magnifications.

HYADES.   A very loose sprinkle of naked-eye stars to the west of Aldebaran. There is no association, however, for Aldebaran is much closer to the sun than is the cluster.

M.1 The Crab Nebula.   Visible with a small telescope as a misty, elongated patch, this is the remains of the supernova observed in A.D. 1054 by Chinese astronomers.

Figure 52.   *The Pleiades.*

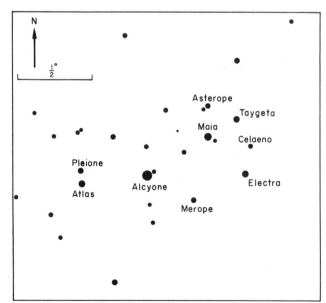

Taurids. A diffuse, long-lasting shower of slow meteors with a complex system of radiants. Noticeable activity lasts between October 26 and November 16.

*Telescopium, the Telescope (Tel; mid-July)

An uninteresting group south of Sagittarius.

6868   A small, centrally condensed nebula. There is a nearby nebula, dimmer and larger; this is N.G.C. 6909.

Triangulum, the Triangle (Tri; late October)

A small but well-defined group south of Gamma (γ) Andromedae. The three principal stars form an obvious elongated triangle; but it must not be confused with Aries, further to the south.

ι (5·0, 6·4; 3″·9; 74°); yellow and blue, fine contrast; also known as 6

Σ 239   (7·0, 8·0; 14″; 212°); yellowish and pale lilac; faint but neat

M.33   A nearby external galaxy, associated with the one in Andromeda. This is a notoriously difficult object, for it is both large and faint, and too high a magnification renders it invisible from lack of contrast. A good finder will show it best, and under good conditions it can be glimpsed with the naked eye. Telescopically, it appears as a barely perceived, extended haze of about the same diameter as the moon.

R (var.)   5·8–12·0, 270$^{\rm d}$

*Triangulum Australe, the Southern Triangle (TrA; late May)

A conspicuous far-southern group lying on the edge of the Milky Way, south of Norma.

L6477   (6·4, 6·6; 2″·1; 151°)
6025   A fine open cluster of bright and faint stars

*Tucana, the Toucan (Tuc; mid-September)

Unremarkable as a constellation, this group contains two noteworthy objects.

β (4·5, 4·5; 27″; 170°); a fine pair
κ (5·1, 7·3; 5″·4; 346°)
δ (4·8, 8·1; 7″·0; 282°)

Tucana (continued)

104 Popularly known as 47 Tucanae, this is a magnificent globular
cluster lying on the *f* border of the Nubecula Minor. To the naked eye
it appears as a hazy star; a low-power eyepiece reveals it as a blazing
mass. In terms of magnificence, it is second only to Omega (ω)
Centauri.

330 A very compressed globular cluster lying within the Nubecula Minor

362 A fine, bright globular cluster, visible to the naked eye

NUBECULA MINOR. This is the smaller Magellanic Cloud, a satellite
galaxy of our own star system. It contains a great many interesting objects,
especially star clusters and variables, but because it is somewhat more
distant than the Nubecula Major it offers a less attractive hunting ground
for a small telescope.

Ursa Major, the Great Bear (UMa; mid-March)

Also known as the Big Dipper, or the Plough, this is the best-known
northern constellation; its sequence of seven bright stars is known to
everyone. To places in latitudes higher than 40°N, the group is circumpolar,
never setting below the northern horizon; at 30°N, however, only the star
Alpha (*a*) remains visible at the constellation's passage below Polaris, the
polestar. Its boundaries extend much farther in the southern and western
directions than is usually supposed, and they enclose a number of galaxies,
mostly faint.

Σ 1349   (6·8, 8·0; 19″; 165°); yellowish and bluish
23   (3·8, 9·0; 23″; 271°); white and lilac; fine contrast
Σ 1415   (6·1, 7·0; 17″; 167°); both white
Σ 1520   (6·5, 7·8; 13″; 345°); white and bluish
ζ (4·4, 4·9; 2″·6; 135°); the first binary star to have its orbit calcu-
         lated; now near its greatest separation; period 60 years
57   (5·2, 8·2; 5″·5; 357°); white and ashen
Σ 1561   (5·9, 8·0; 10″; 252°); primary yellowish
65   (6·0, 8·3; 3″·7; 36°); white and blue
ζ (2·1, 4·2; 14″; 150°); both greenish white. This is Mizar, forming
         a naked-eye pair with Alcor, the nearby 5th-magnitude star. An
         8th-magnitude star lies between the two.
H.I.205 A fairly conspicuous nebulosity with a central condensation
M.81 &   Two bright galaxies which can be included in the same field of
M.82   view; visible in the finder. M.81 appears as a circular nebulosity;
         M.82 has the effect of a narrow, curved streak, somewhat like a

scimitar blade. This is because we are seeing the galaxy at an acute angle.

M.97   A large, dim planetary nebula, best seen with a low-power
R (var.) 6·5–13·0, 302ᵈ

Ursa Minor, the Little Bear (UMi; May)

The north polar constellation, also known as the Little Dipper, invaluable for containing the polestar, Polaris, Alpha (*a*), the most useful star in the northern sky. At the present time Polaris is less than a degree from the true pole, which will approach closest, due to precession, in A.D. 2095, at a distance of only 26'. Thereafter, the slow circling of the earth's axis will carry the celestial pole through Cepheus and Cygnus and, by A.D. 15,000, into Hercules. No star as bright as Polaris lies near the track, although Alpha (*a*) Cephei will make a fairly conspicuous marker in A.D. 8000. In 2000 B.C., Alpha (*α*) Draconis lay fairly near the pole.

a   (2·1, 9·0; 18″; 218°); white and blue; very easy with a 3-inch under good conditions
π^1 (6·1, 7·0; 31″; 80°); yellowish and bluish

*Vela, the Sails (Vel; mid-February)

A Milky Way constellation north of Carina and east of Puppis.

δ   (2·0, 6·6; 3″·0; 160°); a delicate object
H   (4·9, 7·7; 2″·7; 339°)
h4188   (5·5, 6·5; 3″·0; 287°)
h4220   (5·5, 6·0; 2″·1; 210°)
S   (6·2, 6·5; 13″; 219°)
2792   A small but conspicuous planetary nebula
2932   A compressed cluster of bright and faint stars

Virgo, the Virgin (Vir; mid-April)

This extensive constellation accommodates the ecliptic after it has passed through Leo, and its blue-white leader, Spica (mag. 1·0), lies in a region of sky otherwise devoid of bright stars. A mass of faint galaxies lies between Epsilon (*ε*) Virginis and Beta (*β*) Leonis, extending northward into Coma Berenices.

Σ 1627   (5·9, 6·4; 20″; 196°); both yellowish, barren field
17   (6·2, 9·0; 19″; 337°); white and bluish

Virgo (continued)

γ	(3·6, 3·7; 4″·8; 306°); both white; a superb binary pair with a period of 180 years. They are now closing.
Σ 1689	(6·7, 9·0; 29″; 198°); yellowish and bluish
θ	(4·0, 9·0; 7″·2; 343°); white primary
Σ 1904	(6·5, 6·5; 9″·6; 346°); a neat pair
M.84 & M.86	Two nebulosities in the same field, M.84 being slightly the brighter
M.49.	Faint nebulosity positioned between two telescopic stars
M.59 & M.60	Seen in the same field; moderate apertures reveal many faint nebulae in this region
R (var.)	6·2–12·6, 145^d
S (var.)	6·3–13·2, 380^d
SS (var.)	5·9–10·0, 359^d

*Volans, the Flying Fish (Vol; mid-January)

A far-southern constellation, the name being abbreviated from Piscis Volantis. It lies between Beta (β) Carinae and the Nubecula Major.

γ	(3·9, 5·8; 14″; 299°)
ζ	(3·9, 9·0; 17″; 116°); yellow and blue
ε	(4·5, 8·0; 6″·1; 22°)

Vulpecula, the Fox (Vul; late July)

Like its neighbor Sagitta, this is a small group which is often overlooked because it contains no bright stars. But, lying in the Milky Way to the south of Cygnus, it contains some superb star fields.

Σ 2445	(6·3, 8·0; 12″; 263°); white and grayish
Σ 2769	(6·5, 7·5; 18″; 301°); both white
H.VIII.21	A neat sprinkle of 9th-magnitude and fainter stars inside a curious curve of brighter stars
M.27	The Owl Nebula. With a small telescope it appears as a disk of faint luminous haze, with the interior intensified in the rough form of a cotton-reel, or spool. Visible in the finder; and there are several doubles in the low-power field. It is probably the most conspicuous of all planetary nebulae.
H.VIII.20	Surrounding star 20; a coarse group of bright and faint stars lying in an extensive starry region
H.VII.8	A fine, delicate open cluster

22

Astrophotography

Today, many people have taken up photography as a hobby and, by doing their own processing, are achieving results of professional quality. If one's interest in and knowledge of the subject have passed beyond the "snapshot" stage, there is no reason why it should not be turned to good account in astrophotography. This term refers to the photography of large areas of sky, showing stars, comets, and similar objects of interest. The difference between this and planetary photography is that an ordinary camera, strapped to an equatorial telescope, is used. The telescope is used merely as a guider for the camera during the necessarily long exposure of ten minutes, half an hour, or possibly more than an hour.

In planetary photography, as we have seen, there is little chance of the photographic plate competing with the eye. The slightest atmospheric ripple during the exposure will throw a blur across the whole photograph, destroying the finest detail, which the eye can grasp instantly during the rare moments of almost perfect steadiness. But in the case of wide-field photography, the type now to be discussed, the effects of bad seeing are negligible. The area of sky covered is very large, the resultant image scale small; and the object is to record the *faintest possible* star, a task which the photographic emulsion achieves much more successfully than the eye. With a 1½-inch lens, and a considerable amount of care and patience, it is possible to photograph stars that are too faint to be seen clearly with a 3-inch refractor. This is because, unlike the eye—which works instantaneously— the emulsion continues to build up an image for as long as it is exposed.

Image-building

A photographic plate or film consists of a glass or plastic "base" which is coated with a cream-colored emulsion. This emulsion consists essentially of a number of delicate silver compounds that are unstable in the presence of light; when affected by actinic rays they clump together in distinct grains, which are blackened by the subsequent action of the developer. The brighter the light, the more numerous the developable grains and the denser and blacker the layer. The regions receiving only a light exposure produce a gray, semitransparent effect on the negative. If the film receives no exposure at all, none of the grains are affected and the fixer washes them away. We can then see clearly through the colorless base of the developed negative.

When taking an ordinary photograph, it is most important to give the film exactly the right exposure. If it is too short, the darker regions of the subject will not have had time to make even a slight impression on the emulsion, and the corresponding areas on the negative will be quite blank. Conversely, by overexposure the bright- and medium-intensity parts of the subject will appear too dense, with much of the detail obscured. This is because the conversion of the emulsion grains by light is not an instantaneous process; their formation builds up with increased exposure.

This gradual conversion is what makes the process such a boon to the astronomer, for it follows that *the longer the exposure, the fainter the stars recorded.* For example, suppose that the astrocamera in question has a 1-inch lens (note that, just as with visual observation, the clear aperture determines light-gathering power). Using a suitable emulsion, the image of the bright star Vega might be recorded in half a second. It then follows that, since Vega is some 250 times as bright as a star of the 6th magnitude, the latter would be recorded in about two minutes. Bearing in mind the brightness ratio of approximately $2\frac{1}{2}$ between adjacent magnitudes, we could expect to reach the 7th magnitude in five minutes; the 8th in $12\frac{1}{2}$; the 9th in half an hour; and if we have sufficient perseverance to keep the camera guided on the stars for $1\frac{1}{4}$ hours, 10th magnitude stars would presumably be recorded. Yet, if this 1-inch lens were used as the objective of a telescope, it could not normally be expected to reveal stars fainter than the 9th magnitude.

This, then, is the vital difference between the eye and the photographic emulsion. The eye has no cumulative power; by gazing for half an hour it sees no fainter stars than if it gazed half a minute—assuming, of course, that it is fully dark-adapted. Indeed, the eye rapidly fatigues. The emulsion is a relatively slow starter, but since it can maintain this pace almost indefinitely it eventually emerges the winner.

Returning now to the long-exposure photograph, what has happened in the case of Vega? Half a second was enough to print its pinpoint image on the plate. But its light has now been shining down for $1\frac{1}{4}$ hours, giving a degree of overexposure of some 8,000 times! As a result, the light has diffused into all the grains for some considerable distance around the central spot, so that it appears as a large disk, while the 10th-magnitude stars appear as tiny points. The stars of intermediate magnitude show disks of various sizes, depending on their brightness. This means that in stellar photography the magnitude of a star is indicated by the halation disk, and this is indeed a very useful method of calibration: a photograph provides accurate magnitudes as well as precise positions!

Some applications

The great possibilities afforded by the photographic process were obvious to perceptive astronomers from the moment Louis Daguerre introduced his primitive process in 1839; but it was not until the mid-1870s, when the modern dry emulsion was developed, that photography became astronomy's foremost ally. Today, almost all professional research is done photographically; giant telescopes are virtually giant cameras, photographing dim stars and galaxies that could not possibly be seen visually with an instrument of twice the aperture. Only in the observation of close double stars, and in much planetary work, does "the man at the eyepiece" still hold an honored place. Before going into details, let us glance at some of the fields of work that can be usefully tackled with an astrocamera.

STAR CHARTING.   All modern star charts are compiled photographically. The reason is obvious enough: An exposure of an hour or two can reveal thousands of stars, and to chart these individually might take years.

The advantage of the photographic process for this kind of work was proved dramatically when the great comet of 1882 appeared in the sky. At what was then the Royal Observatory at the Cape of Good Hope, the director, Sir David Gill, decided to take some photographs of the comet. Later, he wrote (*Annals of the Cape Observatory*, Vol. 2 Pt. 1, 1886):

> *Several photographers in the Cape Colony found it possible to obtain impressions of the comet, but they were unable to secure pictures of scientific value, because they were unprovided with means to follow the diurnal motion [produced by the rotation of the earth]. I had no available camera belonging to the observatory, and no experience in the development of modern dry plates. In these circumstances I applied to Mr. Allis, a skilful photographer in my neighbourhood, who eagerly consented to co-operate*

with me in the work. I arranged means to attach his camera to the stand of
an equatorial telescope, and the telescope itself was employed to follow the
nucleus of the comet accurately during the whole time of exposure by aid
of the driving-clock and with small corrections given by hand. The lens
employed had an aperture of only 2 inches, and a focal length of 11 inches,
but the result . . . shows a very satisfactory delineation of the tail and
envelope of the comet.

More important still, the photographs showed a great many stars. It
was this unexpected result that inspired Gill to build a special camera, and,
he constructed the first photographic chart of the sky, covering the far-
southern region that could not be reached by Argelander in his visual work
on the *Bonner Durchmusterung*. It also provided the initiative for many
other charts and projects that came to fruition in the late nineteenth
century, including the colossal Astrographic Chart, an international
photographic star catalogue that is still unfinished. It is worth remembering
that all this came about through the results of a 2-inch lens with a focal
length of 11 inches, exposed for an hour or two in conjunction with the
relatively insensitive plates then available.

Although few amateurs will have the inclination to compile their own
personal photographic charts, there is clear scope for photography of small
regions of the sky. In this way, the fluctuations of variable stars and the
movements of minor planets can be followed; the Milky Way regions can
be shown to splendid effect, and some of the very extensive nebulae are
rendered with a prominence that amazes the visual observer.

COMET PHOTOGRAPHY. A handful of enthusiastic amateurs have considered carrying out a photographic hunt for new comets, photographing
regions of the sky near the sun and examining the plates for signs of a suspicious, hazy object. The advantage of this method is that a large area can be
covered in one night; but the examination of the plates is an exhausting
business, and it remains to be seen whether this is a more fruitful procedure
than direct telescopic sweeping.

In the case of known comets, however, photography is an invaluable
tool. When a known comet makes a return, it is almost always located
photographically by a professional observatory—usually the U.S. Naval
Observatory at Flagstaff, Arizona, which specializes in this work. But the
amateur can make a big contribution in the case of a bright comet near
perihelion. The faintest extremities of the tail, and any delicate detail in
the brighter parts, can often be recorded much more effectively by photographic means than visually. Some really splendid results have been
achieved with limited equipment. From Gill's time to the present day, the

appearance of one of these celestial visitors acts as a general inspiration for impromptu effort!

METEOR PHOTOGRAPHY. This is a matter of luck, experience, and, once again, patience. During intense showers, such as the Quadrantids, Perseids, and Geminids, a camera pointed to the radiant may record a number of meteor trails, which can then be examined at leisure and used to plot an accurate radiant point. However, only the brightest meteors leave an appreciable streak unless a very powerful lens is used, and it must be admitted that this is a field in which professional activity is rapidly reducing the scope for useful amateur research. On the other hand, it is very satisfying to record a number of meteor trails on a single photograph.

Cameras and lenses

Successful stellar photographs have been taken with an ordinary miniature or box camera, mounted on an equatorial telescope for guidance purposes. Using such a camera, it is quite possible to record all the naked-eye stars in fifteen or twenty minutes, and the results should encourage the experimenter to attempt further efforts.

There are two drawbacks associated with the use of small cameras for this work. First of all, the lens used with a 35mm or roll-film camera is unlikely to have an aperture of more than an inch, which means that a very long exposure is necessary to record faint stars; secondly, the image scale is very small, and this will lead to confusion in the identification of individual stars. For proper work, a larger lens with a longer focal length is required, and since the lens is the nucleus of the whole affair, it is worth investigating the problem rather more closely.

To be of wide application, an astrocamera should cover a field at least 15° square, and 20° square is much better. Since the image scale increases with the focal length of the lens, it follows that the actual size of the photographic plate required to cover a given area of sky also increases with the focal length; and, since large plates are very expensive, it is best to decide on the plate size first of all, and to carry on the calculations from there. The sizes most widely available are quarter- and half-plate ($3\frac{1}{4} \times 4\frac{1}{4}$ and $4\frac{3}{4} \times 6\frac{1}{2}$ inches, respectively). If we want to produce fields of roughly 15° × 20° on these plates, lenses of about 11 and 18 inches focal length will be required. For wider fields (which may be desirable for meteor work, for example), a shorter focal length is required; a long-focus lens will give a more close-up view of a smaller area of sky.

The actual aperture is the critical factor. The greater the lens opening, the quicker a star is recorded, and the shorter the necessary exposure. This

Photographic telescope. *Cmdr. Hatfield's tubeless 6-inch reflector. It is on a German mounting, with an 18-inch pulley wheel to take the synchronous motor drive. The telescope and mounting are homemade.*

not only means that there is less chance of slightly erratic guiding destroying the perfect circularity of the stars' images; it also allows useful work to be carried out in poor weather conditions, when there are only short periods of unclouded sky; in the case of an "emergency" object, such as a comet or nova, this advantage may prove to be a vital one. Table XI offers a guide to probable exposures with different apertures, using a reasonably fast plate.

TABLE XI.   Exposure Times

LENS APERTURE (INCHES)	EXPOSURE TO REACH 9TH MAG.		FAINTEST STAR REACHED IN 30M. (MAGNITUDE)
1	30^m		9·0
2	8		10·5
3	3	30^s	11·4
4	2	0	12·0
5	1	12	12·5
6		50	12·8

The exposure lessens more or less with the area of the lens, so that a 4-inch aperture is clearly 16 times (4²) as fast as a 1-inch. On the other hand, the efficiency of large lenses is to some extent reduced by their greater thickness, more light being absorbed by the glass.

A large lens is expensive; and the larger it is relative to its focal length, the greater the additional expense. This—the same f/ratio mentioned earlier in connection with mirrors and objectives—means that while, for example, a 2-inch lens of 20-inch focal length (f/10) is a feasible proposition, a 2-inch lens of 5-inch focal length (f/2·5) is extremely difficult to make. So, in the case of an 11-inch focus lens to be used with a quarter-plate, we should be very lucky indeed to find a usable one of 4-inch aperture (f/2·75). Even a 3-inch (f/3·7) would be a good find. It is probably better not to hope for anything bigger than a 2-inch (f/5·5), unless, of course, one has extra money on hand. Many amateur astrocameras work in the f/5 to f/6 range.

There is a further difficulty in the use of wide-aperture lenses. To appreciate this, one must consider the difference between the image of a star and that of an extended object—say, a nebula or a comet's tail. A star is a pinpoint, no matter how great the focal length or magnification of the telescope, but a nebula shows a perceptible area. It therefore follows that the shorter the focal length of a lens of given aperture, the smaller and more intense the nebula's image will be, and the shorter the necessary exposure. For instance, if we have two 2-inch aperture lenses, one of f/3, the other of f/6, the f/3 lens will more quickly produce an image of an extended object; the stars, on the other hand, will be recorded by both lenses in the same time. This is why the ordinary photographer, who is concerned exclusively with terrestrial, and therefore extended, objects, is so anxious to have a "fast" lens—that is, one with a small f/ratio.

This consideration has an important bearing on astrophotography, since the sky is never perfectly dark; various glows, whether auroral or terrestrial, conspire to intensify the sky background so that it readily affects, or "fogs," the photographic plate. Hence, if we wish to give a long exposure in order to record faint stars, this fogging will matter less if the lens is a slow one, with a fairly high f/ratio. Of course, this applies only to stars; if a diffuse object, such as a comet, is being photographed, a fast lens is needed to bring out the faintest reaches of its tail, and it becomes a matter of compromise!

Obviously, then, the best f/ratio depends on both the kind of object to be photographed, and the nocturnal conditions at the site. If money is no object, and the observer lives in a rural area, a ratio as small as f/2·5 should be usable for exposures of up to three-quarters of an hour; on the other hand, an astrocamera used in or near a town would probably fog hopelessly in a matter of minutes at any ratio of less than f/4·5.

For very extended objects, the focal ratio can be of more account than the diameter of the lens. This was proved by E. E. Barnard, who experimented with wide-field photography at the end of the last century and took some of the finest of all Milky Way photographs with a 6-inch portrait lens of 36-inch focal length. He was also, incidentally, the first person to discover a comet photographically when, on October 12, 1892, he found its image on one of his photographs. Here is his comment on lenses:

> *One is too apt to think that, for astronomical investigations of any value nowadays (when single telescopes have run up to a hundred thousand dollars or so in cost), we must have great expensive instruments—the results, in a sort of way, being expected to bear a certain proportion in point of value to the cost of the telescope . . . . What, therefore, must be thought of the performance of an ordinary "magic lantern" lens only 1½ inches in diameter and 3 or 4 inches focus?*
>
> *During the fall of 1894 the writer made a series of experiments with such a lens in photographing certain regions of the heavens . . . . Some of the cloud forms of the Milky Way were shown in ten minutes' time, which had required from two to three hours' exposure with the 6-inch lens! With it a large and previously unknown nebula was photographed about the star v Scorpii.*
>
> *With this lens a photograph was made of the constellation of Orion with about an hour's exposure. To my astonishment this picture showed an enormous curved nebula covering almost the entire figure of Orion. This tremendous nebula is the largest—in point of extent—in the entire heavens. It cannot be seen with any telescope in existence.*

The fact that these words were written seventy years ago (*The Photographic Times*, August 1895) does not alter their relevance for us today. A small lens, under good conditions, can achieve amazing results, as is shown

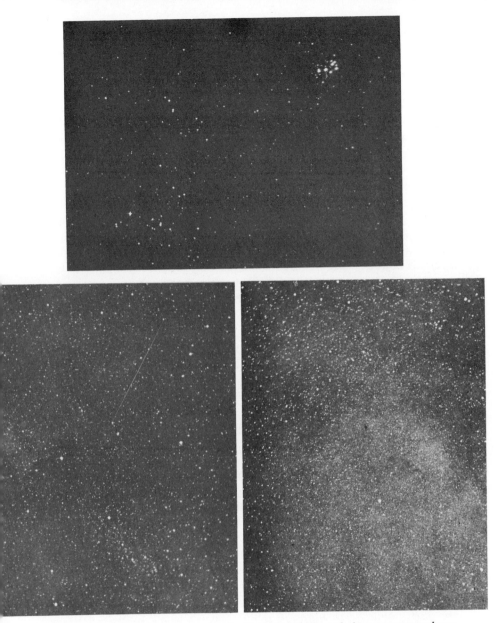

Stellar Photographs. *These were taken by H. N. D. Wright with the astrocamera shown on page 311. (a) The Hyades (very scattered) and Pleiades (top right). (b) Clusters in Cygnus. (c) The Milky Way in the Aquila-Sagitta region, with the effect of the star clouds well brought out.*

by the Milky Way photograph here—which, it should be remembered, was taken from the suburbs of London!

A useful lens for astrophotography is most likely to be found in a government and industrial surplus store specializing in scientific instruments. Some of these stores advertise in *Sky & Telescope* and other scientific magazines. Lenses designed for use in aircraft cameras give good definition over a wide field of view, and so are excellently suited for astronomical work. Perhaps the best known of these is the Kodak Aero-Ektar, which works at f/2·5 and comes in focal lengths of 7 and 12 inches; a 7-inch lens can sometimes be bought for as little as $15, although they are now becoming scarce. It gives a wide field of view—a 7-inch lens will cover a field of 50°. The Ross Xpres (f/4; focal length 5 inches) embraces an even wider area of sky (about 65°), although its aperture is smaller than that of the Aero-Ektar. Another fine lens, ideal for photography of aurorae and other extended objects, is the 8-inch f/2·9 Pentac. Anyone purchasing one of these lenses has made a fine start in the field of astrophotography.

If these types are too expensive, there is no need to be disheartened. In the heyday of the plate camera, many large lenses were made commercially, and these may be picked up nowadays—often with the camera itself— for just a few dollars. These "landscape," or *portrait*, lenses, as they are called, usually work at about f/6 with a focal length of between 10 and 20 inches.

A good portrait lens, many of which were made by the firms of Cooke and Taylor & Hobson, has fulfilled the wishes of many an amateur; unfortunately, there are many bad ones. They can have two faults: bad color correction (chromatic aberration), and a serious deterioration of definition toward the edge of the field. These defects were not too grave for their original purpose, since in the early days of photography a certain diffuseness was frequently considered esthetic, but astronomical work is more demanding. The chromatic aberration will manifest itself as a circular haze around the stars, while the margins of the plate will show them looking like half-closed umbrellas, a defect known as "coma". Generally speaking, however, a lens bought from a reputable optician is its own guarantee, and it should be possible to arrange a refund against testing.

There is no room here to discuss the construction and testing of an astrocamera, but in any case it is largely a matter of common sense. There are three points to be borne in mind: first, the body must be extremely rigid, so that the lens and plate are held firmly in line; second, the plate must be inserted exactly at the focus every time and be perfectly square-on, so that the definition is good over the whole area; third, there should be some means of knowing just what area of sky is being covered. The easiest way of doing this is to make a wire frame-finder similar to those used on press cameras. If the frame is painted white, it will be sufficiently conspicuous to mark off the region, and may prove invaluable when an extensive object, such as a large comet, is being photographed.

Mounting and accessories

The quality of the telescope and mounting used for an astrocamera is of vital importance. It must be solid, with the polar axis accurately aligned (a small error will result in the stars slowly drifting in declination), and there should be good slow-motion action on both axes so that errors can be corrected. For best results, the main telescope—which is used for guiding—should have a focal length at least twice, and preferably three times, that of the camera lens. A normal 3-inch refractor would therefore be adequate for camera lenses of between 10 and 15 inches focal length, provided, of course, that the mounting is strong enough to take the extra weight of the camera. Some counterbalancing will be necessary, in any case, but in the interests of stability this should be reduced to the lowest possible level by mounting the camera itself as far "inboard" as possible. The photograph here shows a satisfactory mounting for a small camera.

To facilitate smooth guiding, the telescope's eyepiece must be equipped with cross wires, so that the image of a star near the center of the photographed field can be bisected. A high magnification must be used, and it is an excellent idea to throw the image slightly out of focus, so that it shows a moderate disk. This can be bisected by the wires more accurately than is possible with a focused image. The longer the focal length of the camera lens, and the greater the resultant image scale, the more accurately everything must be arranged. If the focal length is only 3 or 4 inches, a certain amount of image drifting can be tolerated, since the scale of the negative is so small. But with focal lengths of 12 inches and more, the guiding must

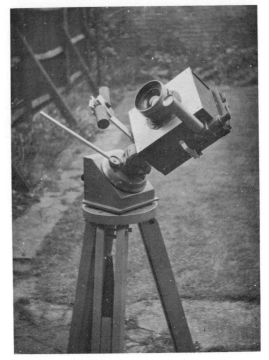

Astrocamera. *This astrocamera, belonging to H. N. D. Wright, has an f/4 lens with a 5-inch focus, and is mounted on a simple equatorial stand. It is guided during the exposure by visual tracking through the attached elbow telescope.*

be done with scrupulous care. Practical experimenting is the only way of bringing hidden flaws to light. Though keeping one's eye glued to the eye-piece for half an hour at a time is never an attractive proposition, such devotion is necessary if good results are to be obtained.

Experience with ordinary telescopes will have introduced the nuisance of dewing, which can also plague the photographer. Unfortunately, a simple dew cap does not answer the problem here, for the field of view is so wide that the margins of the plate will be seriously obstructed. One answer is to make the tube in the form of a funnel, but this does not provide such efficient protection. The most direct solution is the one employed by professional astronomers: to *warm* the camera lens. Unless conditions are extreme, a minute amount of heat is enough to raise the temperature of the lens above that of the air; and this makes it impossible for any dew to be deposited. A length of 1,000-ohm resistance wire, wound around the front of the lens mount and worked off a flashlight battery or suitable mains transformer, will have a magical effect—and it will avoid those angry exclamations which might otherwise be heard when, after an hour's patient guiding, the camera lens is found to have been hopelessly fogged with dew for the last fifty minutes!

Exposure, plates, processing

Since the camera is to be used at night, the simplest of shutters will serve. A flap of aluminium or cardboard, painted dull-black and hinged in front of the lens, can be operated by a string carried back to the rear of the guiding telescope. This allows the observer to get comfortably into position before the exposure is commenced; it also means that the exposure can be stopped during those infuriating moments when an airplane or satellite passes across the field. Before taking the photograph, it is a good idea to swing the telescope through the arc that will be traced out during the exposure, to make sure that the guiding eyepiece is comfortably accessible.

It might be thought that the fastest emulsions, such as Kodak Royal-X Pan or Ilford HPS, would be the best choice for this work. But, strangely enough, some slower types actually record faint stars more quickly. This is because most commercial films are designed for very brief exposures, whereas astronomical work demands exposures of far greater length than in other fields of photography. Most fast emulsions show a rapid falling-off of sensitivity under these circumstances, and special plates are therefore required which maintain their sensitivity during these long exposures, or which, to use the correct term, have a low *reciprocity failure*. Ilford's Zenith Astronomical plate is one example, and the Kodak Oa–J another. If photographic work is being undertaken on a serious basis, it is worth going into the question in more detail, since any reduction of exposure time is bound to improve the quality and pleasure of the work.

Every astrophotographer must be prepared to do his own processing. Each plate demands its own special treatment, and experience will soon dictate the best technique, the perfection of which will add greatly to the worth of the photograph. Furthermore, there may be urgent need to have the picture developed as quickly as possible, so that if it shows flaws there is a chance of securing another one on the same night.

Stellar photography

Amateurs who undertake photography of the Milky Way or of individual constellations frequently find this a fascinating pastime in itself. There are many hazards: The sky may cloud up, or a momentary lapse of concentration produces ruinous irregularities around the brighter stars. (Faint stars build up their images slowly, so that errors of guiding, provided they are quickly corrected, are not so disastrous.) Sometimes a distant thunderstorm or flashes from a nearby electric railway can cause sufficient illumination to ruin the work. Those who live in built-up regions have a more permanent hazard to face; but here the secret is to choose a plate that is relatively insensitive to the color of the glow. For instance, an observer living in a sodium-light district can at least partly overcome the problem by using a plate sensitive to blue rather than yellow light; while filters can also be tried.

These color idiosyncrasies will come out clearly in the resultant photographs. A picture of Orion taken with a blue-sensitive plate, such as Kodak 103a–O, will show Betelgeuse as the least conspicuous of the seven bright stars, since its pronounced reddish color has less action on the emulsion than has the white light of the others. Alternatively, a red-sensitive plate, such as Kodak 103a–E, will exaggerate Betelgeuse. Clearly, we have here the elements of a systematic color-gradation system, a method that has been used extensively by professional workers. Since it is impossible to judge color visually when the star falls below a certain threshhold (about magnitude 9 with a 3-inch refractor), the amateur can at least distinguish between the faint red and blue-white stars in a certain region by comparing a blue-sensitive photograph with the ordinary telescopic view. If a certain star appears brighter in the photograph relative to its companions, it must be bluish; if it appears even fainter, then it is red. Since even a small lens can photograph stars down to the 11th magnitude, this tool is a powerful one.

Photographic observations are also of interest in nova work. If a long-focus lens is available, so that the region around the nova can be photo-

Nova Herculis, 1963. *Photograph taken by D. S. Brown on February 27, 1963. The nova, which is at the centre of the field, was still relatively bright. A short-focus 6½-inch reflector was used; the exposure time was 15 minutes. The faintest stars shown are of the 13th magnitude. Comparison stars are identified by numbers.*

graphed on a large scale, its dimming relative to the surrounding comparison stars can be followed very accurately. The star field of Nova Herculis 1963, as photographed by an amateur living in England, is shown here.

The most direct method of recording stellar tints is, obviously enough, to use a color film, but this method is fraught with snags. A color emulsion requires very accurate exposure; if this is in error to even a small degree, the color registered will be false. Without some means of accurately gauging the exposure in advance, the pictures are not likely to be of much scientific value. It is certainly interesting, however, to experiment with a few frames of color film in a miniature camera.

Comet photography

Photographs of comets are, or can be, the most spectacular of all. They are also the most difficult to capture on film successfully, for two reasons: They are brightest when situated near the sun, so that the precious minutes for exposure are few, and they move quite rapidly relative to the stars.

The first difficulty can be overcome only by taking one's chances as they occur. It is useless to expose when the sky is even faintly lit by twilight, for

314

the plate will fog rapidly and obscure the delicate reaches of the comet's tail. Neither can much be hoped for when it is very near the horizon. However, since these difficulties affect everyone in the same way, there is still a chance of securing a relatively worthwhile photograph. The most treacherous conditions occur before dawn, when the sky lightens so unobtrusively that the plate can be wrecked before one realizes it. Every regular watcher of the skies is taken unawares by the strengthening dawn, which at first trims the faint margins of the Milky Way and then, quite suddenly, leaves the sky still almost dark, but magically shorn of its powdery background of stars.

Since a comet has orbital motion of its own, it is essential to guide on *it* rather than on the stars. The bright nucleus is therefore bisected by the cross wires and kept firmly in place, so that the stars themselves appear as short trails on the plate. An automatic drive is a tremendous help in all astrophotography, but particularly so in the case of comets, since adjustments for its motion have to be made in both right ascension and declination, and this, coupled with the general diurnal motion, puts something of a burden on the average two-handed amateur.

When taking a comet photograph, it is best to arrange the head in one corner of the plate, with the tail stretching across the diagonal. This allows the faintest extensions, invisible with the eye, to be recorded on the plate instead of being cut off at the edge. Provision must be made to tilt the camera so that the guiding telescope can be directed at the nucleus.

Meteor photography

Since a bright meteor may appear anywhere in the sky, it is not, strictly speaking, necessary to guide the camera at all. It can simply be pointed to a certain region of the firmament (the radiant in the case of a known shower), and left for 30 minutes or an hour. The stars will appear as trails, due to the earth's rotation, and any meteor will leave its mark as a streak. On the other hand, unless a visual watch is kept and the moment of the meteor's appearance noted, it is impossible to know its true path relative to the stars, since it might have appeared at any time during their trailing period.

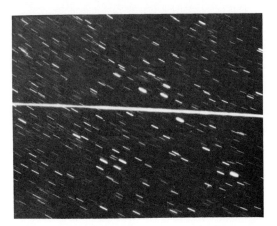

Echo I. *The satellite passing through Hercules, July 24, 1962. (Stephen A. Walther, Stevens Point, Wisconsin.)*

If an automatic drive is used, so that the camera follows the stars and registers them as dots, all need for visual observation vanishes. Moreover, there is no need to guide with scrupulous accuracy, since a short-focus lens embracing the widest possible field of view gives the best results, and minor errors will have little effect on the results. Provided that the motor is accurately rated, the camera can be left to its own devices for half an hour at a time.

Since meteors are almost instantaneous streaks of light, we must use the fastest possible emulsion. HPS or Royal–X plates, used in conjunction with a 2-inch aperture lens, can record meteors down to the 3rd or 4th magnitude, so that an intense shower such as the Quadrantids can be expected to produce a number of trails. One most interesting experiment is to fit a rotating shutter in front of the lens. If this is arranged so that the lens is occulted, say, ten times per second, every meteor trail will be recorded as a series of dashes, and the distance between each break will give an accurate measure of its velocity across the sky.

Another interesting program in meteor observation is to experiment with two cameras separated by between 40 and 60 miles. If these are exposed simultaneously, and the same meteor is caught by both, its two different *apparent* lines of flight against the stars will, due to the parallactic effect, afford a direct trigonometrical key to its *actual* path through the atmosphere, and hence the meteor's orbit around the sun. This is just one of the ways in which keen amateurs, drawn together by mutual love of their science, can work together not only to produce results of increased value, but (more important still) to foster and enhance their own enjoyment of the sky's inexhaustible fascination.

Appendices

Forthcoming Lunar Eclipses
1968–1980

DATE	TYPE	DATE	TYPE
1968 April 13	*Total*	1974 June 4	*Partial**
October 6	*Total*	November 29	*Total**
1970 February 21	*Small partial*	1975 May 25	*Total*
		November 18	*Total*
August 17	*Partial*	1976 May 13	*Small partial**
1971 February 10	*Total*		
August 6	*Total*	1977 April 4	*Small partial*
1972 January 30	*Total*	1978 March 24	*Total**
July 26	*Partial*	September 16	*Total**
1973 December 10	*Small partial*	1979 March 13	*Partial**
		September 6	*Total*

*An asterisk indicates that the eclipse cannot be seen from anywhere in the United States.

317

Forthcoming Solar Eclipses
1968–1980

DATE		TYPE	REGION OF VISIBILITY
1968	September 22	*Total*	Arctic; central Asia.
1969	March 18	*Annular*	Indian Ocean; Pacific.
	September 11	*Annular*	Pacific; S. America.
1970	March 7	*Total*	Pacific; Mexico; Florida; N. Atlantic.
	August 31	*Annular*	S. Pacific.
1972	January 16	*Annular*	Antarctic.
	July 10	*Total*	Japan; Pacific; Canada; mid-Atlantic.
1973	January 4	*Annular*	Antarctic.
	June 30	*Total*	S. America; Atlantic; N. Africa; Indian Ocean.
	December 24	*Annular*	S. America; Atlantic; N. Africa.
1974	June 20	*Total*	Indian Ocean.
1976	April 29	*Annular*	Atlantic; N. Africa; Mediterranean; Asia.
	October 23	*Total*	Central Africa; Indian Ocean; Antarctica.
1977	April 18	*Annular*	Atlantic; Central Africa; Indian Ocean.
	October 12	*Total*	Pacific; S. America.
1979	February 26	*Total*	N. Pacific; N. United States; Canada; Greenland.
	August 22	*Annular*	Antarctic.
1980	February 16	*Total*	Central Africa; India; China.
	August 10	*Annular*	Pacific; S. America.

Elongations of the Inferior Planets
1968–1980

MERCURY

Evening		Morning		
DATE	ELONGATION (°)	DATE		ELONGATION (°)
1968 January 31	18	1968	March 13	$27\frac{1}{2}$
May 24	23		July 11	21
September 20	26		October 31	19
1969 January 13	19	1969	February 23	27
May 5	21		June 23	23
September 3	27		October 14	18
December 27	20			
1970 April 18	20	1970	February 5	$25\frac{1}{2}$
August 16	27		June 5	24
December 10	21		September 28	18
1971 April 1	19	1971	January 19	24
July 29	27		May 17	26
November 23	22		September 12	18
1972 March 14	18	1972	January 1	23
July 10	26		April 28	27
November 5	23		August 25	18
			December 14	21
1973 February 25	18	1973	April 10	28
June 22	25		August 8	19
October 18	25		November 27	20
1974 February 9	18	1974	March 23	28
June 4	$23\frac{1}{2}$		July 22	20
October 1	26		November 10	19
1975 January 23	19	1975	March 6	27
May 16	22		July 4	22
September 13	27		October 25	18
1976 January 7	19	1976	February 16	26
April 28	20		June 15	23
August 26	27		October 7	20
December 20	20			

319

DATE		ELONGATION (°)	DATE		ELONGATION (°)
1977	April 10	19½	1977	January 28	25
	August 8	27		May 27	25
	December 3	21		September 21	18
1978	March 24	19	1978	January 11	23½
	July 22	27		May 9	26
	November 16	23		September 4	18
				December 24	22
1979	March 8	18	1979	April 21	27
	July 3	26		August 19	19
	October 29	24		December 7	21
1980	February 19	18	1980	April 2	28
	June 14	24½		August 1	19½
	October 11	25		November 19	20

VENUS

	EVENING ELONGATION	INFERIOR CONJUNCTION	MORNING ELONGATION	SUPERIOR CONJUNCTION
1968				June 20
1969	January 26	April 8	June 17	
1970	September 1	November 10		January 24
1971			January 20	August 27
1972	April 8	June 17	August 27	
1973	November 13			April 9
1974		January 23	April 4	November 6
1975	June 18	August 27	November 7	
1976				June 18
1977	January 24	April 6	June 15	
1978	August 29	November 7		January 22
1979			January 18	August 25
1980	April 5	June 15	August 24	

Because of the almost perfect circularity of the orbit, elongations of Venus are always between 46° and 48°.

Oppositions of Mars, Jupiter, and Saturn 1968–1980

MARS

	DATE	DIAMETER (")	MAGNITUDE
1969	May 31	19·3	−2·0
1971	August 10	24·9	−2·7
1973	October 25	21·1	−2·2
1975	December 15	16·2	−1·5
1978	January 22	14·3	−1·1
1980	February 25	13·8	−0·8

JUPITER

	DATE	DIAMETER (")	MAGNITUDE
1968	February 20	44·8	−2·1
1969	March 21	44·2	−2·0
1970	April 21	44·3	−2·0
1971	May 23	45·2	−2·1
1972	June 24	46·6	−2·2
1973	July 30	48·2	−2·3
1974	September 5	49·5	−2·4
1975	October 13	49·9	−2·5
1976	November 18	48·9	−2·4
1977	December 23	47·4	−2·3
1979	January 24	45·8	−2·2
1980	February 24	44·7	−2·1

SATURN

DATE		MAGNITUDE
1968	October 15	+0·3
1969	October 28	+0·1
1970	November 11	−0·1
1971	November 25	−0·2
1972	December 8	−0·2
1973	December 23	−0·3
1975	January 6	−0·2
1976	January 20	−0·1
1977	February 2	0·0
1978	February 16	+0·3
1979	March 1	+0·5
1980	March 13	+0·8

APPENDIX V

Minor Planet Data

No. & Name	Diam- eter (miles)	Max. Mag.	Orbital Period (years)	Inclina- tion (°)	Ampli- tude (mag.)	Fluctuation Period h m
(1) Ceres	480	7·0	4·6	10·6	0·04	9 05
(2) Pallas	304	6·3	4·61	34·8	0·13	5ʰ—6ʰ or 10ʰ— 12ʰ
(3) Juno	118	6·9	4·36	13·0	0·15	7 12·6
(4) Vesta	236	5·5	3·63	7·1	0·13	5 20·5 or 10 41·0
(6) Hebe	70	7·1	3·77	11·7	0·16	7 17
(7) Iris	78	6·7	3·69	5·5	0·29	7 05
(8) Flora	56	7·8	3·27	5·9	0·04	13 36
(9) Metis	78	8·1	3·69	5·6	0·26	5 04·6
(15) Eunomia	?	7·4	4·30	11·8	0·53	6 05·0
(20) Massalia	66	8·2	3·74	0·7	0·20	8 05·9

These are among other minor planets reaching magnitude 9·0 or brighter at a favorable opposition:

NO. & NAME	MAGNITUDE	NO. & NAME	MAGNITUDE
(5) Astraea	8·7	(42) Isis	8·8
(10) Hygeia	8·8	(43) Ariadne	8·8
(11) Parthenope	8·7	(44) Nysa	8·8
(12) Victoria	8·1	(97) Clotho	8·9
(14) Irene	8·7	(129) Antigone	8·9
(16) Psyche	8·8	(132) Aethra	8·5
(18) Melpomene	7·7	(192) Nausicaa	7·5
(19) Fortuna	8·7	(194) Procne	8·9
(23) Thalia	8·9	(216) Cleopatra	8·4
(25) Phocaea	9·0	(313) Chaldaea	9·0
(27) Euterpe	8·5	(324) Bamberga	7·4
(29) Amphitrite	8·6	(372) Palma	8·8
(39) Laetitia	8·8	(387) Aquitania	8·2
(40) Harmonia	8·9	(393) Lampetia	8·6
(41) Daphne	8·7	(433) Eros	6·5

APPENDIX VI

Tables of Precession
for Ten Years

1. Precession in Right Ascension

R.A.—If N., read top; if S., read lower

Dec.	0,12ʰ	1,11ʰ	2,10ʰ	3,9ʰ	4,8ʰ	5,7ʰ	6ʰ
	m	m	m	m	m	m	m
80°	+0·51	+0·84	+1·14	+1·40	+1·60	+1·73	+1·77
70°	0·51	0·67	0·82	0·94	1·04	1·10	1·12
60°	0·51	0·61	0·70	0·78	0·84	0·88	0·90
50°	0·51	0·58	0·64	0·70	0·74	0·77	0·78
40°	0·51	0·56	0·61	0·64	0·67	0·69	0·70
30°	0·51	0·54	0·58	0·60	0·62	0·64	0·64
20°	0·51	0·53	0·55	0·57	0·58	0·59	0·59
10°	0·51	0·52	0·53	0·54	0·55	0·55	0·55
0°	0·51	0·51	0·51	0·51	0·51	0·51	0·51
	0,12ʰ	23,13ʰ	22,14ʰ	21,15ʰ	20,16ʰ	19,17ʰ	18ʰ

R.A.—If N., read top; if S., read lower

Dec.	18ʰ	19,17ʰ	20,16ʰ	21,15ʰ	22,14ʰ	23,13ʰ
	m	m	m	m	m	m
80°	−0·75	−0·70	−0·58	−0·38	−0·12	+0·19
70°	−0·10	−0·08	−0·02	+0·08	+0·21	0·35
60°	+0·13	+0·14	+0·18	0·24	0·32	0·41
50°	0·25	0·26	0·28	0·32	0·38	0·44
40°	0·33	0·33	0·35	0·38	0·42	0·46
30°	0·38	0·39	0·40	0·42	0·45	0·48
20°	0·43	0·43	0·44	0·45	0·47	0·49
10°	0·47	0·47	0·48	0·48	0·49	0·50
0°	0·51	0·51	0·51	0·51	0·51	0·51
	6ʰ	5,7ʰ	4,8ʰ	3,9ʰ	2,10ʰ	1,11ʰ

If positions are being converted to an earlier epoch, the signs must be reversed.

2. Precession in Declination

This table is for objects north of the celestial equator; for southern objects, reverse the signs.

○

R.A.	PREC.	R.A.	PREC.
h	′	h	′
0,24	+3·3	7,17	−0·9
1,23	3·2	8,16	1·7
2,22	2·9	9,15	2·4
3,21	2·4	10,14	2·9
4,20	1·7	11,13	3·2
5,19	0·9	12	3·3
6,18	0		

If positions are being converted to an earlier epoch, the signs must be reversed.

APPENDIX VII

The Latitude of the Center of the Sun's Disk (B_0) Throughout the Year

DATE		B_0	DATE		B_0	DATE		B_0
Jan.	4	−3·5°	May	4	−3·8°	Sept.	1	+7·2°
	9	4·0		9	3·2		6	7·3
	14	4·5		14	2·7		11	7·2
	19	5·0		19	2·1		16	7·1
	24	5·5		24	1·5		21	7·0
	29	5·9		29	0·9		26	6·9
Feb.	3	−6·2	June	3	−0·4	Oct.	1	+6·7
	8	6·5		8	+0·3		6	6·4
	13	6·8		13	0·9		11	6·1
	18	7·0		18	1·5		16	5·7
	23	7·1		23	2·0		21	5·3
	28	7·2		28	2·6		26	4·9
							31	4·4
Mar.	5	−7·3	July	3	+3·2	Nov.	5	+3·9
	10	7·2		8	3·7		10	3·3
	15	7·1		13	4·2		15	2·8
	20	7·1		18	4·7		20	2·1
	25	6·8		23	5·1		25	1·5
	30	6·6		28	5·5		30	0·9
Apr.	4	−6·4	Aug.	2	+5·9	Dec.	5	+0·2
	9	6·0		7	6·3		10	−0·4
	14	5·6		12	6·6		15	1·0
	19	5·2		17	6·8		20	1·6
	24	4·8		22	7·0		25	2·2
	29	4·3		27	7·2		30	2·9

The positive and negative prefixes refer to north and south latitudes, respectively.

Sidereal Time at 00ʰ U.T. Throughout the Year

The conversion is given for 8-day intervals. It can be calculated for intervening days by adding 3·9 minutes for every complete day. By remembering that a sidereal day consists of 23 hours 56 minutes, the sidereal time for any hour during the day can be calculated with sufficient accuracy for most purposes. The conversion is subject to an error of ± 2 minutes due to leap-year adjustments.

Date		Sidereal Time		Date		Sidereal Time		Date		Sidereal Time	
		h	m			h	m			h	m
Jan.	1	6	40	May	1	14	33	Sept.	6	22	58
	9	7	11		9	15	04		14	23	29
	17	7	43		17	15	36		22	0	01
	25	8	14		25	16	07		30	0	32
Feb.	2	8	46	June	2	16	39	Oct.	8	1	04
	10	9	17		10	17	11		16	1	35
	18	9	49		18	17	42		24	2	07
	26	10	21		26	18	14				
Mar.	6	10	52	July	4	18	45	Nov.	1	2	38
	14	11	24		12	19	17		9	3	10
	22	11	55		20	19	48		17	3	41
	30	12	27		28	20	20		25	4	13
Apr.	7	12	58	Aug.	5	20	51	Dec.	3	4	44
	15	13	30		13	21	23		11	5	16
	23	14	01		21	21	54		19	5	48
					29	22	26		27	6	19

Glossary

Aberration. The apparent annual displacement of a star caused by the "bending" of its light, due to the earth's orbital motion. Its effect is to make every star appear to revolve around a fixed point, its maximum distance from this point being about 20"·5. *Chromatic aberration:* The formation of a colored fringe around the image produced by a simple lens. *Spherical aberration:* Imperfect image caused by the lens or mirror not bringing all rays to a point.

Absolute magnitude. The brightness a star would appear to have if viewed from a standard distance (10 parsecs, or 32·6 light-years). It is therefore a measure of a star's actual luminosity.

Albedo. The ratio of light reflected to that received. Approximate albedos for the planets are: Mercury ·06; Venus ·65; Earth ·39; Moon ·07; Mars ·15; Jupiter ·42; Saturn ·45; Uranus ·46; Neptune ·53. Some authorities consider the four last-named planets to be as reflective as Venus.

Almanac. A yearly publication containing relevant astronomical data. The principal one is *The American Ephemeris and Nautical Almanac;* in Great Britain this is published as the *Astronomical Ephemeris*. Other almanacs are the *Connaissance de Temps* (France) and the *Astronomisch-Geodatisches Jahrbuch* (Germany).

Altazimuth mount. A telescope mounted with axes in the horizontal and vertical planes.

Annular eclipse. A solar eclipse occurring with the moon near apogee, so that it appears smaller than the sun and cannot block it out completely.

Ansae. Term used to describe the eastern and western extremities of Saturn's rings as viewed from the earth.

Aphelion. The point on a planet's or comet's orbit at the greatest distance from the sun.

Apogee. The point on a satellite's orbit at the greatest distance from its primary.

Apparent magnitude. The brightness of a star as seen from the earth, a value dependent on both its absolute magnitude and its distance.

Appulse. A close approach of one celestial body to another, as seen from the earth. It is a line-of-sight effect, and does not imply physical proximity.

Asteroid. An alternative name for a minor planet.

Astronomical Unit. The mean distance from the earth to the sun, now taken as 92,900,000 miles.

Baily's beads. A phenomenon occurring at the beginning and/or end of a total solar eclipse, when fragments of the photosphere shine out brilliantly through deep rifts in the moon's limb.

Barlow lens. A concave (negative) achromatic lens placed a short distance inside the focal point of the objective. This has the effect of increasing the image scale.

Barycenter. The point of the imaginary line joining two bodies under mutual gravitational influence, around which they revolve.

Binary system. Two or more stars revolving around each other.

Bode's law. An empirical guide to the relative distances from the sun of all the planets except Mercury, Neptune, and Pluto. It is obtained by taking the series, 3, 6, 12, and so on, and adding 4 to each.

Cassegrain telescope. A reflecting telescope using a convex as well as a concave mirror. This increases the effective focal length and gives a large image scale.

Celestial sphere. An imaginary sphere surrounding Earth and carrying all the celestial objects. It rotates in 23 hours 56 minutes and is inscribed with the celestial equivalents of the terrestrial poles, equator, latitude, and longitude.

Chronograph. A device for recording the instant at which an observation is made.

Circumpolar. An object so close to the celestial pole that it remains permanently above the horizon.

Conjunction. Strictly speaking, the condition of two celestial bodies when their R.A. or Dec. become the same. In practice, it is equivalent to an appulse. For instance, a superior planet is in conjunction when it appears near the sun in the sky. An inferior planet is said to be in *inferior* or *superior* conjunction when it appears nearest to the sun on the near side and far side, respectively, of its orbit.

Constellation. One of the 88 defined regions of the celestial sphere.

Culmination. The condition of a celestial object when at its greatest possible altitude above the horizon. Unless very near the pole, this occurs when it is due south (to an observer in the northern hemisphere).

Cusp. A horn of the moon, Mercury, or Venus when in the crescent phase.

Declination (*Dec.*). The angular distance of a celestial body north (+) or south (−) of the celestial equator.

Doppler effect. The shift of a source's spectral lines due to its motion toward or away from the observer.

Earthshine. Illumination of the moon's dark side due to sunlight reflected back from the earth.

Eclipse. Passage of the moon wholly or partly across the sun, or the passage of a satellite wholly or partly through its primary's shadow.

Eclipsing variable. A binary system at so great a distance that its individual components cannot be seen from the earth. The light of the "single" star fluctuates as one component is occulted by the other.

Ecliptic. The apparent path of the sun around the celestial sphere, approximately marking the plane of the solar system.

Elongation. The condition of an inferior planet when at its greatest angular distance from the sun.

Emersion. The reappearance of an object after occultation.

Ephemeris. A table giving the calculated future positions of a celestial body.

Ephemeris time. A time system used in astronomical computing that ignores the slight irregularities in the earth's rotation upon its axis. During this century, the difference between "observed" and "predicted" rotation has so far amounted to more than 30 seconds.

Epoch. Generally speaking, the date for which star positions (as on a chart) are correct.

Equation of time. The discrepancy between the sun's southing and the instant of noon. This varies, because the sun does not move along the ecliptic in a regular manner. The sun is 14 minutes slow in February and 16 minutes fast in October–November.

Equatorial mount. A telescope stand with one axis parallel to that of the earth, making it easy to follow the diurnal motion of a celestial body.

Equinoxes. The two points at which the ecliptic crosses the celestial equator. The sun reaches these points in March and September.

Gibbous. Phase intermediate between half and full.

Greenwich Mean Time (G.M.T.). Standard world time system, with 0 and 24 hours occurring at midnight on 0° longitude. This line passed through the old Greenwich Observatory in England. Usually referred to as U.T. (q.v.).

Gregorian telescope. Mainly obsolete form of reflecting telescope, using a second concave mirror. Most "compound" telescopes use the Cassegrain system.

Halation. The appearance of a star as a disk in a long-exposure photograph, due to its light spreading into the emulsion.

Hour angle. The interval, measured in sidereal time, since a given celestial object was last on the meridian.

Hyperbola. The path followed by many comets. Unlike an ellipse, it is not continuous; this means that a body traveling along such an orbit can never return to the vicinity of the sun.

Immersion. The disappearance visually of a body when occulted.

Inclination. The angle formed by the plane of one orbit with respect to another plane.

Inferior planet. A planet whose orbit is smaller than that of the earth.

International Astronomical Union (I.A.U.). A body coordinating the work of astronomers throughout the world. A number of committees have been established to specialize in various important departments of astronomy; these hold discussions at symposia held in various countries. I.A.U. conferences are held every three years.

Irradiation. The apparent augmentation in size of a celestial body due to its brightness against the dark sky.

Julian date. The number of days that have elapsed between the day in question and 1 January 4713 B.C. It is expressed in days and decimals of a day, and is used in much computing work. The selection of the original date is arbitrary.

Libration. The axial swinging of the moon with respect to the earth, due to its varying orbital velocity.

Light-year. An arbitrary measure of distance, taken as the distance traveled by light in one terrestrial year. It is equal to 5,880,000,000,000 miles.

Limb. The "edge" of the sun, moon, or a planet, as seen from the earth.

Lunation. The period elapsing between successive similar phases of the moon, also known as the *synodic period*. It is roughly 29¾ days. The term also refers to the phase progress from new to new.

Magnitude. The classification of a star's real (*absolute*) or *apparent* brightness.

Maksutov telescope. A reflecting telescope using a spheroidal instead of paraboloidal main mirror. Before reaching this, the light passes through a concave lens almost as large as the mirror itself to remove the spherical aberration.

Meridian. The great circle passing through the zenith and touching the horizon at the north and south points. The meridian of the sun, moon, or a planet is the straight line joining the north and south poles and passing across the center of the disk.

Meridian circle. A telescope constrained so that it can be pointed only at the meridian. It is used to time the instant at which stars pass across the meridian and so to keep a check on the rotation of the earth.

Micrometer. A device in the eyepiece of a telescope for measuring the angular dimensions of a celestial object.

Nadir. The point on the celestial sphere directly beneath the observer.

Newtonian telescope. A reflecting telescope using a concave paraboloidal mirror, with a small plane mirror to reflect the converging rays out of the tube.

New General Catalogue (N.G.C.). Standard list of the brighter star clusters, nebulae, and galaxies, published in 1888 and listing more than 7,000 objects.

Node. The apparent crossing of two paths, or orbits. An example is the intersection of the ecliptic and the celestial equator at the equinoxes.

Nutation. A minute oscillation of the earth's axis, due to lunar perturbations, superimposed on the much more marked precession.

Objective. The focusing and light-gathering agent of an astronomical telescope, whether mirror or lens.

Occultation. The passage of a nearby celestial body in front of a more remote one.

Opposition. The condition of the moon or a planet when opposite the sun in the sky as seen from the earth.

Orbit. The path followed through space by a celestial body.

Parallax. The apparent displacement of a body against its background when seen from different stations.

Parsec. A distance of about 32·6 light-years, at which the earth's orbit, with a diameter of 186,000,000 miles, would subtend an angle of 1″.

Penumbra. The partly illuminated outer region of the shadow cast by a solid body from a light source of appreciable diameter.

Periastron. The point in their orbits at which the two components of a binary pair are closest to each other.

Perigee. The point on a satellite's orbit which is closest to its primary.

Perihelion.   The point on a planet's or comet's orbit which is closest to the sun.

Period.   The time taken for a planet, comet, or satellite to achieve one circuit of its orbit.

Personal equation.   The fractional discrepancy between the observation of an instantaneous phenomenon (such as an occultation) and the recording of it.

Perturbation.   The gravitational influence of a nearby mass, causing a body to deviate from its true path.

Phase.   The percentage area of a body seen illuminated.

Phase angle.   The angular distance between the sun and the earth as seen from the moon or a particular planet.

Position angle.   The bearing of the fainter member of a double star measured from its primary. It is reckoned in degrees, starting at the north point and working counterclockwise.

Precession.   A slow oscillation of the earth's axis which takes 25,900 years to complete. This has the effect of changing the celestial coordinates, though to a very small extent.

Quadrature.   The condition of the moon or a superior planet when it subtends a right angle with the sun as seen from the earth.

Radial velocity.   The speed at which a celestial body, particularly a star, appears to be moving toward or away from the earth.

Radiant.   The point on the celestial sphere from which meteors appear to radiate during a shower.

Red shift.   The displacement toward the red end of the lines in the spectrum of a distant galaxy.   This is taken to imply recession of the galaxy.

Resolving power.   The ability of a telescope to resolve, or separate, fine detail, such as the individual components of a close double star. The limiting angular distance is a direct function of aperture.

Retrograde motion.   Real or apparent motion of a planet, comet, or satellite in the opposite sense to that usual in the solar system. It can also be applied to binary stars.

Right ascension (R.A.).   The celestial equivalent of longitude, measured eastward from the spring or vernal equinox.

Saros.   An interval of roughly 18 years 10¼ days, after which the sun and moon are in almost exactly the same relative positions in the sky. It was an ancient method of predicting eclipses.

Scintillation.   More usually known as "twinkling," this is the flickering of a star when viewed with the naked eye, caused by heat currents in the atmosphere.

Seeing. The steadiness of the telescopic image, which is affected by atmospheric currents. Some observers rate it from 1 to 10, 1 being hopelessly bad and 10 unattainably good.

Shadow transit. The passage of a satellite's shadow across the disk of Jupiter or Saturn.

Sidereal period. The time it takes for a planet or satellite to achieve one circuit of its orbit, relative to a fixed point.

Sidereal time. Time system based on the true rotation of the earth (relative to a fixed point and not to the sun), which takes only 23 hours 56 minutes.

Solar Time. Time system based on the earth's rotation relative to the sun, the basis of all civil time reckoning.

Solstices. The two points on the ecliptic farthest removed from the celestial equator; the sun is at these points at midsummer and midwinter.

Southing. A celestial object's crossing of the meridian.

Spectroscope. A device for dispersing the light received from a source into its component wave lengths. Examination of the light distribution in the spectrum can give information about the composition of the source.

Superior planet. A planet whose orbit is larger than that of the earth.

Synodic period. The time it takes for a planet or satellite to achieve one circuit of its orbit as seen from the earth.

Terminator. The division between the illuminated and dark hemispheres of the moon or a planet.

Time zone. A division on the earth's surface in which civil time is taken as a whole number of hours earlier or later than G.M.T.

Transit. There are three meanings of the word. A star or planet transits when it crosses the meridian; a detail on a planet's disk transits when it is carried across the planet's meridian by its rotation; and a satellite (or its shadow) transits when it crosses in front of its primary's disk.

Umbra. The region of the shadow, cast by a solid body, in which all direct light from the source is cut off.

Universal Time (U.T.). The 24-hour time system used by astronomers all over the world. The reckoning is the same as for G.M.T.

Vertex. The point on the limb of the sun, moon, or a planet that is highest above the horizon.

Zenith. The point on the celestial sphere directly above the observer.

Zodiac. A zone 18° wide, centered along the ecliptic, inside which the major planets (except Pluto) and many of the minor planets are always to be found. The twelve constellations through which it passes are called the zodiacal constellations.

Bibliography

CHAPTER 1

King, Henry C. *History of the Telescope.* London: Charles Griffin, 1955. A detailed account, giving vivid insight into the problems faced by telescope-makers down the ages.

Woodbury, D. O. *The Glass Giant of Palomar.* New York: Dodd, Mead, 1953. Really a biography of G. E. Hale, whose initiative and enthusiasm led to the building of the Yerkes 40-inch refractor and the great reflectors at Mount Wilson and Palomar. Contains much practical detail of interest to the amateur astronomer.

CHAPTER 3

Bell, Louis. *The Telescope.* New York: McGraw-Hill, 1922. A classic work on the subject, and still of value.

Howard, Neale E. *Standard Handbook for Telescope Making.* New York: Thomas Y. Crowell, 1959. London: Faber & Faber, 1965. An excellent introduction to mirror-making and the construction of a reflecting telescope.

Ingalls, A., ed. *Amateur Telescope Making.* New York: Scientific American. Now in three volumes, this is a classic assembly of features by amateur telescope-makers, and probably contains more useful information than any other work.

Sidgwick, J. B. *Amateur Astronomer's Handbook.* New York: Macmillan, 1955. London: Faber & Faber, 1961 (2nd ed.). The standard work on the theory and function of astronomical instruments. This and its companion volume, *Observational Astronomy for Amateurs* (*q.v.*) are almost essential for any amateur astronomer's library.

CHAPTER 4

Argelander. *Bonner Durchmusterung.* Bonn, 1865. Long out of print, but still a useful reference book in libraries.

Becvár, A. *Atlas Coeli.* Prague, 1956. A more comprehensive (but bulkier) atlas than Norton's.

Beyer-Graff. *Stern Atlas*. Published in 1925; now out of print. Like the *Bonner Durchmusterung*, a useful reference book in libraries.

Norton's Star Atlas and Reference Handbook. London: Gall & Inglis, 1964 (15th ed.). The best known of all star atlases.

Vehrenberg, Hans. *Photographic Star Atlas*. Cambridge, Mass.: Sky Publishing Corp. Even more comprehensive than Norton's.

Webb, H. B. *Atlas of the Stars*. New York: privately published, 1945 (2nd ed.).

Periodicals

The American Ephemeris and Nautical Almanac (in Britain The Nautical Almanac and Astronomical Ephemeris).

Announcement Cards (Harvard University Observatory) and *Circulars* (British Astronomical Association) give details of astronomical events and discoveries.

Handbook of the British Astronomical Association.

Sky and Telescope. Cambridge, Mass.: Sky Publishing Corp.

CHAPTER 5

Denning, W. F. *Telescopic Work for Starlight Evenings*. London: Longmans, Green, 1891. Although long out of print, this can still be consulted in astronomical libraries and is a useful account of the amateur's tools and methods, written by an observer of distinction.

Sidgwick, J. B. *Observational Astronomy for Amateurs*. New York: Macmillan, 1955. London: Faber & Faber, 1961 (2nd ed.). Gives exhaustive coverage of observational techniques, both visual and photographic, and is an invaluable source of reference for all the observational fields mentioned in this book.

CHAPTER 6

Kopal, Z. *Photographic Atlas of the Moon*. New York: Academic Press, 1965. A collection of superb photographs taken with the 24-inch refractor at the Pic du Midi Observatory, in the French Pyrenees.

Kuiper, Gerard P. *Photographic Lunar Atlas*. Chicago: University of Chicago Press, 1960. A collection of lunar photographs, of rather varying standard, taken with telescopes all over the world. A standard work. The *Orthographic Atlas* (1960) contains more than 5,000 measured positions. The *Rectified Lunar Atlas* (1963) gives "plan-view" photographs of regions very near the lunar limb.

Wilkins, H. P., and P. A. Moore. *The Moon*. New York: Macmillan, 1955. London: Faber & Faber, 1961 (2nd ed.). An excellent verbal description of the lunar features, accompanied by a 100-inch diameter map.

CHAPTER 7

Abetti, G. *The Sun*. New York: Macmillan, 1957. London: Faber & Faber, 1963. An authoritative survey of our knowledge of the sun.

Baxter, W. M. *The Sun and Amateur Astronomy*. New York: Norton, 1962. London: Lutterworth, 1963. A useful introduction to solar observation, written by one of Britain's leading amateurs.

CHAPTER 8

Kuiper, Gerard P., and Barbara M. Middlehurst, ed. *Planets and Satellites.* Chicago: University of Chicago Press, 1961. A specialized treatise by a leading professional astronomer.

Moore, P. A., ed. *Handbook of Practical Amateur Astrononomy.* London: Lutterworth, 1963. New York: Norton, 1964. Deals with the observation of all celestial objects, but particularly with those in the solar system.

————. *The Planets.* New York: Norton, 1962. London: Eyre & Spottiswoode, 1962. A popular work, written for the amateur astronomer.

CHAPTER 9

Sandner, Werner. *The Planet Mercury.* London: Faber & Faber, 1963. New York: Macmillan, 1963. An outline account, but in need of revision because of recent findings.

CHAPTER 10

Moore, P. A. *The Planet Venus.* London: Faber & Faber, 1959. New York: Macmillan, 1961. A popular account of past and present observational work, with a useful bibliography.

CHAPTER 12

Roth, G. *The System of Minor Planets.* London: Faber & Faber, 1963. New York: Van Nostrand, 1963.

CHAPTER 13

Peek, B. M. *The Planet Jupiter.* New York: Macmillan, 1958. London: Faber & Faber, 1959. A detailed description of each region of the planet Jupiter, based on the observational work of the past century.

CHAPTER 14

Alexander, A. F. O'D. *The Planet Saturn.* London: Faber & Faber, 1962. New York: Macmillan, 1962. A definitive survey of practically every published observation of the planet Saturn and its satellites, extending back to pre-Christian times.

CHAPTER 15

Alexander, A. F. O'D. *The Planet Uranus.* London: Faber & Faber, 1965. New York: Elxevier, 1965. A definitive survey of practically every published observation made of the planet Uranus and its satellites, including those made before its planetary nature was known.

CHAPTER 16

Grosser, Morton. *The Discovery of Neptune.* Cambridge, Mass.: Harvard University Press, 1962.

CHAPTER 17

Porter, J. G. *Comets and Meteor Streams*. London: Chapman & Hall, 1952. A scholarly survey, with a useful bibliography.

Richter, N. B. *The Nature of Comets*. New York: Dover, 1963.

CHAPTER 21

Webb, T. W. *Celestial Objects for Common Telescopes*. New York: Dover, 1962. A reissue of the famous classic, one especially valuable for its long lists of stellar objects. It is in need of extensive revision, however; the last edition was in 1917.

CHAPTER 22

Rackham, T. W. *Astronomical Photography at the Telescope*. London: Faber & Faber, 1959. New York: Macmillan, 1959. A useful handbook of photography for the amateur astronomer.

Amateur
Astronomical Societies

The leading amateur organization in the British Isles is the British Astronomical Association, founded in 1890. Divided into Observing Sections, it caters principally to the practical amateur, and has a matchless record of observation during its more than seventy-five years of existence.

Membership in the B.A.A., with its monthly meetings in London (together with one provincial summer meeting) and its bimonthly *Journal*, may be regarded as essential for any amateur, whether or not he has a telescope. Subscription costs 45/– ($5.35) per annum (30/– if under 21 years of age); details are provided by the Assistant Secretary at 303 Bath Road, Hounslow West, Middlesex, England.

An organization existing primarily to help the newcomer to astronomy is the Junior Astronomical Society (Secretary, D. B. P. Beglan, 17 Chanctonbury Chase, Redhill, Surrey, England). Subscription costs 15/–, and the journal and meetings are quarterly.

Since both these societies are London-based, a great number of local groups have been formed. Meetings are usually fortnightly or monthly, and subscriptions range from 10/– to £1 ($2.40). A full list can be found in the current *Yearbook of Astronomy*, published by Eyre & Spottiswoode, Ltd., London.

There are a great number of amateur astronomical societies in the United States. A complete list is published annually by *Sky and Telescope*. The societies listed here are all open to the public. Most of them hold regular meetings once or twice monthly. Details of each society's program can be obtained from the official whose name and address is listed.

    * Member organization of the Astronomical
       League
    † Member organization of the Western
       Amateur Astronomers
    ‡ Society has junior section
    ° Independent junior society

ALABAMA

Birmingham Birmingham Astronomy Club: Miss M. Kimbell, 1218 3rd Ave. W. (8). *

Huntsville Rocket City Astronomical Assn.: Mrs. D. Killion, Rte. 1, Owens Cross Rds. (35763). 536-2051. *

ALASKA

Anchorage Polaris Astronomical Society: F. A. Nelson, Box 4-458. FA 2-2863. ‡

Fairbanks Fairbanks Astronomical Society: L. Stuck, 1007 Noble St. (99701). 907-452-1068. ‡

ARIZONA

Phoenix Phoenix Observatory Assn.: L. Horton, 8720 E. Arlington Rd., Scottsdale (85251). 947-2863. †

Tucson Tucson Astronomical and Astronautical Assn.: D. Strittmatter, 1840 E. Lee St. EA 5-9453. *†

ARKANSAS

Little Rock Arkansas Astronomical Assn.: J. M. Brannen, 2201 E. 9th St. FR 5-5812.

CALIFORNIA

Burbank Burbank Astronomical Society: D. Rhoades, 1474 N. Evergreen St. TH 8-5880.

Canoga Park Polaris Astronomical Society: G. Frie, 11209 Gloria, Granada Hills. 365-5429. †‡

Covina San Gabriel Valley Astronomical Society: Miss S. Spinka, 4441 N. Roxburgh. ED 9-1498. †‡

Escondido Palomar Amateur Astronomers: M. A. Sloan, 2418 Alexander Dr. SH 5-6144. †

Eureka Astronomers of Humboldt: W. N. Abbay, Jr., 1745 Margaret Lane, Arcata. VA 2-4403.

Fresno Central Valley Astronomers: G. Reavis, 234 E. Normal. AM 4-9771. †

Long Beach Excelsior Telescope Club: B. Sproul, 130 5th St. †

Los Angeles
Los Angeles Astronomical Society, Inc.: Griffith Observatory, P.O. Box 27787 (90027). †‡

Los Angeles Junior Astronomical Society: 4613 Ambrose Ave. NO 4-7693. °

Valley Astronomy Club: J. D. Truxton, 6615 Bevis Ave., Van Nuys. ST 2-3736. ‡

Los Gatos Los Gatos Amateur Astronomers: L. Anthenien, 1725 Hicks Ave., San Jose (25). 269-5561.

North Hollywood San Fernando Valley Astronomical Society: T. Thorpe, 12414 Huston St., N. Hollywood. 763-7019.

Oakland Eastbay Astronomical Society: Mrs. S. Burke, 1528 E. 31st (94602). 536-0691. †

Palo Alto Peninsula Astronomical Society: T. C. Terman, 354 Whitclem Dr. 415-326-7054. †

Pasadena Stony Ridge Observatory, Inc.: E. Sloman, 1100 Armada Dr. SY 6-4731. †

Pomona Junior Astronomical Society of Pomona Valley: 1540 Arroyo Ave. 629-0352. †°

Redlands Valley Amateur Astronomers: J. B. and W. Osgood, 1346 La Loma Dr. 793-1394. †

Riverside Riverside Astronomical Society: C. Holmes, 8642 Wells (92503). 689-6893. †

Sacramento Sacramento Valley Astronomical Society: Mrs. E. Williams, 3733 West Way (95821). 487-3799. †‡

San Bernardino Valley Amateur Astronomers of San Bernardino County: B. Graf, 380 W. 10th St. (92410). TU 8-5290. †‡

San Diego
CRA Youth Astronomy Club: D. Weisbrod, 4315 Hermosa Way (3). CY 5-4607. °
San Diego Amateur Astronomers: B. Barnett, 3561 Mt. Aclare Ave. (92111). 278-8285. †
San Diego Astronomical Society: R. K. Larimer, c/o 672 Cunningham Lane, El Cajon.
San Diego Astronomy Associates Inc.: H. L. McCalla, 1845 Primera St., Lemon Grove. 469-3214. †‡
San Diego Lunar Society: T. Smith, 9654 Candy Lane, La Mesa. HO 3-5290.

San Francisco San Francisco Amateur Astronomers, Inc.: E. Taylor, 1626 Pacheco St. 731-4916. †

San Jose
San Jose Amateur Astronomers: W. Krumm, 10628 Larry Way, Cupertino. †
Western Star Observers: J. J. Mancuso, Jr., 1528 Ardenwood Dr. (29). AL 2-8984. °

San Rafael
Marin Astronomical Society, Inc.: A. J. Gnoerich, P.O. Box 356, Kentfield (94901). †
Star Observers of Marin: M. D. Beck, 170 Hillside Ave. (94901). 456-4266. ‡

Santa Barbara Santa Barbara Star Cluster: Capt. C. Adair, 607 Miramonte Dr. WO 2-1717.†

Sonoma Valley of the Moon Astronomical Society: Mrs. G. McDaniel, 515 El Dorado Dr. WY 6-0205

Stockton
Royal Astronomical Society of Stockton: N. Adams, 7313 Coral Lane. 477-2962. °
Stockton Astronomical Society: Miss B. Peterson, 1511 Oxford Way (95204). †

Sunnyvale Skyline Astronomical Society: C. Baughman, 16093 Blossom Hill Rd., Los Gatos.

Whittier Whittier Amateur Astronomers, Inc.: Dr. D. Bender, 1217 Merit Lane.

COLORADO
Boulder Boulder Astronomical Society: C. L. Johnson, 765 S. 46th (80302).

Colorado Springs Colorado Springs Astronomical Society: M. Williams, 1306 E. Columbia. ME 3-9286. *

Denver Denver Astronomical Society: R. A. Spencer, 4430 Gladiola St., Golden. CR 9-4682. *†‡

Pueblo Pueblo Astronomical Society: N. Onstott, 2421 Second Ave. LI 3-3348. *†‡

CONNECTICUT
Greenwich Scanners' Club Astronomical Society: G. Shea, 102 Milbank Ave. TO 9-4474.

Hartford Central Connecticut Amateur Astronomers: C. Hammond, 17 Greystone Rd., W. Hartford. 521-3384. *

New Haven Astronomical Society of New Haven, Inc.: S. J. LeRoy, Northrop Rd., Woodbridge. FU 7-8683. *

New London Thames Amateur Astronomical Society: R. Tumicki, 106 Canterbury Tpk., Norwich. *

Ridgefield Mt. West's Amateur Astronomers League: S. Devlin, 69 W. Mountain Rd. (06877). 438-8528. °

Stamford Fairfield County Astronomical Society: C. E. Scovil, 15 Dover Rd., Westport. 227-8341. *‡

DELAWARE
Wilmington Delaware Astronomical Society: P.O. Box 652 (19899). 302-656-8364. *‡

DISTRICT OF COLUMBIA
Washington
Maret Astronomers Club: P. Moretti, 3435 Yuma St. N.W. (8). °
National Capital Astronomers: Mrs. M. Noble, 2104 32nd Place S.E. 582-6721. *‡
Washington Junior Astronomers: C. Hanback, 2152 F St. N.W. (20037). 338-1452. °

FLORIDA
Bradenton Gulf Coast Astronomical Society: D. L. Schrader, 4530 14th St. W. 745-1185. *‡

Daytona Beach Daytona Beach Star Gazers: W. T. Thomas, 105 N. Halifax. CL 2-8049.

Eglin Air Force Base Choctaw Astronomical Society: Col. M. Marston, 710 Osceola Circle.

Fort Myers Fort Myers Amateur Astronomers Assn.: S. Graf, 222 Lynneda Ave., Tice. OX 4-1801.

Hollywood South Florida Amateur Astronomy Association: H. G. Perry, Hallandale. 923-0016. *‡

Jacksonville
Astro-Gators Junior Astronomy Club: R. S. Hart, Children's Museum, 1061 Riverside Ave. (32204). 355-6781. *°
Jacksonville Astronomy Club, Inc.: K. Simmons, Children's Museum, 1061 Riverside Ave. (32204). 355-6781. *°
Jacksonville Meteor Society: K. Simmons, 4238 Springwood Rd. (32207).

Key West Key West Astronomy Club: Mrs. C. Lott, Box 284.

Lakeland Central Florida Astronomical Society: C. Sammons, 1810 Fredericksburg Ave. MU 2-3223.

Miami
Gulfstream Astronomical Assn., Inc.: L. F. Higgins, 631 Falcon Ave., Miami Springs. TU 8-3341. *
Miami Astronomical Assn.: C. Silverman, 629 S.W. 11th St. FR 9-5202.
Southern Cross Astronomical Society: A. P. Smith, Jr., 1601 S.W. 10th St. FR 4-7145. *

Orlando Martin Orlando Astronomy Club: C. W. Finnigan, 2040 Summerland Ave., Winter Park. 644-5216. *

Pensacola Escambia Celestial Society: R. Blake, 200 Aster St., Warrington (32507). 456-4674. *

St. Petersburg St. Petersburg Astronomy Club: Mrs. R. Angell, 233 5th Ave. N. 79-0544. *

Tampa Tampa Amateur Astronomical Society: E. Z. Randall, 407 W. Chelsea St. (3). 33-6391.

GEORGIA
Atlanta Atlanta Astronomy Club: W. H. Close. 225 Forkner Dr., Decatur. DR 3-3945. *‡

Macon Macon Amateur Astronomers Club: A. B. Domingos, 4182 Forsyth Rd. 745-6549.

Savannah Savannah Astronomical Society: J. Benton, Jr., 305 Surrey Rd. (31404). 897-2523. ‡

HAWAII
Honolulu Hawaiian Astronomical Society: G. W. Bunton, B. P. Bishop Museum (17). 85951. †

IDAHO
Boise Boise Valley Astronomical Assn.: S. Piepgrass, 3330 Wagon Wheel Rd. 344-5203.

Twin Falls Southern Idaho Amateur Astronomers: N. Herrett, 1220 Kimberly Rd. RE 3-0868.

ILLINOIS
Chicago
Aldebaran Astronomical Assn.: M. Porcellino, 4020 N. Marmosa. PE 6-1736.
Chicago Astronomical Assn.: E. A. Giese, 2618 N. Magnolia. GR 7-5017. °
Chicago Astronomical Society: E. Ganek, 818 S. La Grange Rd., La Grange (60525). 312-352-0678.
Illini Astro-Observers: W. Wedmore, 79A S. Westmore Ave., Lombard. MA 7-1871.

Galesburg Galesburg Amateur Astronomers: H. L. Horein, 1246 N. Morton Ave. DI 2-0873.

Macon Macon Astronomical Society: Rev. A. J. Tamulis, 375 Miller St. RO 4-3795. *

Peoria Peoria Astronomical Society: R. Van Zandt, 1100 N. Parkside Dr. 4-5621. *

Rockford
Rockford Amateur Astronomers: A. R. Eastman, 2406 Clinton Rd. WO 3-5733. *
Rockford Astronomical Society: J. Brodine, 2125 Oxford St. WO 4-2933. °

Springfield Sangamon Astronomical Society: D. G. Van Wie, 1418 S. 8th St. 522-4617.

INDIANA
Evansville Evansville Astronomical Society: Dr. R. T. Dufford, 512 S. Weinbach Ave. (14). GR 6-7856. *

Fort Wayne Fort Wayne Astronomical Society, Inc.: W. E. Herriman, R. R. 10, Southcrest Trailer Court (46806). 639-3916.

Indianapolis Indiana Astronomical Society, Inc.: W. Wilkins, 6124 Dewey Ave. (19). FL 7-5946. *‡

Madison Madison Junior Astronomy Society: T. A. Winkel, 607 N. East St. 387-R. °

IOWA
Burlington Burlington Astronomy Club: J. Polson, 2214 Barrett St. PL 4-6064.

Des Moines Des Moines Div., Great Plains Astronomical Soc.: R. T. Morehead, R. R. 1, Beaver Ave. (10).

Dubuque Dubuque Astronomical Society: H. W. Klauer, 1795 Adair St.

KANSAS

Topeka Topeka Astronomical Society: J. Simpson, 4218 W. 30th St. CR 2-7130.

Wichita Wichita Astronomical Society: S. Whitehead, 425 N. Lorraine (14). MU 2-6642. *

KENTUCKY

Bowling Green Jaggers Astronomical Society: Mrs. J. C. Cottrell, 1530 State St. VI 3-8164. *

Covington
Covington Astronomical Assn.: S. L. Black, Box 264, Burlington.
Covington Variable Star Observers Assn.: P. Hartmann, 832 Madison Ave.

Lexington Bluegrass Astronomical Society: J. Hayden, 336 Colony Blvd. 6-7657. *‡

Louisville
Louisville Astronomical Society: Mrs. T. E. Field, 3017 Sherbrooke (40205). 458-3885. *
Louisville Junior Astronomical Society: C. Allen, 4005 St. Germaine Ct. (40207). *°

LOUISIANA

Lake Charles Lake Charles Amateur Astronomers Club: C. Fronczek, 2511 German Rd., Westlake. HE 6-1797.

New Orleans New Orleans Amateur Astronomers Assn.: W. E. Wulf, 2107 Annunciation St. JA 5-0706.

Shreveport Shreveport Astronomical Society: R. A. Worley, 550 Lloyd Lane. 868-2946. ‡

MAINE

Portland Astronomical Society of Maine: Mrs. O. H. Mayberry, Millbrook Rd., Scarboro. *

MARYLAND

Baltimore Baltimore Astronomical Society: Maryland Academy of Sciences, 7 W. Mulberry St. (21201). 685-2370. *

Silver Spring Applied Physics Laboratory Astronomy Club: I. Schroader, Applied Physics Lab., Johns Hopkins Univ., 8621 Georgia Ave. 776-7100.

MASSACHUSETTS

Cambridge
Amateur Telescope Makers of Boston: D. E. Argentini, 12 Rowell Rd., Danvers (01923). 774-3767. *

Bond Astronomical Club: R. C. Smith, 519 Morrissey Blvd., N. Quincy (71). GR 2-1938. *

New Bedford
Amateur Astronomy Club of New Bedford: M. Correia, 22 Ashley St. WY 2-6305.
Greater New Bedford Astronomical Society: H. N. Patnaude, 1203 Ashley Blvd. (02745).

Rutland Pommagussett Astronomical Society: M. S. Lubin, 45 Granite St., Worcester (4). PL 7-7278.

Springfield Springfield Stars Club: W. I. Fillmore, 11 Ridgewood Rd., Wilbraham (01095). 413-596-4067. *‡

Worcester Aldrich Astronomical Society: A. Nieuwenhoff, 3 Crestview Dr., Holden (01520). 829-2281. *

MICHIGAN

Ann Arbor Ann Arbor Amateur Astronomers Assn.: E. Holland-Moritz, 2920 Valley Dr. 662-2458. ‡

Battle Creek Battle Creek Amateur Astronomy Club: Mrs. W. V. Eichenlaub, 47 Everett Ave. WO 2-3059.

Detroit Detroit Astronomical Society, Inc.: F. N. Lewis, 807 Ellen, Royal Oak. 585-3433. *†

Flint
Flint Astronomy Club: Mrs. C. Adams, 610 Grand Blanc Rd., Grand Blanc.
Flint Junior Astronomy Club: D. G. Blondin, 3505 Holly Ave. (6). °

Grand Rapids Grand Rapids Amateur Astronomical Assn.: R. Larson, 3706 Lawn St. N.W. 453-9301. *‡

Kalamazoo Kalamazoo Astronomy Club: Mrs. V. Shellman, 3811 Allandale Ave. *

Lansing Lansing Amateur Astronomers: R. D. Bonner, 725 N. Magnolia Ave. IV 4-9834. ‡

Pontiac Pontiac-Northwest Detroit Astronomers Assn.: Mrs. M. Klarick, 17390 Wiltshire, Lathrup Village. EL 7-0364. ‡

Wyandotte Huron Valley Astronomy Club: A. E. Nolder, 13467 Kerr, Southgate.

MINNESOTA

Detroit Lakes: Detroit Lakes Amateur Astronomy Club: T. Albright, 1108 Rossman Ave. (56501).

St. Paul Astronomers Club of St. Paul: M. J. Charland, 1614 Stanford Ave. (5). °

MISSISSIPPI

Laurel Laurel Astronomy and Space Assn.: Mrs. R. Waters, 13 Country Club Dr. 87068. *

Raymond Amateur Astronomers Club: F. Stephenson, Hinds Junior College. 857-5085.

MISSOURI

Fayette Central Missouri Amateur Astronomers, Inc.: W. C. Shewmon, 518 Monroe Ave., Moberly. 816-263-0438. *

Joplin Joplin Astronomical Society: B. Vance, 622 Pearl Ave. MA 3-0842. °

Kansas City Astronomy Club of Kansas City: Mrs. L. Kinsey, 1522 Brush Creek (10). WA 3-3410. *

St. Joseph
International Amateur Astronomical Society: J. Milnar, 1817 Dalton St. AD 4-3424. ‡
Midland Empire Astronomical Society: L. White, 806 N. 25th St. (64506). *‡

St. Louis
Astronomers' Club of St. Louis: K. Hornberger, 1111 Avant Dr. (37). °
St. Louis Astronomical Society: Mrs. W. Fallert, 448 Hill Trail, Manchester (63062). *‡

MONTANA

Livingston Big Sky Astronomical Society: L. Shorthill, 511 N. 2nd St. (59047).

NEBRASKA

Lincoln Prairie Astronomy Club: J. Williams, 7844 S. Sycamore Dr. (68520). ‡

Omaha Omaha Astronomical Society: Mrs. E. Heinz, 13592 Walnut St. (68114). 731-1237. *‡

NEVADA

Las Vegas Unistars Astronomical League: E. Bold, 700 Easy St. 878-1442. ‡

Reno Astronomical Society of Nevada: A. A. Garroway, 2040 Meadow View Lane. FA 3-0696. †

NEW HAMPSHIRE

Keene Keene Amateur Astronomers, Inc.: P. N. Atwood, 12 Gardner St. (03431). 352-5058. *

Manchester
Clearview Astronomical Society: Mrs. D. Trudeau, 1050 Hayward St. NA 3-8951. °
Manchester Astronomical Society: R. E. Durette, 8 Keene St., Bedford. NA 5-8167.

Nashua Merrimack Valley Astronomical Society, Inc.: D. E. Pickering, Naticook Rd., Merrimack (03054).

NEW JERSEY

Caldwell West Essex Astronomical Society: R. M. Greenley, 412 Bloomfield Ave. CA 6-6751.

Clifton Clifton Astronomical Society: J. Ziemba, 144 Piaget Ave. 772-1857. °

Hackensack Bergen County Telescope Club: J. Norczyk, 54 Pehle Ave., Saddle Brook. (07663). 843-2694.

Jersey City Gregory Mem. Obs. of Paul Revere Boys Club: E. F. Jones, 339 Wayne St. (2). °

Newark Newark Museum Astronomy Club: A. Frielink, Jr., 43 Washington St. MI 2-0011.

Princeton Amateur Astronomers Assn. of Princeton: F. V. Shallcross, 3 Harrison Lane, Princeton Junction (08550). 609-799-0011.

Rutherford Astronomical Society of Rutherford: Mrs. A. Cox, 478 Riverside Terr. WE 9-0453.

Teaneck Bergen County Astronomical Society: W. DeForge, Jr., 424 W. Anderson St., Hackensack. HU 9-3436.

Upper Montclair Montclair Telescope Club: R. Boeghold, 280 N. Mountain Ave. PI 6-0495.

NEW MEXICO

Albuquerque Albuquerque Astronomers: D. Judd, 320 13th St. N.W. CH 3-4955. *

Las Cruces Astronomical Society of Las Cruces: J. E. Durrenberger, Box 921. JA 6-2968. *†

NEW YORK

Albany Albany Amateur Astronomers: R. E. Coon, Dudley Observatory, 140 S. Lake Ave. (12208). 518-462-0831.

Binghamton Astronomical Society of Broome County: F. S. Maddocks, 3213 Woodberry Dr., Vestal (13850). 607-729-2846. ‡

Brooklyn Kingsway Ast. and Rocketry Soc.: P. Harrison, 720 Ave. P (11223). NI 5-3067. *°

Buffalo
Buffalo Astronomical Assn., Inc.: R. S. Zygmunt, 48 Colonial Ave., Kenmore (14217). 877-7625. *
Buffalo Junior Astronomical Society: M. Fink, 69 Pine Ridge Rd., Cheektowaga. TX 6-6271. °

Chappaqua Northern Westchester Astronomical Society: W. P. Smith, 130 Castle Rd. CE 8-3853.

Corning Corning Astronomy Club: Mrs. E. Johnston, 106 Jennings St. 2-5142.

Farmingdale
Astronomical Society of Long Island: F. Chapman, 5 Garden Ave., N. Massapequa (11758). 516-541-2860.
Long Island Students of Advanced Astronomy: W. Huebner, 53-114B Piedmont Dr., Port Jefferson Sta. (11776). 516-928-0152.

Huntington Long Island Observers' Assn., Inc.: 109-A Browns Rd. (11743). AN 1-8602. *

Lake Success Sperry Telescope and Astronomy Group: N. F. Van Gelder, 130 Main Ave., Wyandanch (11798). 516-643-7938. *

Newburgh
Association of Junior Celestial Observers: E. Ashton, 40 Upper Ave. 914-561-9039. °
Newburgh Astronomy Club: R. Maharay, 238 Windsor Hwy. (12550). °

New York
Amateur Astronomers Assn., Inc.: P. V. Rizzo, 212 W. 79th St. (10024). 874-9064. *
Amateur Observers Society: M. Suarez, 29-11 Ditmars Blvd., Long Island City (11105).
Astronomical Society of New York City: T. W. Hamilton, 235 Seaman Ave. (34). LO 9-1712.

Junior Astronomy Club: New York Univ., 100 Washington Sq. E. (3). °

Patchogue Long Island Astronomical Society: W. J. Brookes, 128 Avon Place, W. Hempstead.

Poughkeepsie IBM Astronomical Society: R. Ogden, Dept. 380, Bldg. 002-2. 36207.

Rochester Astronomy Section, Academy of Science: R. K. Dakin, 720 Pittsford-Victor Rd., Pittsford (14534). 716-586-4519. *‡

Schenectady
Bishop Gibbons Astronomy Club: Br. A. E. Newman, F.S.C.H., 2602 Albany St. EX 3-3131. °
Schenectady Astronomy Club: L. Kroger, 764 State St. *

Syracuse Syracuse Astronomical Society: J. Italiano, 1115 E. Colvin St. (13210). *

Troy
Rensselaer Astrophysical Society: S. Ross, 272 Hoosick St. (12181). 272-9413.
Troy Astronomy Club: D. Harris, 1032 19th St., Watervliet. AR 3-1266.

Utica
Utica Amateur Astronomers, Inc.: F. Staudaher, 8 Tanglewood Rd., New Hartford. RA 4-6211. *‡
Utica Junior Amateur Astronomers: P. Reddick, 1640½ Howard Ave. RE 5-3494. °

Watertown Northern New York Amateur Astronomers: L. Beaumont, Box 133, Evans Mills.

Yonkers Yonkers Astronomy Club: B. Simon, 9 Valley View Dr. YO 8-7681.

NORTH CAROLINA

Chapel Hill Chapel Hill Astronomy Club: B. Melvin, Rte. 2. 9-9447.

Charlotte Charlotte Amateur Astronomers Club: C. Gallant, Jr., 4527 Wentworth Place.

Greensboro Greensboro Astronomy Club: J. P. Patton, Jr., 3504 Tanglewood Dr. CY 9-0194. *

Raleigh Raleigh Amateur Astronomers: O. N. Rich, 126 Fenton Rd. 833-8420.

Winston-Salem Forsyth Astronomical Society: K. A. Shepherd, 903 West End Blvd. PA 2-1631.

NORTH DAKOTA

Grand Forks Red River Astronomy Club: Miss M. Barlow, 704 Cottonwood St. 2-2473.

OHIO

Akron Astronomy Club of Akron: H. Brock, 345 Trigonia Dr. (44302). 535-9829. ‡

Canton Stark County Astronomical Society: Mrs. M. Terembis, 1153 Spring Ave., N.E. (47704). 452-8755. *

Cincinnati
  Cincinnati Astronomical Assn.: D. Wessling, 946 Deblin Dr., Milford. 831-5763. ‡
  Cincinnati Astronomical Society: Miss M. Stone, 5767 Sheviot Rd. (39). WE 1-0954.

Cleveland
  Cleveland Astronomical Society: Warner and Swasey Obs., Taylor Rd., E. Cleveland (12). GL 1-5625.
  Cuyahoga Astronomy Club: C. R. Peck, 3278 W. 122nd St. (44111). 941-3044. ‡

Columbus
  Battelle Astronomy Club: W. Orahood, 1181 Penn. Ave.
  Columbus Astronomical Society: Mrs. J. Gann, 420 N. Cassady Rd. (9). CL 2-8421. *

Dayton Miami Valley Astronomical Society: F. Sutter, 5038 Far Hills Ave. (45429). 434-1176. *‡

Kent Kent Quadrangle Astronomical Society: T. Dietz, 141 E. Elm. 673-4154. ‡

Lima Lima Astronomy Club: Miss V. Schmitz, 823 Gloria Dr. (45805). 991-5991. ‡

Mansfield Richland Astronomy Society: F. Cary, 549 Connor Dr. 522-4918. *‡

Marietta Marietta Astronomical Society: Miss L. E. Cisler, Cisler Terrace. 614-373-0231. ‡

Newark Newark Astronomical Society: G. Cooperrider, 326 N. 11th St. FA 3-0452.

Toledo
  Star and Sky Group of Toledo Naturalists: Dr. M. Bell, 2257 Upton Ave. (43606). 472-7827.
  Toledo Astronomical Society: C. Schalow, 706 Culley Dr., Holland. UN 5-5392. ‡

Warren Mahoning Valley Astronomical Society: Mrs. C. R. Prather, 1363 Drexel Ave. N.W. (44485). 393-4483.

Wooster Wayne County Astronomical Society: M. Specht, 452 N. Buckeye St. ‡

Youngstown Youngstown Astronomy Club: T. Pedas, 626 Fruit Ave., Farrell (16121). 342-3798.

OKLAHOMA

Oklahoma City Astronomy Club of Oklahoma City: E. W. Davis, 2428 N.W. 48 St. (73112). VI 2-7202.

Tulsa
  Asteroids: M. Madden, 2737 E. Newton Pl. WE 9-7750. °
  Astronomy Club of Tulsa: Mrs. G. Rose, 4697 S. Columbia Ave. (5). RI 7-6729. *

OREGON

Eugene Eugene Astronomical Society: R. Fidler, 669 E. 13th St., Apt. 4. DI 3-5387. ‡

Portland
  Amateur Telescope Makers and Observers: Miss M. Kobs, 5215 N.E. 30th Ave. (11). AT 2-8843. †
  Portland Astronomical Society: Mrs. M. Krutsinger, 6525 N.E. Davis (16). AL 4-1491. *

Salem Salem Astronomical Society: Mrs. B. W. Christensen, 1430 Marshall Dr. EM 4-6626. ‡

PENNSYLVANIA

Allentown Lehigh Valley Amateur Astronomical Society: W. J. Ference, 554 Main St., Bethlehem (18018). 215-868-7721. *‡

Erie M31 Astronomical Society: R. S. Cadwallader, 916 Kahkwa Blvd. GL 4-0229.

Harrisburg Astronomical Society of Harrisburg: E. L. Naylor, 320 Wilhelm Rd., Paxtany. 564-0370. *‡

Philadelphia
  Amateur Astronomers of Franklin Inst.: E. F. Bailey, Franklin Inst. (34). LO 4-3600. *
  Association of General Celestial Observers: M. McCrery, 3000-G Tasker St. DE 6-4230.
  Brahe Astronomical Society: S. Karpchuk, Jr., 3304 Oakmont Ave. (36). °
  Rittenhouse Astronomical Society: E. F. Bailey, Franklin Inst. (34). 484-1294. *

Pittsburgh
Amateur Astronomers Assn. of Pittsburgh: F. M. Garland, 210 Park Pl. (37). 364-3211. *

Astrophysical Society of Pittsburgh: J. Apt, 40 Woodland Rd. (15232). 361-0047. °

Junior Amateur Astronomers Assn. of Pittsburgh: A. Zappa, 314 S. Evaline St. 361-1691. °

Scranton Lackawanna Astronomical Society: Miss S. Owens, 916 Prospect Ave. (18505). *‡

Villanova Villanova Astronomical Society: Rev. E. F. Jenkins, O.S.A., Villanova Univ. LA 5-4600.

Waynesboro Astronomical Society of Waynesboro: J. Snider, 1021 S. Coldbrook Ave., Chambersburg (17201). 717-264-4838. *‡

PUERTO RICO
Vieques Vieques Amateur Astronomy Society: Father R. Kringel, Apartado 308 (00765). 741-2731.

RHODE ISLAND
Providence
Rhode Island Stellar Society: J. McGuirk, 12 Oakdale St. 751-8606. °

Skyscrapers, Inc.: Miss M. Gildea, 25 Hymer St. (02908). 831-8928.

SOUTH CAROLINA
Columbia Columbia Astronomical Society: Science Museum, 1519 Senate St. AL 2-6975.

Hartsville Hartsville Astronomical Society: B. Hopkins, Box 423. 1540. °

SOUTH DAKOTA
Rapid City Rapid City Astronomical Society: Dr. R. Heckman, S. D. School of Mines and Technology. FI 3-1600. ‡

Sioux Falls Sioux Falls Amateur Astronomy Club: D. Ness, 2305 Carter Pl. ED 2-5893.

TENNESSEE
Chattanooga Barnard Astronomical Society: W. G. Swafford, Jr., 5321 Connell St. (37412). 622-5309. *

Greeneville Greeneville Astronomical Society: D. Rockhill, R.F.D. 8, College View. ME 8-6875.

Kingsport Kingsport Astronomical Society: J. Brown, 1329 Belmeade Dr. CI 5-7513.

Knoxville Knoxville Astronomical Assn.: D. L. Bower, 2110 Fairmont Blvd. 2-1798. ‡

Memphis Memphis Astronomical Society: Miss C. Whiteleather, 71 N. Perkins Rd. (38117). 683-8862. *‡

Nashville Barnard Astronomical Society: Miss P. H. Hudgens, Dyer Obs., Vanderbilt Univ. CY 7-8811.

TEXAS
Abilene Abilene Astronomical Society: R. B. Edmundson, 1849 N. 8th St. OR 4-5932. ‡

Amarillo Panhandle Astronomical Society: K. Peyton, 205 Santa Fe Bldg. DR 4-3389.

Austin Schwartz Astronomical Society: F. D. Talbert, Dept. of Ast., Univ. of Texas.

Corpus Christi Corpus Christi Astronomical Society: G. McLerran, 910 Delaine (78411). UL 3-8621. *‡

Dallas
Junior Texas Astronomical Society: J. Wulf, 9305 Waterview Rd. (75218). DA 1-6804. °

Texas Astronomical Society: E. M. Brewer, 5218 Morningside Ave. (75206). TA 6-3894. *‡

Fort Worth
Fort Worth Astronomical Society: Dr. H. C. Sehested, 3223 Wescliff Rd. W. 924-6886. *

Fort Worth Junior Astronomical Society: D. H. Gallagher, Children's Museum, 1501 Montgomery. PE 2-1461. *°

Houston Houston Amateur Astronomy Club: W. W. Myers, 7424 Tipps St. (23). WA 6-5947.

Laredo Laredo Astronomy Club: S. Freidin, 2220 Davis Ave.

Lubbock South Plains Astronomy Club: K. Little, 3629 60th. SW 5-2012. *‡

Midland Midland Astronomical Society: M. Sloan, 116 Eisenhower. 694-9933. °

Richardson Richardson Junior Astronomical Society: D. C. Baer, 105 Thompson Dr. AD 5-2450. °

San Angelo San Angelo Amateur Astronomy Assn.: D. V. Payne, 212 W. First St. (76901). 655-3792. *

Wichita Falls North Texas Astronomical Society: J. M. Marshall, Box 300. 692-1220, ext. 316.

UTAH

Provo Utah County Amateur Astronomers: J. S. Beardall, P.O. Box 1, Springville (84663). 489-5775

Salt Lake City Astronomical Society of Utah: J. W. Geertsen, 4461 S. 9th East St. (17).

VERMONT

Burlington Vermont Astronomical Society: E. Salvas, Box 132, Shelburne (05482). 985-3692. *

Springfield Springfield Telescope Makers: C. R. Ranney, 3 Hillcrest Rd. 5-2436. *

VIRGINIA

Arlington STOSTH: R. Walker, 2802 S. Wakefield.

Danville Piedmont Amateur Astronomical Society: D. L. Motley, 418 Kemper Rd. SW 2-0552.

Lynchburg Blue Ridge Amateur Astronomers: J. E. Ardery, 2900 Rivermont Ave. VI 6-3584. *

Norfolk Norfolk Astronomical Society: D. Berent, 1109 Brunswick Ave. (8). MA 2-8069. ‡

Richmond
    Richmond Assn. of Junior Astronomers: Dr. E. Hoff, 117 Gaymont Rd. (26). AT 8-3368. *°
    Richmond Astronomical Society: F. S. Clark, 6205 Clover Lane (28). *

Roanoke Amateur Astronomers of Roanoke: J. Newman, 401 Elden Ave. N.W. 362-1793. ‡

WASHINGTON

Seattle Seattle Amateur Astronomical Society, Inc.: Miss D. Reilly, 4220 N.E. 105th (55). LA 2-5427. *‡

Spokane Amateur Telescope Makers of Spokane: T. L. Keel, N. 1223 Hollis St. (99201). FA 8-0249. *

Tacoma Tacoma Amateur Astronomers, Inc.: C. Stevens, 2207 S. 41st (98409). 474-9026. *

Yakima Yakima Amateur Astronomers: E. J. Newman, 509 N. 6th St. (98901). GL 2-9825. *

WEST VIRGINIA

Charleston Carbide Astronomy Club: W. Casto, 333 Parkview Dr., St. Albans. *

Wheeling Oglebay Inst. Astronomical Assn.: S. Brooks, Oglebay Inst., Speidel Obs. CH 3-6855

WISCONSIN

Beloit Beloit Astronomical Society: Dr. K. E. Patterson, 813 Lilac Rd. (53511). 362-2242.

Eau Claire Memorial High School Astronomy Club: Mrs. K. German, 1615 State St. TE 5-3207. °

Kenosha Kenosha Amateur Astronomers: R. Henkel, 7625 18th Ave. OL 2-5225.

Madison Madison Astronomical Society: G. N. Harris, 1938 Sheridan St. CH 9-3714. *‡

Milwaukee Milwaukee Astronomical Society: E. Halbach, 2971 S. 52nd St. (19). LI 1-1181. *

Oshkosh Fox River Valley Amateur Astronomers Club: D. Zwicky, R. R. 5, Box 505. BE 5-7163.

Racine Racine Astronomical Society, Inc.: Mrs. M. Lizik, 1216 W. Colonial Dr. (53404). 634-2175. *

[The information given here has been drawn from the lists given in *Sky and Telescope*, for whose kind assistance we are most grateful.]

Index